90 relate

*Science Policy
and the University*

HAROLD ORLANS *Editor*

Science Policy and the University

Contributors
CHRISTIAN K. ARNOLD
HOMER D. BABBIDGE, JR.
HENDRIK W. BODE
HARVEY BROOKS
WILLIAM D. CAREY
HARRY MELVILLE
JOHN F. MORSE
HOWARD E. PAGE
WOLFGANG K. H. PANOFSKY
DON K. PRICE
HERBERT ROBACK
DAVID Z. ROBINSON
ELMER B. STAATS
ALVIN M. WEINBERG

The Brookings Institution
WASHINGTON, D.C.

THE BROOKINGS INSTITUTION is an independent organization devoted to nonpartisan research, education, and publication in economics, government, foreign policy, and the social sciences generally. Its principal purposes are to aid in the development of sound public policies and to promote public understanding of issues of national importance.

The Institution was founded on December 8, 1927, to merge the activities of the Institute for Government Research, founded in 1916, the Institute of Economics, founded in 1922, and the Robert Brookings Graduate School of Economics and Government, founded in 1924.

The general administration of the Institution is the responsibility of a self-perpetuating Board of Trustees. The trustees are likewise charged with maintaining the independence of the staff and fostering the most favorable conditions for creative research and education. The immediate direction of the policies, program, and staff of the Institution is vested in the President, assisted by an advisory council chosen from the staff of the Institution.

In publishing a study, the Institution presents it as a competent treatment of a subject worthy of public consideration. The interpretations and conclusions in such publications are those of the author or authors and do not purport to represent the views of the other staff members, officers, or trustees of the Brookings Institution.

Foreword

IN THE FALL OF 1964, the Brookings Institution began a seminar on "Science, Technology, and Public Policy" to advance understanding of some current problems of policy regarding government programs of scientific research and development by providing an opportunity for the informal, dispassionate discussion of these problems by public officials and private citizens.

Initially, the participants examined a number of specific government R&D program decisions, in the hope that, thereby, some useful general observations might emerge. Despite the interest which some of these cases aroused, it soon became clear that a seminar of this type was not the best means to conduct an essentially historical analysis of the factors underlying a specific decision to proceed or not to proceed with particular research or engineering ventures. Accordingly, of the seven sessions held during the 1964–65 year, only three are represented in this volume (in the papers of Robinson, Roback, and Carey).

The following year, 1965–66, the seminar found a more coherent intellectual outlook in exploring various issues of government policy toward university science. Seven of the eight papers presented during that period are included here (those of Price, Brooks, Page, Bode, Panofsky, Staats, and Morse).

Literary detectives searching for either timely or cumulative elements in the discussions may be interested in their original dates and sequence. These are as follows: *1965*—Robinson, January 26; Roback, March 23; Carey, April 27; Price, October 6; Bode, November 3; Weinberg, November 12; Brooks, December 1; *1966*—Page, January 5; Staats, February 2; Panofsky, March 2; Morse, May 4.

To provide a broader perspective on some of the issues discussed by the seminar, three additional papers were invited for this volume: one by Christian Arnold arguing the merits of institutional grants calculated on a tripartite formula geared to the volume of an institution's educational and research activities in the sciences; one by Harry Melville reviewing current issues in British policy toward university science; and a concluding paper by Homer Babbidge offering one university president's impressions of the Washington science scene.

The seminar was initiated by George A. Graham, then director of the Governmental Studies program at Brookings, with the help of John McCollum, then in the Office of the Secretary of Health, Education, and Welfare, and Charles R. Bowen of the International Business Machines Corporation, as a Washington version of the Columbia University Seminar on Technology and Social Change, which they had been attending. It was chaired during the first year by Dael Wolfle, executive officer of the American Association for the Advancement of Science, and during the second by Kermit Gordon, then vice president of Brookings, with George Graham substituting whenever required. The latter three, together with Charles Kidd, of the Office of Science and Technology; Chalmers Sherwin, then of the Office of the Assistant Secretary of Defense for Research and Engineering; Edward Wenk, of the Legislative Reference Service; Bowen Dees, then of the National Science Foundation; and Herbert Roback, of the Military Operations Subcommittee of the House Committee on Government Operations, constituted an informal advisory committee which helped to shape the program. Harold Orlans, a Brookings Senior Fellow, served as executive secretary of the seminar.

Miss Janet Porter and Mrs. Andrea Manfredonia efficiently performed the secretarial work for both the seminar sessions and this volume, Mrs. Nancy Romoser edited the manuscript for the printer, and Mrs. Rachel Johnson prepared the index.

The Institution is grateful to the International Business Machines

Corporation for a grant and to the Office of Science and Technology for a contract which helped to finance the seminar. Of course, neither organization, nor the trustees, officers, or other staff of the Brookings Institution should be assumed to agree with the views presented in this volume, which are solely those of each author.

KERMIT GORDON
President

June 1968
Washington, D.C.

Contents

PART IV. **A BROADER VIEW**

ABBREVIATIONS

AAUP   American Association of University Professors
ACE   American Council on Education
AEC   Atomic Energy Commission
AGS   Alternating Gradient Synchrotron
Bev   Billion electron volts (U.S. usage)
BOB   Bureau of the Budget
CERN   European Organization for Nuclear Research
COSPUP   Committee on Science and Public Policy, National Academy of Sciences
DDR&E   Director of Defense Research and Engineering, Department of Defense
DOD   Department of Defense
ESRO   European Space Research Organization
FY   Fiscal year (July 1–June 30)
GAC   General Advisory Committee, Atomic Energy Commission
GAO   General Accounting Office
GeV   Billion electron volts (European usage)
HEW   Department of Health, Education, and Welfare
LRS   Legislative Reference Service, Library of Congress
Mev   Million electron volts
MURA   Midwestern Universities Research Association
NAS   National Academy of Sciences
NAS-NRC   National Academy of Sciences–National Research Council
NASA   National Aeronautics and Space Administration
NIH   National Institutes of Health, Public Health Service, Department of Health, Education, and Welfare
NSF   National Science Foundation
OE   Office of Education, Department of Health, Education, and Welfare
ONR   Office of Naval Research, Department of the Navy
OST   Office of Science and Technology, Executive Office of the President
PSAC   President's Science Advisory Committee
R&D   Research and development
RDT&E   Research, development, testing, and evaluation (Department of Defense usage)
SNAP   Systems for Nuclear Auxiliary Power
UGC   University Grants Committee (United Kingdom)

*Science Policy
and the University*

HAROLD ORLANS

Editor's Introduction

To SUMMARIZE the summaries in this volume would be to masticate them unduly. Ideas are not always, like cud, improved by rumination; they may simply lose their flavor. Accordingly, this introduction will seek not so much to summarize as to comment selectively on some policy issues that were of recurrent concern to the seminar.

The Character of the Seminar

Before doing so, however, something should be said about the character of the discussions, which were, in turn, a reflection of the character of the group.

The seminar format called for a dinner followed by discussion, approximately monthly from the fall through the spring. Normally, the speaker's paper was circulated in advance so that it was only necessary for him briefly to summarize or extend his main observations. Thereby, most of the two after-dinner hours was available for a discussion that had three basic ground rules: it was to be directed at the issues, not at the speaker who was to participate as any other member; remarks were to be brief, so that no one would monopolize the floor; and to encourage candor, nothing said was to be attributed to any participant in public, or used against him in private, without his permission. The summaries, prepared by the editor from stenotype transcripts, attempt to convey not only the main points raised during the discussion but also some of the liveliness of the occasion.

Of course, this was a Washington group—which is to say, a group of men close to the seats of power, politically sophisticated, and displaying (at least on these occasions) more of a pragmatic than a scholarly interest in ideas and knowledge. One scholarly critic of this manuscript found the "Washington orientation . . . overwhelming. . ."; but it is precisely from that orientation that readers may obtain some insight into the ways of democratic government. Thus, another reader of the manuscript felt that the discussions "convey a realistic appreciation of the real current pressures, cross currents, subtleties, influence of personalities, complexity of forces, etc., that influence actions." The seminar was, he suggested, characterized by

a. The "professional" nature of the discussions. Most of the people knew what they were talking about, and were able (as I see it) to view their own problems "from outside themselves."

b. The ease of communication, and the directness of the conversation.

c. The general flexibility of the participants. There was an interesting combination of tolerance and bluntness on some fundamentals.

d. The "style" of the meetings may be significant in that it seems to me to represent an American approach. When you think that this kind of exchange goes on daily in hundreds of places, and that there is pretty good communication, the real nature of "science policy formulation" in the U.S. may become clearer. The book may be more revealing to foreigners than to us.

Inevitably, the seminar also had limitations which were the obverse side of its strengths. A free-ranging discussion can hop, skip, and jump all over a problem without subjecting it to rigorous or systematic logical and empirical analysis. In such a discussion, an assertion of "fact" should be construed as an honest, but not necessarily valid, belief or recollection, and, if valid, as part, not all, of the truth. And plainly, as part of the truth was discerned, so another part was either disregarded or, occasionally, withheld. Before Budget Bureau officials, congressmen of both parties, and senior government officials from other departments, there are always some things that no one in his right mind would say. Thus, candor was constantly balanced against, and occasionally outweighed by, discretion. A good example is afforded by one of the signally less revealing sessions not reported in this volume. Though there were present several authorities well qualified to answer the questions that had been set down on the agenda to stimulate discussion, none chose to do so. Subsequently, one authority demonstrated, off-the-record, how readily the questions could be answered. With congressional hearings and White House action impending, that evening had simply not been opportune for candor on that subject. Nonetheless, it may be claimed (and the reader can judge the merit of this claim for himself) that a high order of candor generally prevailed, that special pleading was generally forsaken, and that participants sought the truth with the same earnestness and disinterest that marks any genuine intellectual inquiry.

Institutional vs. Project Funding

One issue with which the seminar was much concerned was the balance that should now be struck, in the federal financing of academic research, between project funds awarded to individual investigators by the advisers and staff of Washington agencies, and funds awarded to academic institutions for local allocation. Plainly, the group favored a relative (not absolute) decrease in project, and a corresponding increase in institutional, funding. One hardy soul even specified how much: the volume of institutional awards should rise to 25 percent from an estimated 12 percent in fiscal year 1966, while project funds should decline to 50 percent from a 1966 level of 74 percent (see p. 45).[1]

Many reasons were cited and more could be added why a shift would be desirable. It would simplify the labor and cost of obtaining, awarding, and accounting for federal funds; it would allow the money to be used more flexibly and perhaps more parsimoniously to meet special

[1] On this calculation, the residue assigned to fellowships and traineeships would rise to 25 percent from a 1966 level of 14 percent. See Harvard president Nathan Pusey's suggestion: "There is a widespread belief that the scientific productivity of the Nation would be enhanced if a substantial portion of the Federal funds for science, perhaps a quarter, were allocated to universities for deployment as they saw fit within their structures, another quarter allocated to the universities selectively and earmarked by broad area—physical science, medicine, public health, meteorology, oceanography, etc.; the remaining half to be managed as at present in terms of project, fellowship, and training grant support" (in *Impact of Public Health Grant Programs on Medical Research and Education,* Results of Questionnaire Survey Participated in by 19 Selected Institutions, Prepared for the Use of the House Committee on Interstate and Foreign Commerce, 88 Cong. 2 Sess. [August 1964], p. 141).

local requirements rather than general national regulations; and it would restore to the institution some of the power over its affairs now wielded by distant forces. "What the college president wants more than anything else . . . is grant support . . . that can be deployed at the discretion of the institution," says Homer Babbidge in the last chapter (p. 326), echoing Don Price's statement in the first that "the government . . . [should] move in the direction of support on a broader basis, putting more general substantive as well as financial responsibility in the hands of the university faculties and administration" (pp. 32–33).

The proposition is no longer radical; to its traditional advocates, the university administrators, have been added in recent years numbers of senior faculty, public officials, and men who often help to form new government policies toward university science. It has been endorsed even by the American Medical Association's Commission on Research.[2] And the logic is as clear as spring water. Since World War II, one *ad hoc* measure or special purpose program has succeeded another at higher educational institutions until it lies beyond the power of mortal man to comprehend the lot. What is evident is that the total amount of money rises each year; it comes from the federal treasury; and it goes to more and more institutions. Is it not time to rationalize the process, to acknowledge that the federal government is supporting higher research and education, and to go about it more simply and directly? "We now face the question of whether the support of scientific research and higher education can be seen as a public purpose in itself," Don Price observes (p. 37). "Has the Federal Government acquired any responsibility for the continuing and general support of higher education in the United States?" Dael Wolfle asks.[3]

To answer yes is, however, easier than to implement that answer wisely.

Confining ourselves solely to the sphere of science and setting aside, as beyond the scope of this volume, the larger question of general aid to higher education, significant issues of public policy remain. It may be said that, in principle, these issues have already been resolved by two existing programs of general aid to university science, the institutional

[2] "Several investigative bodies and many distinguished leaders are now urging—and we concur—that a higher percentage of the Federal research monies now going into project grants be shifted to institutional grants and that this money be administered by and in the discretion of the medical schools" (American Medical Association, *Report of the Commission on Research* [February 1967], p. 9).

[3] Dael Wolfle, "Stable Federal Support," editorial in *Science,* July 8, 1966.

grants of the National Institutes of Health (NIH) and the National Science Foundation (NSF), which are geared to the volume of each institution's project grants.[4] But evidently they have not been resolved to the satisfaction of institutions which rank higher in the number of science degrees they confer than in the volume of federal research funds they receive. Some important institutions of this sort are members of the National Association of State Universities and Land-Grant Colleges, which has endorsed the proposal outlined by Christian Arnold (see pp. 96–100) and introduced as a bill in 1966 by Representative George Miller, Chairman of the House Committee on Science and Astronautics. Under this proposal, unrestricted grants for scientific education and research (ranging initially up to $300,000 a year) would be awarded in accordance with a formula two-thirds of which would be determined by the number of undergraduate students taught and graduate degrees conferred in the natural and social sciences.

Whereas, as Price relates (p. 35), Vannevar Bush and "conservative leaders of scientific institutions" successfully opposed Senator Kilgore's comparable proposal more than twenty years ago, the Miller bill has been backed by, among others, NSF Director Leland Haworth and the Association of American Universities (see p. 97). Why the change? Various explanations can be offered; but among them, surely, practical political considerations occupy a larger place today, when annual federal expenditures for academic science exceed $2 billion, than in former years. These considerations have been voiced with utmost candor by Frederick Seitz, president of the National Academy of Sciences:

> Quite apart from whether or not one believes that geographical imbalance is good or bad—and much has been said on both sides of this issue—the fact remains that representation in Congress is geographical, and unless funds are distributed with some relation to geography, everyone will suffer to some degree in the future, including the so-called rich. The significant

[4] In fiscal year 1967, for example, the NSF institutional grant formula was 100 percent of the first $10,000 in applicable NSF grants for research or research participation, with progressively smaller percentages of larger amounts; 517 institutions thereby received sums ranging from $709 to $159,186; while most institutions received less than $20,000, 55 received more than $100,000 (see *Seventeenth Annual Report of the National Science Foundation* [1968], p. 155).

For fiscal year 1968, NIH proposed to award each health professional school 10 percent of the first million dollars of its nonfederal research expenditures plus 5 percent of the first, and 3 percent of the second, million dollars of federal research expenditures as well as a base grant of $25,000 (see *Departments of Labor and Health, Education, and Welfare Appropriations for 1968*, Hearings before a Subcommittee of the House Committee on Appropriations, 90 Cong. 1 sess. [1967], pt. 5, p. 723).

numbers of Representatives in "have-not" areas will lose interest in the
support of science by the Federal Government. This principle is so nearly
self-evident that I would have felt that it would have been recognized and
adopted by practically all Federal agencies long ago. Even at this late date I
can only urge each Federal agency to reexamine the geographical distribution of its funds for basic science with the thought that this will probably
mean more for all in the future. The argument that money must go where
quality is has, of course, much wisdom associated with it, but it must also
be realized that human nature is such that good men will also go where
money is—particularly under circumstances like those we now face in
which funds are not rising as rapidly as the scientific community can absorb
them. There are those who will say that this point of view is too political
or too pragmatic. To them I can only say that if Federal funds can be effective in building up science and engineering in one part of the country, they
can also be effective in building up science in other parts if reasonable institutions are available.[5]

It is not at all paradoxical, as Arnold points out, that a formula cater-
ing to political interests dissatisfied with the present pattern of project
funding would obviate the kinds of politics that can enter into project
awards (pp. 98–99). For the politics that can enter the administration
of one system is incorporated in the structure of the other. The main
weakness of a formula system derives from the same source as its
strength—its inflexibility and indiscriminativeness. Just as one man is
worth one vote at the polls, so one science student is worth as much as
another from the Treasury. The principle is entirely democratic—but
how democratic is nature? How readily does she yield her secrets, if not
to popular vote then to diligent inquiry by any "competent" scientist (to
use a term popular among officials who must defend large science budgets before the Congress)?

Once, this question could have received only one answer: the secrets
of nature, like those of Skull & Bones, are revealed only to a select few.
"Ten second-rate scientists or engineers cannot do the work of one who
is in the first rank," said Harvard president James Conant, and the president of the California Institute of Technology, Lee DuBridge, raised
him a hundred-fold: "One top-rate scientist can produce more science
than a thousand second-rate people."[6] However, as the legions of science

[5] Frederick Seitz, "Promises and Constraints on Science" (address at the Vicennial
Convocation of Office of Naval Research, May 4, 1966), pp. 17–18.
[6] See James Conant's Foreword to *The First Annual Report of the National Science
Foundation, 1950–51* (1951), p. viii; and Lee DuBridge, in *Government and Science,*
Hearings before the Subcommittee on Science, Research, and Development of the House
Committee on Science and Astronautics, 88 Cong. 2 sess. (1964), p. 387.

multiply, they no longer march under elite banners. If they agree about little else, Christian Arnold and Harvey Brooks apparently agree about that. Arnold extravagantly endorses the massive federal expenditures for research and development (p. 89), all of which could not go to geniuses even if we tried (and there is scant evidence that we have tried); while Brooks rejects the "genius theory" of scientific progress on the grounds that the genius' contribution "is never as isolated or unique as the layman believes" and "usually rests on the lesser but essential contributions of hundreds of other people" (pp. 147–48). And, of course, the public investments in "big science" are made on the assumption, not that an apple may ripen and fall on the head of a second Newton but that immodest nature will reveal her charms on a schedule appointed jointly by high energy physicists, the Congress, and the Bureau of the Budget. To the extent that science has become more of an industry and less of an art, the production of knowledge can be mechanized—and Panofsky describes a new cadre of "data reducers" bred to tend the factories of physics (see pp. 196–97). And if science can be at least partly mechanized, why not partly mechanize the financing of science?

Development Grants

The operation of a more selective kind of institutional grant program, the National Science Foundation's science development grants, is explained by Howard Page (pp. 101–13). Although these grants are decidedly larger than the NSF formula grants, they lack the element of continuity and, of course, they have gone to only a few schools (twenty all told during fiscal years 1965 and 1966). Nonetheless, selectivity is worthy of praise, not criticism, for it is precisely the feature difficult to maintain in a publicly financed program. Though the institutional development program has been operating for only three years, it already shows signs of losing some of its initial selectivity. NSF staff were understandably concerned about their inability to help all institutions which applied to them, and new graduate departmental and college science improvement programs have been initiated to offer some solace to schools which do not get institutional grants. (A commendable effort has been made, however, to increase the size and reduce the annual number of institutional grants.)

The choice of particular institutions may, of course, be faulted, although it is difficult to do so intelligently without knowing the specific proposals from which NSF staff had to choose. But several more fundamental difficulties remain. One, noted by the seminar (see p. 118), is the apparent inability of different government agencies (and, often, of the same agency) to concert their programs to achieve a common purpose. Clark Kerr has rightly observed that "the selection of designated 'centers of strength' assumes a single source of designation—a single over-all federal agency or committee."[7] But it is hard indeed to imagine a single list of institutions being designated as our next twenty centers of scientific excellence or any official (other than the President) making such a designation surviving long in office.

Another difficulty is the inadequacy of the resources provided for the job. The maximum size of NSF development grants was formerly $5 million, and is now $6 million, for a three-year period. By contrast, Harvard's operating budget for three years is over $300 million. And, of course, the disparity between rich and poor institutions is not confined to their operating budgets but extends to their land, buildings, equipment, endowment, alumni, reputation, and good will accumulated over the years. Harvard's endowment alone has a market value of some $800 million. A proposal to bring such capital resources of lesser universities up to the level of major ones has not been seriously entertained in this country, though it has been suggested in Britain.[8] However, as the instruments and ideas of science turn over so rapidly, it is probably cheaper, and certainly more practicable, to equip a university rapidly for distinction in science than in the humanities and arts, which require not new instruments but old books and *objets d'art* that must be assembled through painstaking and protracted effort.

Finally, a point government officials cannot readily make and some scientific entrepreneurs have too readily discounted: the areas of this nation most in need of a distinguished university are often those where money will not suffice to create one. No amount of money will induce

[7] Clark Kerr, *The Uses of the University* (Harvard University Press, 1963), p. 74.

[8] Alan Peacock and Jack Wiseman have proposed that a commission be appointed "to assess the capital endowment of the existing university-type institutions in order to provide a basis for once-for-all capital grants intended to equalize the 'capital-student ratio' . . . , for example, by bringing all the 'poorer' universities up year by year to some specified percentage of the endowments of the richer ones" (in *Education for Democrats* [Institute of Economic Affairs, London, 1964], p. 60). As Britain has fewer universities than the United States, relative to population, such grants would be correspondingly more expensive here.

some eminent men, who enjoy the freedom that eminence bestows, to suffer the general sense of discomfort and isolation in what is to them an environment alien (if not hostile) to scholarship, to ideas, and to their personal habits and values. This is the larger significance of the Atomic Energy Commission's effort to locate its 200 Bev accelerator near a center that "will provide intellectual and cultural opportunities for staff and families," and it sets certain limits, which have been inadequately acknowledged, on optimistic efforts to bring instant science to the hinterland.[9]

But, of course, a great university, like a great oak, cannot be established merely by eliminating local hostility; it must receive exceptional, steady, and protracted nourishment. There are in this nation a number of vigorous institutions, in friendly locations, which have prospered markedly in recent decades and now enjoy prospects for national recognition. What they lack, apparently, is the requisite scale and range of scholarly activity and the requisite concentration not just of bright young faculty (which they have) but of nationally and internationally renowned authorities. The demands—the clannishness and fussiness—of some scientists and scholars can surely rival those of society dames and are not easy for any community to satisfy. How many more intellectual than financial or cultural capitals can a nation have?

What Are the University's Goals?

A consequence—indeed, an objective—of both formula and development grants is a shift in power from individual faculty to that ineffable body which some seminar members called the "collective faculty" or the "faculty as a whole" and to more readily identifiable administrators with

[9] Cf. the following observation in a report of the Graduate Research Center of the Southwest: ". . . [T]he attracting and holding in numbers of faculty of outstanding accomplishment and international reputation has been difficult in the Southwest. A major institution tried six years ago to use offers of $25,000 per year along with endowed research to lure top people to this region, but the efforts were unsuccessful even though the salary was 50% above salaries being earned in the Midwest by the men sought. Fortunately, this picture is changing . . ." ("Report of the Visiting Committee of the Graduate Research Center of the Southwest, April 9, 1964" [Richardson, Tex.], p. 3). For the considerations involved in siting a major new accelerator, see the statement submitted by Commissioner G. F. Tape to Congressman Chet Holifield, in *High Energy Physics Research*, Hearings before the Subcommittee on Research, Development, and Radiation of the Joint Committee on Atomic Energy, 89 Cong. 1 sess. (March 1965), p. 695.

broad institutional responsibilities such as presidents, deans, and department chairmen. Page describes the shift and the reasons for it:

> In the Science Development Program, as in other federal forms of institutional support, it is essential that there be careful and continuous planning which encompasses the institution's entire educational and research program. . . . Where an academic anarchy of autonomous departments and colleges prevails, an institution will have to bring order. . . . The president and his top lieutenants must exert more authority in setting policy and seeing to its execution. Resistance from faculty members who have been free agents . . . must be expected. . . . [Presidents] alone are charged with responsibility for the administration of the entire institution, and they cannot discharge that responsibility effectively without controls which many have let slip away in recent years. Correspondingly, faculty members must start thinking institutionally, and academic administrators will have to help them to do so (pp. 111–12).

The specialized, self-generated goals of individual scientists and scientific professions have found a natural outlet, a natural administrative expression, in the project system. What broader and more communal goals will be expressed in the broader forms of institutional support? What *should* be the goals of scientific research and education in the modern university?

The seminar grappled with this problem repeatedly, but did not subdue it. Page expressed disappointment that so many institutional plans are so conventional: ". . . [P]lans are usually projections of present actualities, not imaginative ventures into unknown academic frontiers" (p. 109). Independently, Dael Wolfle observed the same phenomenon and expressed the hope that more diverse and original institutional goals can be encouraged:

> Too many of the institutions that are changing their roles—typically but by no means exclusively the state teachers colleges that are becoming state colleges or universities—seem to see only one proper model to follow: the great, complex university. . . . We need to foster the development of diverse criteria of excellence so that, with realistic appreciation of their own special situations, different institutions can strive toward different goals instead of all trying to head in the same direction.[10]

Wolfle assigned to the government considerable responsibility for this situation, since "[m]ost of the federal money for higher education is so administered as to put a premium on size, number of students, amount of research, or other characteristics of the big university."[11] Though this

---

[10] Dael Wolfle, "Diversity of Institutional Goals," editorial in *Science*, November 19, 1965.

[11] *Ibid.*

is doubtless true, it is also true that the government does not bear sole responsibility and that, to a considerable extent, government programs are formulated to give special constituencies at least some of the things that they want. Which returns us to the question: What does the scientific university want? Insofar as anyone answered that question explicitly, it was probably Harvey Brooks:

> I would list the primary functions of the university as follows: (1) to add through research and scholarship to man's understanding of himself and the world in which he lives; (2) to integrate newly acquired knowledge into our total intellectual structure, to systematize and organize knowledge for each generation; (3) to communicate existing understanding and knowledge through formal teaching, writing, and other kinds of communication to the intellectual public and to train the next generation of scholars through apprenticeship; (4) to be the custodian of the intellectual standards of society and to maintain intellectual leadership in the major fields of human knowledge and its long-term applications.
> Research is essential to all of these functions, but especially to the maintenance of intellectual leadership. The universities must be able to attract and hold a fair proportion of the best minds in each generation in each major intellectual field (p. 64).

These are noble enough goals, which many universities would probably accept; but are they narrow enough for the purposes of academic and public policy? Several additional points must first be clarified: (*a*) the degree to which it is essential or desirable for each function to be performed by each and every university and the degree to which it may, instead, be performed only somewhere in the national university complex; (*b*) the degree to which each function is unique to the university or shared with other institutions such as industrial, governmental, and independent nonprofit laboratories; and (*c*) the weight or priority that should be assigned to each function.

The position that "the university" adopts on these points is founded on its particular traditions and immediate practical alternatives. And, since 1945, the practical alternatives, and the horizons, of many American universities have expanded greatly. As Don Price observes, the universities, "especially the great public institutions, have grown into a powerful interest group which, in influence with the Congress, takes its place along with the businessman and the farmer" (p. 26). (A modest Harvard dean, he singles out "the great public institutions," but *their* spokesmen are apt to single out the private. In fact, the political prizes have been shared, although opinions differ on which group has won more than its share and, for that matter, on what its fair share should come to.) It could be argued that what the strong modern university needs more than income and influence is the power to say no—or, as Babbidge puts it, "the integrity and the will power to walk past parts of the Great Society Smorgasbord" (p. 330). The ability (or inability) to delimit a set of goals which are both attainable and worth attaining and to hew to them despite countless temptations and the downward turns of fortune defines the character of an institution as it does that of a man.

Bigger and Bigger Science

"Big science," and particularly the biggest pure science of all, high energy physics, holds many fascinations—the scale and nicety of its engineering, the complexities of its politics and administration, the exotic character of its knowledge (and of some of its scientists). But it poses a special challenge to that intimate, intertwined process of research and education involving professor and graduate student in the academic model of "little science," which Panofsky holds to be in part a romantic illusion (pp. 189 ff.). To fulfill the ideal of participating in "each major intellectual field," the university can hardly forgo an interest in high energy physics; but for a graduate student to engage in research at a large high energy accelerator, Panofsky acknowledges, the university must forgo the traditional requirement that his doctoral dissertation represent an independent contribution to knowledge. Lloyd Berkner has gone farther, declaring that "the great machines can certainly not be used for education or training activities in the ordinary sense, because their capacity must be reserved for those experiments likely to extend the boundaries of knowledge most effectively." The primary function of a national laboratory's operating a major accelerator, he has stated, "must be pure research at the most advanced level with educational activities as distinctly secondary"; the educational function must be performed at many small accelerators that should be provided on campus.[12]

[12] Lloyd Berkner, "The Role of the National Laboratory in American Scientific Progress," *Physics Today*, April 1958, p. 20. Cf. the conclusion of the Ramsey committee: "The larger the installation, the more difficult it becomes to give an inexperienced graduate student independent responsibility for a given piece of research. For this reason, the principal educational function of the high energy centers is shifting gradually from pre-doctoral to post-doctoral education. Nevertheless, the accelerator center should consider the training of graduate students to be an essential goal, and the centers and the cooperating universities should make all possible efforts to facilitate constructive grad-

Doubtless, as was noted during the discussions, graduate students can find intellectual excitement doing their part in a critical experiment as a member of a large team (pp. 203–04). But is it unduly cynical to suggest that the teams are organized by professors and that the accelerators are built for them and not for the students? It may be said that the accelerators are not built for the pleasure of professors (who dislike the delays and complications of obtaining access) any more than for that of the engineers who design them, the contractors who construct them, or the utilities who satisfy their cavernous hunger for electricity. They are built to pursue the truth, and many physicists are deeply troubled about how expensive this is getting to be. For, if the rich grades of scientific ore have already been gutted and it costs more and more to exploit the poorer grades, pure science, which once prided itself on its cheapness, will eventually become uneconomic. That is one of several equally dismal prospects for the eventual fate of science envisaged by Nobel physicist Richard Feynman.[13]

Statesmen and physicists have devoted much effort to stabilizing the technology of nuclear weapons and missiles. The doctrine enunciated by Edward Teller that there should be no limit to the nation's search for new nuclear knowledge and technology has been resisted by many, if not most, of his fellow physicists. Will they also try to stabilize the escalating technology of pure physics?

A Global View of Research and Development

If there is one handicap native to close and continuing observers of the Washington scene, it is the difficulty of getting a global view of the kind

---

uate-student participation" (U.S. Atomic Energy Commission, *Report of the Panel on High Energy Accelerator Physics of the General Advisory Committee to the Atomic Energy Commission and the President's Science Advisory Committee*, April 26, 1963, p. 11).

[13] "What of the future of this adventure? What will happen ultimately? . . . It seems to me that what can happen in the future is either that all the laws become known . . . or it may happen that the experiments get harder and harder to make, more and more expensive, so you get 99.9 per cent of the phenomena, but there is always some phenomenon which has just been discovered, which is very hard to measure, and which disagrees; and as soon as you have the explanation of that one there is always another one, and it gets slower and slower and more and more uninteresting. That is another way it may end. But I think it has to end one way or another" (Richard Feynman, *The Character of Physical Law* [The M.I.T. Press, 1967], p. 172).

that, from afar, seems so obvious (and is often so superficial). As experienced Washington hands, seminar members were so familiar with the individualized pragmatic character of scientific agencies and their overlord and patron committees on the Hill that they may well have underestimated the government-wide and interagency forces that can arise in peace as well as war. So they tended to evaluate the prospects of an agency's scientific program or appropriation in isolation from any other, as if a national budget did not exist or were infinitely distensible and as if a decision about the budget of one agency had no effect upon that of another. This attitude was exhibited most clearly in the seminar's reaction to William Carey's proposal that a yearly report on federal programs of scientific research and development be submitted by the Executive to the Congress (see pp. 271 ff.). Basically, the group rejected the notion that "research" and "development"—for example, academic research and military development—had anything in common or enough in common to warrant the preparation of such a report; and they were equally dubious about either the technical or the political comparability of the varied agency research programs that end up on campuses.

Since Carey made that proposal, it has been endorsed by the *New York Times;* a similar recommendation by the House Committee on Government Operations has been endorsed by the National Academy of Sciences' Committee on Science and Public Policy; whilst the House Committee on Science and Astronautics has proposed that the National Science Board prepare such a report, and staff are already working on a first draft.[14] Perhaps it may not prove to be so impossible or undesirable after all.

[14] Following publication of Carey's paper in the November 6, 1965, *Saturday Review,* a *New York Times* editorial, "Allocating Science Funds," concluded: "William Carey of the Bureau of the Budget has suggested that there might be an annual scientific report to the nation comparable to the President's annual Economic Report. Taken together, such a comprehensive overview of the field, plus the briefs prepared by spokesmen for each major area of research, would permit more intelligent discussion of the problems of allocating science funds and perhaps lead to more rational decisions on those problems" (December 7, 1965).

The House Committee on Government Operations recommended that "[t]he Executive Office should publish yearly a 'Science and Technology Report,' similar in scope to the Economic Report. The report should discuss the outlines and directions of policy on science and technology on which Federal actions have been based, an evaluation of the economy and efficiency of Federal program performance in the light of R&D invested, and recommendations for the period ahead. The report should discuss the Federal role in science and technology in relation to other sectors, private and public, and with respect

Nevertheless, the seminar was probably quite right about the nature of most R&D budgeting. Elmer Staats's account of the preparation of the fiscal year 1967 budget (pp. 213–22) makes amply clear how discrete and independent most major budgetary decisions remain—as well as the efforts of the Executive Office of the President to impose upon them such order and rationality as circumstances permit.

After Hiroshima and Nagasaki, the connection between pure science and military technology seemed close; after Project Hindsight, it seems more remote.[15] Around Cambridge, the relation between basic research

---

to scientific manpower as well as money" (*Federal Research and Development Programs: The Decisionmaking Process,* Thirty-fourth Report by the House Committee on Government Operations, H. Rept. 1664, 89 Cong. 2 sess. [June 27, 1966], p. 41).

On this recommendation, the NAS Committee on Science and Public Policy commented, "We concur, while recognizing the unusual difficulty and magnitude of such a task." Budget Director Charles Schultze was more equivocal: ". . . I believe that such a report might well be useful in providing broad perspectives on the content, goals, and priorities of federally sponsored R&D. It does seem to me, however, that for such a report to be the high-quality product that is envisaged, a considerable investment of scarce man-hours would be required, and I am not sure that such an intensive effort can be accommodated at this time in the face of other priorities. However, I would defer to the views of the Director of the Office of Science and Technology for further comment on this matter" (*Federal Research and Development Programs: The Decisionmaking Process,* Eighth Report by the House Committee on Government Operations, 90 Cong. 1 sess. [August 28, 1967], pp. 11, 16).

In its report on proposed legislation to amend the National Science Foundation Act, the House Committee on Science and Astronautics stated: "The [National Science] Board has been given a major new responsibility—that of rendering an annual report to the Congress on the status and health of science and its various disciplines. The committee believes that such a report will be of inestimable value to Congress in its deliberations on policy matters which depend or impinge upon science and technology—and that the Board is admirably conceived and composed to do the job.

"However, there is no intent here to pin a time-consuming, repetitive task on either the Board or the Foundation staff. The committee would not expect a complete evaluation and report each year on every science discipline or every phase of technology. The committee would expect the Board to be selective, to report on areas and developments which appear to it most significant, most timely, where achievement has occurred, or where the greatest gaps and needs exist. The committee is thinking, in this regard, in terms of a report to the Nation somewhat akin to the President's annual Economic Report" (*Amending the National Science Foundation Act of 1950 To Make Improvements in the Organization and Operation of the Foundation,* H. Rept. No. 1650, 89 Cong. 2 sess. [June 23, 1966], p. 21).

[15] Project Hindsight, a major investigation by the Department of Defense of the scientific and technical foundations of new military weapons systems, concluded that an insignificant proportion rested upon ideas or knowledge yielded by the pure or undirected (as distinct from applied or directed) research of the last twenty years. "The results of the study do not call in question the value of undirected science on the 50-

and industrial innovation seems clear; around Cleveland, it is less evident (see p. 226). Advocates of federal expenditures for academic science have taken both positions: that as the progress of technology is tied to the progress of science, the government should devote to science some fraction of its expenditures on technological development; and that as science differs inherently from technology, the two should not be lumped together for budgetary purposes. In recent years, the latter position has become more popular, and insofar as the complications of the budgetary and political processes permit, an effort has been made to formulate a government-wide budget for academic science and engineering. This approach was reflected in the March 1964 letter from presidential science adviser Donald Hornig to Senator John O. Pastore (see pp. 333–36);[16] in the March 1965 recommendation of various members of the National Academy of Sciences that the National Science Foundation serve as a "balance wheel" in agency expenditures for academic research;[17] in the implementation of that recommendation during the preparation of the fiscal year 1966 budget;[18] and in attempts to improve

---

year-or-more time scale. In light of our finding that 5 to 10 years are often required before even a piece of highly applied research is 'fitted in' as an effective contributing member of a large assembly of Events [discoveries], it is not surprising that 'fragments' of undirected science are infrequently utilized on even a 20-year time scale" (Chalmers W. Sherwin and Raymond S. Isenson, "Project Hindsight," *Science,* June 23, 1967, p. 1577).

[16] Of particular significance was Hornig's statement that the level of federal support for high energy physics "must be determined and periodically reassessed in the context of . . . the overall national science program (rather than in relation to the applied research and development programs of the AEC) . . ." (p. 335). See also the discussion on pp. 186–88.

[17] See *Basic Research and National Goals,* A Report to the House Committee on Science and Astronautics by the National Academy of Sciences, 89 Cong. 1 sess. (March 1965), p. 24.

[18] ". . . [I]t is estimated that in fiscal year 1966 an overall increase of about 15 percent in total Federal support for research at academic institutions will be needed merely to maintain a constant relative level of research activity in those institutions—to hold our own, so to speak. A substantial part of this increase will be provided by Federal agencies that have specific missions to perform. . . . Inspection of the budgets being proposed for fiscal year 1966 by these agencies provide for somewhat less than the desired 15 percent increase in the support of academic research. Because of the Foundation's responsibility for the strength of basic science and for science education, the Office of Science and Technology and the Bureau of the Budget proposed, and the President adopted the concept that the Foundation's budget for academic research should be sufficiently large to assure the neccessary 15 percent increase in overall Federal support" (NSF Director Leland Haworth, in *Independent Offices Appropriations for 1966,* Hear-

statistics on scientific expenditures at higher educational institutions so that they can be more useful for policy purposes.[19]

Harvey Brooks's conclusion that federal expenditures for academic research should increase at least 15 percent a year for a number of years (see pp. 71–76) was one significant outcome of this effort to prepare, in effect, a special (or between-the-acts) federal budget for university science.[20] That conclusion was accepted by the administration in fiscal years 1966 and 1967 but not, apparently (in view of the Vietnam war), in fiscal year 1968.[21]

---

ings before a Subcommittee of the House Committee on Appropriations, 89 Cong. 1 sess. [March 23, 1965], p. 574).

[19] The most significant of these new statistical series has been initiated under the auspices of the interagency Committee on Academic Science and Engineering, chaired by NSF Director Haworth (see *Federal Support for Academic Science and Other Educational Activities in Universities and Colleges, Fiscal Year 1965,* Prepared by the National Science Foundation for the Office of Science and Technology, National Science Foundation [1966], and *Federal Support for Academic Science and Other Educational Activities in Universities and Colleges, Fiscal Years 1963–66,* Prepared by the National Science Foundation for the Office of Science and Technology [National Science Foundation, 1967]).

[20] That is, adjustments were made by the Budget Bureau in the proposed budget of the National Science Foundation after the university research budgets of other agencies were in but before the entire Executive budget was submitted to Congress.

[21] See Elmer Staats, p. 220: "In the 1966 budget, we [the Bureau of the Budget] agreed with Leland Haworth [director of the National Science Foundation] and Donald Hornig [director of the Office of Science and Technology] to aim for a 15 percent growth in basic research funds going to the universities. We came out of Congress with some 17 percent in toto. . . . This year [fiscal 1967], because of the budget stringency, we are not doing as well."

In August 1966, HEW Secretary John Gardner stated: "Much speculation has been directed to the identification of the necessary rate of growth of graduate research and education. Some say that a rate of 15 percent per year is the necessary minimum increase in level of support. But I have not yet encountered the thorough economic analysis that one might expect to lie behind such a widely quoted figure" (remarks to a Meeting of Consultants, National Institutes of Health, August 23, 1966). By the following spring, OST Director Donald Hornig was talking along similar lines: ". . . [O]ver all the doubling period [in federal expenditures for basic research] was of the order of 4 to 5 years through much of the two decades following World War II. What has changed now is not that there are restraints to be imposed on science either by the Congress or by the Executive, but that the initial vacuum has largely been filled and a new situation has arisen which requires new thought. . . . We accept as the goals that America must be second to none in most of the significant fields of science. . . . What is *not* accepted is the notion that every part of science should grow at some automatic and predetermined rate, 15 percent per year or any other number . . ." (address to the American Physical Society, Washington, D.C., April 26, 1967, pp. 7–8).

On Rationalizing the Irrational

One need not agree entirely with Brooks to recognize his contributions
to the difficult craft of budgeting—the more touchy word is "planning"
—for science. "It is a most capricious kind of activity," remarked one
seminar member of federal science budgeting, and anyone who has had
any contact with the process would have to agree. No theme preoccupied
the seminar more than the amount of planning which is both possible
and desirable in government science programs: the balance that can and
should be struck between arbitrariness and rationality, between politics
and rationality, between the capricious or accidental and the systematiz-
able or plannable elements in federal allocations for science.

"Why should we expect more of scientific programs than of other government programs?" a government physicist asked. Perhaps we should
not; but it seems particularly ignominious for scientists who are such advocates of reason in their professional work to forsake it in their public
affairs. And so the efforts of Hendrik Bode (pp. 123–36) and Alvin
Weinberg (pp. 153–64) to explicate the criteria upon which funds
might rationally be allocated among various scientific fields are a distinct
service to political rationality. It may be, as Bode observes, that, while
these efforts are intellectually stimulating, they do not yet give the administrator any practical help in making budgetary decisions (p. 125).
They do, however, discharge the scientist's responsibility to foster informed public discussion of government decisions in the scientific arena
and to engage in that discussion not solely as advocate but also as analyst
and, if need be, critic.

In the process of public discussion, the role of the Congress has been
indispensable, as Roback indicates (pp. 233–54). Some readers may
agree with some seminar participants that the authorizing committees of
Congress could profitably sharpen their critical function and, at least
upon occasion, offer a forum for critics as well as proponents of Executive
R&D programs (see p. 255). Nonetheless, on balance it is the lay
Congress which has of late been asking the searching questions about
government science policies and which has generated the largest volume
of fresh information needed to answer these questions, whereas Executive
science agencies have usually employed their expertise to defend rather
than to evaluate their policies.

The more compact British scene reviewed by Harry Melville (pp. 311–12) affords useful insights for American policy. As we have noted, American policy has been moving slowly toward the award of relatively more funds in broader forms; the British University Grants Committee's five-year institutional grants unfettered by categorical purpose or parliamentary review are often cited as a model we should emulate. But in Britain, the movement has been in precisely the opposite direction, toward a greater emphasis upon project research. And the reason is clear: whereas Britain needs to modernize its industry and to increase the number of industrial personnel with advanced scientific and technical qualifications, the call of the classics and of pure science is still so strong that unfettered grants would simply not be used sufficiently for such mundane purposes.

In brief, the purposes of the academy and those of the nation are not identical—or, as Weinberg remarks, "society is not a university"[22]—and one would not want them to be. Broadly as one may define the university's interests in scientific research and education, they are not identical with those of the nation; nor should they be. The resultant tensions between the university's service to the nation and to itself, between science's homage to government and to nature, are explored in succeeding pages.

[22] Alvin Weinberg, "But Is the Teacher Also a Citizen?" in Boyd Keenan (ed.), *Science and the University* (Columbia University Press, 1966), p. 175.

PART I

*Federal Money
and Academic Science*

DON K. PRICE

Federal Money
and University Research

THE RECENT hearings by the Daddario subcommittee
on the record and the mission of the National Science Foundation give
us an opportunity to reconsider the whole subject of government support
of university research. When I was asked, along with many other witnesses, to submit my views, I said that I thought the foundation had
been a remarkable success.‾ And so it has. By any crude measure of political or financial success it would be hard to beat. Vannevar Bush and
his cohorts first proved their ability to turn basic theory into practical ac-
complishments during World War II. Then they persuaded a suspicious
and jealous Congress that basic science was worth supporting for its own
sake—or at any rate without inquiring too closely about its connection
with practical results.

This was an impressive short-run triumph. Even more impressive was
the fact that it reversed, apparently, some of the nation's most cherished
long-range political habits or prejudices. Tocqueville, for example, had
observed a century earlier that in the United States "a science is taken up
as a matter of business, and the only branch of it which is attended to is

This paper, which was originally presented to the Brookings seminar on October 6,
1965, was published by permission in the January 21, 1966, issue of *Science,* pp. 285–90.

[1] *Government and Science: Review of the National Science Foundation,* Hearings before the Subcommittee on Science, Research, and Development of the House Committee
on Science and Astronautics, 89 Cong. 1 sess. (1965), no. 6, vol. 1, p. 241.

such as admits of an immediate practical application."[2] Later he went on
to say that "the spirit of Americans is averse to general ideas; and it
does not seek theoretical discoveries."[3] This general observation could
have still been considered applicable to American science one hundred
years later, in the 1930's. For a century or so Americans not only accepted Tocqueville's verdict but gloried in it. Mark Twain's *Connecticut
Yankee* typified the pride in the practical and useful, the scorn for
theory, the glory in self-support and contempt for government authority,
that seemed at the end of the nineteenth century typical of the United
States.

It was no mean feat to overturn this traditional attitude. Yet by the
middle of the twentieth century, the picture was radically different. Federal tax funds were going to the support of academic science that made
no claim of immediate utility. You can measure the input by the hundreds of millions of dollars per year and the output in Nobel prizes and
articles in scientific journals; by either standard it has been an impressive
performance. These are the things that impress scientists most. But students of politics should, I think, be more interested in a by-product of
this revolution in the relation of science and politics—should be concerned not merely with the impact of government support on science but
with the impact of science on government.

The Impact of Science on Government

Tocqueville's was only one of two characteristic European predictions
about America in the nineteenth century that turned out to be all wrong
in the twentieth. The other was Macaulay's. He observed—and it is significant that this came not from a Tory but from a Liberal and the father
of the reformed civil service—that the American Constitution was "all
sail and no anchor"; by abolishing the special status of the aristocracy
and the special privileges of the wealthy, Thomas Jefferson had turned
over political power to the envious masses, who would soon tear down all
the institutions on which civilization depended and bring us to anarchy
or socialism or—by way of reaction—to military despotism in the style
of Napoleon III.[4]

[2] Alexis de Tocqueville, *Democracy in America* (Colonial Press, 1899), p. 52.
[3] *Ibid.*, p. 320.
[4] Letter of Lord Macaulay to H. S. Randall, May 23, 1857, published in *Harper's
New Monthly Magazine*, February 1877, p. 460.

It seems to me that the failure of Macaulay's prediction had some relation to the failure of Tocqueville's. The building up of strong independent scientific institutions, now supported in part by government
money and with a long history of interest in government policy, and the
tremendous strength, within the federal system, of corps of scientific
personnel with an extraordinary influence on policy and an extraordinary
capacity to resist political control or discipline have helped us create a
constitutional system that, to admirers of parliamentary responsibility,
seems all anchor and no sail.

But even though this general political speculation may be relevant, let
us get down to the precise topic of this seminar. It is clear that we have
made a revolution in the relation of the federal government to colleges
and universities. In that sense, we are dealing with a new problem. But
even though we have come a long way from Tocqueville and Macaulay,
we have not completely abandoned all our old political habits. And political and administrative professionals cannot afford to waste time indulg-
ing themselves in political self-congratulation. For nothing is so tempo-
rary in politics as a great victory.

This particular victory, it seems to me, rests on a rather shaky pair of
foundations—namely, the reaction to the depression and the fear of war.
You remember the couplet,

> The Devil was sick, the Devil a monk would be;
> The Devil was well, the devil a monk was he.

The immediate occasion of our conversion to government support of
basic science was of course the fright of World War II. The scientists
had performed miracles that enabled us to win the war and that prom-
ised to help us establish endless prosperity. They accordingly became as
popular and respected as the businessmen had become in the 1920's,
after they helped mobilize America's industrial power in World War I.
As the experience of the businessmen in 1929 suggests, this is not necessarily a guarantee of permanent popularity.

The depression was probably responsible for a change in our national
mood or attitude that, even before World War II, did much to change
the status of science in our political system. It was the notion of automatic progress, based on a union of applied science and free private enterprise, that had let the leaders of America assume that politics and
government were not things that need concern the best minds in the
country. The depression shattered that faith. Moreover, it came along at
a time when leading scientists were painfully aware that wherever sci-

ence is taken up only as a matter of business, as Tocqueville observed, it is sure to be a second-class kind of science and also at a time when Marxist intellectuals throughout Europe were posing fundamental questions regarding the connections between the philosophy of science and political ideas.

Out of all this ferment something had to bubble up. To the extent that, even before World War II, the depression had begun to lead politicians and scientists to take each other more seriously, it probably provided a more enduring basis for a satisfactory relationship between the two than did the threat of war.

Predicting Difficulties

Yet it would be naïve to assume that the present volume of government grants to universities for theoretical science could have been stimulated solely by a zeal for pure learning on the part of administrators or congressmen. The mixed motives that have led to this tremendous volume of appropriations are likely to lead to difficulties in the long run. If we want to try to predict the main types of trouble that are likely to arise in the future, in order to safeguard against them, we should do two things.

First, we should quit hypnotizing ourselves by projecting the trends of the past fifteen or twenty years. Even if this rate of increase could continue indefinitely, which I take to be impossible, it could do so only by including within our definition of research a lot of work that would necessarily be different in kind or in quality from the type of science we have been seeking to support in the past.

In terms of sheer quantity, however, I venture the guess that we shall continue to try to explore the endless frontiers of federal subsidy for scientific research. Businesses have been persuaded that scientific progress is the key to industrial prosperity. Military planners are certain that it is the key to military strength. The universities themselves, especially the great public institutions, have grown into a powerful interest group which, in influence with the Congress, takes its place along with the businessman and the farmer. And perhaps the most powerful fact of all is that the executive hierarchy is infiltrated at the top levels with men whose personal interests and training are conditioned by scientific and technical education or by career patterns which lead them to look to institutions outside the government service for intellectual leadership. The nature of the executive hierarchy is reinforced by the nature of the constitutional structure: the committees of Congress are not as disposed to follow the leadership of a disciplined political party, or a disciplined central bureaucracy, as to follow the rather diverse leadership of the specialized committees. They, of course, are tempted to run off in all directions at once and to give far more weight to the opinion of experts, or to the results of scientific research, than to any central political leadership.

We used to think that this would work only in fields where hardheaded politicians would be persuaded by practical results—the big bang of modern weapons or the magic bullets by which medical research would provide miraculous cures for dangerous diseases. But now that the Office of Education has managed to persuade congressmen to support research on the process of education itself—and has even wangled support for its program from the professional educators themselves—it seems clear that there are hardly any limits on the amount of money we will choose to spend on research grants.

But the availability of money is not the only thing to worry about. Even though universities may be getting ample grants, they are certain to run into other political difficulties. And so my second suggestion, if we are to try to guess at the types of political problems that may arise in the near future, is that we should look to the past for some lessons. For this purpose we should quit, for the moment, admiring the great success story of the Bush report and the National Science Foundation and look back on some of the earlier political failures that are within the memory of living men. The record of some of our failures will perhaps suggest some of the major problems, some of the fundamental political attitudes, that complicate the relation of government to science in our political history.

Quite arbitrarily, I think I would choose four of the failures as starting points for speculation. These are the Science Advisory Board of 1933–35; the National Research Fund; the Kilgore bill, in which a national science foundation was first seriously proposed; and the Research Board for National Security. Let me take up each of them in turn, not merely to explore ancient history, but in order to introduce some contemporary problems.

Science Advisory Board, 1933–35

The Science Advisory Board was the first committee of eminent scientists that the executive branch ever asked for comprehensive advice on national policy. President Roosevelt commissioned a blue-ribbon panel from the National Academy of Sciences and National Research Council, under the chairmanship of Karl T. Compton, to produce a program to beat the depression. The program, to the horror of the Sanhedrin of the academy, proposed federal grants to universities, private and public alike, and cited as precedent for government grants to the Ivy League the long history of federal aid to the land-grant colleges. The program might have gone through in spite of the fear on the part of the private universities that their status would be compromised if it had not been for Honest Harold Ickes, who stood pat on the old tradition: public aid should go only to public institutions.[5]

On the face of the matter, we have completely abandoned Ickes' point of view. He represented the staunch old faith that public funds should be devoted only to public purposes and, moreover, that a strict line should be drawn between private institutions, which are not dedicated to public purposes, and government agencies, which are. This was the distinction that led the United States to end its support of ecclesiastical establishments, discontinue the awarding of monopolies to private business, and stop the licensing of privateers in time of war—in short, to eliminate the last vestiges of guilds and feudalism in our political system.

Since we are now clearly relying heavily on private institutions, through various types of governmental grants or contractual arrangements, we have the automatic impulse to safeguard the public interest by tightening the specifications and the inspection of performance under the contracts. This is all to the good if the government is buying goods or services that can be precisely specified in advance. On the other hand, if it makes a deliberate political judgment that our national purposes will be advanced by supporting and enlarging the amount of scientific research that is carried on in independent universities (whether private or state), because the very quality of independence produces results that are more in the public interest than results that could be produced within the regular administrative hierarchy, then we have a very different situation. Then we are obliged to ask whether our administrative and contractual arrangements are really designed to carry out this policy judgment. It seems clear to me that they are not, perhaps because we never explicitly made such a national policy judgment. Instead, we

[5] Lewis E. Auerbach, "Scientists in the New Deal," *Minerva*, Summer 1965, pp. 457–82.

backed into it, making every effort not to look at what we were doing. We pretended that we were only buying specific pieces of research from independent sellers or that we were only supporting by grants particular projects that would add to the sum total of science. And we woke up in surprise to find that these bits of support were about to convert our national system of independent universities into a system dependent in large measure on federal support, since project grants had displaced other funds within university budgets, with the result that, indirectly, even the humanities had benefited from them.

Now, of course, the terms of that relationship are being debated between government and university officials. And the ways in which universities have traditionally run their affairs do not make it easy to assure conscientious auditors and contract officers that the public interest is being protected. In the past, much of the private money that has come to the universities has come from bequests, or from enthusiastic alumni who do not know or care very much about the details of the scholarly interests that are being supported, or from knowledgeable donors who do know and who respect the necessity of leaving researchers a great deal of freedom to pursue their unpredictable purposes. In none of these relationships do university scientists become accustomed to justifying the details of their work to the sources of their funds.

Moreover, universities have commonly tolerated, or encouraged, a large amount of individual entrepreneurship; their professors have never been entirely dependent on their salaries for their incomes. The resistance of the faculty of the University of Chicago a generation ago to an employment contract which offered somewhat higher salary in return for an agreement to turn outside earnings over to the university is a good illustration of the practical faith in freewheeling individual enterprise even among those who doubt its merits in political theory. The general freedom of professors to accept royalties from their writings, fees for consulting and lecturing, and various kinds of special payments from special sources has encouraged habits that make the government-university relationship difficult. The inclination, for example, to pick up a bit of extra money for work during the summer or on weekends could be ignored when such opportunities were open only in exceptional cases. But when universities began to use federal funds to offer prospective faculty members extra compensation for summer work or reduced teaching loads so that they could earn outside consulting fees, the matter of outside earnings obviously became a policy issue of some importance.

But the problem is hard to deal with because this kind of individual enterprise in financial matters corresponds to the kind of freedom and initiative in intellectual matters that characterizes the most productive centers of scientific research.

Now I am unable to join those who deny that there is a problem or that it can be dealt with by asserting that professors are morally superior to other people and can be trusted with funds without being subjected to any administrative check whatever. A few years of experience in a grant-making foundation is likely to give anyone a more pessimistic view of human nature. Nevertheless, it is by no means clear that we can solve the problem by imposing on the universities the kind of overly detailed centralized checks that, within the government itself, have proved so wasteful and so destructive of responsibility.

Perhaps the first thing is for the universities themselves to recognize their responsibilities more clearly. It is obvious that their relationship to the government is now for them big business, and it is up to them to organize themselves to handle matters accordingly. On this point, I need say no more than was said in 1964 by the Committee on Science and Public Policy of the National Academy of Sciences in its report *Federal Support of Basic Research in Institutions of Higher Learning:* The strengthening of university administration, in order to discharge fully whatever responsibility for the custody and expenditure of public funds may be involved in research grants, is a basic necessity.

But from the point of view of the federal government, it is by no means clear that its own interests are protected by the maximum amount of detailed supervision of universities or detailed bookkeeping within universities. We learned (at least in theory) more than a generation ago that the kind of detailed checking that then went on in the General Accounting Office saved very little in the way of expenditures and cost tremendous amounts in the effectiveness of management. Something analogous seems to me to be going on now in the relation of grant-making agencies to universities.

The auditors and investigators who are the guardians of our public conscience tell us that we must check on the detailed performance of detailed obligations in this relationship, just as in any other. Thus we see the beginnings of a steady multiplication of paper work and the filling out of reports on time spent on work done under particular project grants. Thus, too, we see a new requirement for cost sharing. And the question is raised whether a questionnaire circulated by a university aided by a federal grant should not be controlled by the Budget Bureau as if it were a government questionnaire.

It is easier for the President to say, perhaps on the advice of his Science Advisory Committee, that "more support will be provided under terms which give the university and the investigator wider scope for inquiry, as contrasted with highly specific, narrowly defined projects," and to emphasize the fact that in "the vital top segment" of higher education "education and research become inseparable"[6] than to get these fine generalizations translated into practice by auditors and contracting officers. From my personal point of view, the worst thing about the nature of this relationship at the working level is that it gives the leaders of American higher education, who are going to have a profound influence on what the next generation of college students thinks about government and politics, a wrong impression of what "administration" is and one that is a powerful deterrent to the selection of public service as a career.

Similarly, the principle of cost sharing, which makes a great deal of sense if a small foundation is about to go 50–50 with a university, has very little effect on the way business is handled if the proportion is set at 5 percent, as the National Science Foundation now suggests, or at $1\frac{1}{2}$ percent, which is more to the taste of Representative Melvin Laird. Matching in much larger proportions cannot be required without wrecking university programs, but matching in these proportions, even though it is better than the refusal to pay the total amount of indirect costs, is still relatively ineffectual. On the government's side, it is mainly a pious gesture, and on the university's, a continuous minor irritation and not much of an incentive toward economy.

Nevertheless, at the very minimum, those interested in the government-university relationship have to take into account the fact that there is a deeply rooted distrust of irresponsible establishments in our political tradition, our inherited ways of thinking. I for one think it is a healthy distrust if only it is put into effect in ways that correspond to the modern problem. The essence of the modern problem is that the extent of government interests is too great, and the need for positive action too broad, for the public interest to be satisfied adequately by detailed supervision at routine subordinate levels. We must find ways to delegate authority and encourage initiative and responsibility in the relation between government and universities. We should be able to do at least as well in this

---

[6] President Johnson's Statement to the Cabinet of Sept. 13, 1965, and his Memorandum to the Heads of Departments and Agencies, Sept. 14, 1965.

relationship as in state grants-in-aid, where the institution which receives the grant is made more generally responsible for the detailed accountability.

But this depends on a proper system of incentives, and *that* we do not yet have. We need something to substitute for the type of requirement that in effect asks a scholar to punch a time clock when he quits research and begins teaching or when he quits thinking about university-supported research and begins thinking about government-supported research. The filling out of forms along these lines is nothing but an invitation to creative fiction; if a university scholar is any good, he cannot possibly know where one type of activity begins and the other ends.

The problem cannot be solved by detailed bookkeeping requirements. It can only be solved by a system which gives the university an incentive to take the same point of view as that required by the higher interests of government policy. And this is of course the most powerful argument for moving, at least in part, from a system which bases support for research on a series of small, narrowly defined projects to a system of broader general grants—to the "program project" or the institutional grant.

The argument here is exactly the same as the argument against detailed line-item budgeting. Money that is available only for a narrow specific purpose is money that the general administrator has no incentive to avoid wasting, because he cannot apply any savings to any other purpose. The university cannot be given an incentive toward rigorous economy by the principle of cost sharing; this can only be done by making the grant funds available for longer periods and over broader areas of subject matter, so that the university administrator thinks of them as his "own" funds and economizes accordingly.

The main difficulty comes from contrasting government grant funds with the university's "own" funds. The very notion of private ownership is misleading in thinking about the incentives that control a university's business. The general unrestricted funds of a university are not available to be converted into personal profit. It is rather the precisely restricted funds, controlled by the intentions of the donor, which a university administration has no incentive to control in the interest of academic austerity. For this reason, I think that waste of funds would be greatly reduced if, on the whole, the government—without giving up the project grant as its main instrument of support—would move in the direction of support on a broader basis, putting more general substantive as well as financial responsibility in the hands of the university faculties and administration.

National Research Fund

The second traditional public attitude which complicates the government-university relationship is our congenital mistrust of the government career servant. The episode in our recent history that best illustrates this point was the action of the National Academy of Sciences, during the late 1920's and 1930's, in setting up the National Research Fund for the purpose of raising private funds to supply the rapidly growing basic research needs of the scientific community. To many of those who lent this effort their support, it must have seemed that this was the last chance to avert the necessity of government subsidy, which had always been anathema to the academy. It is hard to recall how deep and conscientious the objections of the scientific leaders of only a generation ago were to accepting general subsidies from government sources.

Later, when it was clear that the subsidies had to be swallowed, the pill was sugared either by an approach (especially in the initial Office of Naval Research program) that paid great deference to the academic traditions of free research or by arrangements which made the awards depend in the main on decisions, not by members of the career government service, but by panels of advisers from independent universities. Hence the statutory framework of the National Institutes of Health advisory councils and the popular practice of using outside panels for decisions on project grants.

This system obviously has great merit, especially in the making of decisions on the scientific aspects of any question. These are the aspects that predominate in judgments on particular research projects. But as the government broadens the basis on which it gives support to universities and begins to make much broader grants for institutional or program support, the specialized knowledge of a scientific advisory panel becomes proportionally less important. For a detailed argument on the decreasing extent to which the responsible official may lean on his specialized advisers, as grant-making programs come to be based less on specific research projects and more on broader types of institutional grants, I refer you to the report of the review procedures panel in *Biomedical Science and Its Administration,* a study of the National Institutes of Health.[7]

I have suggested that we should not think about the relationship of government to university research programs as one in which an increase of control by government agencies would ensure more responsible use of public funds. In fact, the reverse is true: we have reached a stage in this relationship in which it is no longer in the university's interest to keep the government weak at the level where the key decisions are made. It would be positively to the advantage of the universities, I believe, if their own members did not have so predominant an influence in making grants to each other and if the government relied a great deal more on a career government service of high quality. For if these funds are controlled entirely by panels of outside advisers, the system is in danger of degenerating into petty academic politics, because the major nonscientific issues will not be recognized and faced up to squarely. This situation can be prevented only if a strong group of career officers can, by high-quality staff work, identify the major issues for debate and decision. This will not keep the universities and the private advisers out of the act; indeed, their voice will always be more influential than that of the career bureaucracy at the top political levels where the key decisions will ultimately be made. It will only let those decisions be framed in the light of a consideration of general alternatives, which our present system does not identify clearly.

The Kilgore Bill

So far we have dealt with the broader policy issues regarding the support of science by sweeping them under the rug and by pretending that a completely free enterprise system of project grants can be backed by an unlimited continuation of increases in the amount of available funds. If we are to face these questions, we have to confront squarely the conflict between the view that governmental decisions regarding scientific institutions should be made according to the judgment of the leaders in the scientific community and the view that they should be made by political authority. This brings me to the third big failure that I would like to recall. *Failure* is not the word that most leading scientists would apply to

[7] The White House, February 1965, pp. 191–213.

it—they would consider the outcome fortunate. But the successful en-
actment, in the main, of Vannevar Bush's program was the defeat of
Senator Kilgore's. It may be useful to stop to recall that the first major
political effort for the establishment of a national science foundation was
not that of Dr. Bush but that of a West Virginia senator, who frightened all of the leading scientists by his apparent assumption that science
should be under government guidance.

In some ways, Senator Kilgore and his closest advisers took an approach to science that resembled that of Bernal, Haldane, and other
Marxists. Senator Kilgore thought that the sciences could be advanced
through subsidization as applied sciences, with an eye on practical development. Moreover, he was willing to support the social sciences on equal
terms with the natural sciences, assuming that the ultimate end of science was to solve social problems and advance the purposes of human
welfare. The similarity of these views to Marxist thought did not go un-
noticed among conservative leaders of scientific institutions. But they
might well also have noticed that in these respects Thomas Jefferson had
anticipated the Marxists. And on a key political test—the point on
which Jefferson differed most sharply from the Marxists—Senator Kilgore was clearly a Jeffersonian; in his mind science did not fit into a
tightly integrated national system in which decisions would be made on
a centralized basis. He wanted a quota system which would require that
grants be distributed among the several states much on the pattern of the
agricultural research grants and the land-grant colleges. If it was a planning of science that he favored, as the frightened leaders of the academy
warned each other, it was a populist sort of planning growing out of a
deeply American political tradition.

The Kilgore bill was defeated. Moreover, it was generally forgotten
through almost a positive effort on the part of scientists. It was pushed
back deep in our national political subconscious. But its central notions
are slipping up on us again rapidly—as the Commerce Department proposes that the "trickle down" theory will not let the nation devote a fair
share of its science to applied programs affecting domestic prosperity
and human welfare; and as the social sciences creep into the programs of
the National Institutes of Health (NIH) and the National Science
Foundation (NSF); and even more important, as the National Academy
of Sciences begins to study systematically, with the help of social scientists, the problems of organizing and supporting the natural sciences
themselves. And they are creeping back, finally, as natural scientists and

their university administrations throughout the country organize political action toward getting their share of the grants, being convinced that the problems of competition will grow worse rather than better in the future as the rate of increase of the federal research budget slows down.

What we have to worry about, it seems to me, is not that government as such will decide at high levels of authority to restrict the freedom of universities and scientific institutions. It is not that social planning will impose itself from some central power center on institutions throughout the country. It is, rather, that an even more damaging form of political interference will be generated from within the scientific community itself and that local and regional rivalries will throw so many general policy decisions into the political arena that it will be hard to work out any orderly and systematic policy for supporting science on standards of scientific quality.

Research Board for National Security

The fourth political problem of which I am reminded by one of our historic failures is the civil-military double standard. Not many people remember the brief episode, shortly after the war, of the effort to create a research board for national security. During the time when the plans for the NSF were stalemated by the disagreement over whether the director should or should not be responsible to the President, there was a considerable danger that the military services would cut off the wartime support of science before any civilian agencies were prepared to take it up. This led to the proposal that the National Academy of Sciences create a "Research Board for National Security," to which the military services would transfer funds to be given out in grants to universities and research laboratories. The director of the Bureau of the Budget stopped this move, largely because he thought that public funds should not be dispensed by a nongovernment agency like the academy and also because he anticipated President Eisenhower in his distrust of the scientific-technological elite in alliance with military power.

Harold Smith, the budget director in question, had a good bit of Harold Ickes in his political makeup. He distrusted establishments. But on this issue his opponents were more in tune with the national mood than he. As a nation we distrust only civilian establishments. It is only career civilian officers who have no political appeal—and only the civilian departments that cannot wangle from Congress a high measure of delegated authority and administrative discretion.

From the point of view of the universities and the scientific community, it was a magnificent accomplishment when the Office of Naval Research stepped into the breach and held the fort until NSF and NIH could bring up their resources—and went on holding a good part of the fort thereafter. From that time until the present, of course, the vast majority of research and development funds—even a majority of basic research funds—has come from federal agencies whose missions are not primarily the support of basic science or higher education but national security and military strength.

On this issue, I am far from being against the military services. I would give them more money for science and not less. But as a matter of balance, I think that the military basic research funds themselves are in danger of waste because to a large extent they are spent in universities which do not have adequate general support for their general functions of research and education. The Department of Defense, as a matter of fact, has shown more awareness of this point in its development of institutional and programmatic forms of support than have most of its civilian competitors. The qualities of independence and critical scholarship and leadership in basic theory, on which the whole research and development enterprise depends, will be threatened unless the central structure of the universities is made strong enough to sustain the structure of specialized research grants.

We now face the question whether the support of scientific research and higher education can be seen as a public purpose in itself. From the educational point of view we are supporting universities throughout the country by something perilously close to political subterfuge. We are putting so much larger a proportion of our money for science into specific projects, on account of the financial double standard within the United States budget which favors military over civilian purposes, that we are in danger of a serious lack of balance. It still remains true today, in spite of all the recent advances in support of research for educational purposes, that it is much easier to get funds from the Congress for purposes of military power than for general civilian objectives. The Atomic Energy Commission and National Aeronautics and Space Administration, as well as the military services, depend largely for congressional support on considerations of international power and rivalry. Aside from the case of NIH, the grants for support of applied science for civilian purposes are either tied to obsolete patterns of support, as in agriculture, or stalemated by the fear that social action will interfere with private enterprise, as in the case of the Commerce Department.

We are separated from the era of the Science Advisory Board of the mid-1930's only by a single generation, but we are now required to deal with a set of political problems—problems in which science is inescapably involved—that its members could never have foreseen. We have to learn how to support an educational and scientific establishment, including private as well as public institutions, without either destroying its freedom or leaving it in a position of privileged irresponsibility. We have to learn how to fit the research interests of free scientists into a pattern of public policy and to take account of the need for balanced national development while building up our existing centers of high scientific quality. And we need, equally obviously, to devote our knowledge to the service of human welfare as effectively as it has been enlisted in the service of national defense. We obviously have not yet learned how to do all these things. But we can at least begin, if we are not afraid to make some changes in some of our most stubborn political and administrative habits.

DISCUSSION

On the Virtues
of Broader Grants

THE DISCUSSION dwelled mainly on the virtues of broader, institutional forms of research support and the balance that should be struck between them and project support at the present juncture.

Unquestionably, the project system has great merits, permitting able men to conduct work of their own choosing, the value of which is determined by their professional peers on the basis of national standards. Indeed, its merits were so evident that they did not require (or at any rate, receive) much elaboration. It was simply noted that "the freewheeling system that exists today has all of the merits of private enterprise in any other field." Moreover, one seminar member observed sardonically, projects with limited objectives are ideally suited to a heterogeneous, pragmatic society with diverse and shifting goals, which is seemingly incapable of establishing and hewing to larger national purposes:

> . . . [I]n a society where you have very little in the way of particular goals on what research should do, . . . a project orientation should be perfect. That is, you can move and you can shift and you can make grants in terms of whims, in terms of power and influence as it may develop. . . . Now, if we had even general goals—and this is where Congress should play a very important role—then . . . institutional grants would be very, very important. We would begin to say, "Well, we ought to have a center of education some place, we ought to have a center of biology some place," and you would have these things beginning to develop. But in the kind of society where we don't have any articulate goals, who decides whether we ought to put money in biology or physics? It just seems to float up to the top. A project orientation is perfect.

This view was challenged on two grounds. For one, the Congress has clearly enunciated and consistently backed certain national goals (such as the development of advanced weapons and nuclear energy, space exploration, and medical and agricultural research). And for another, the apparent chaos of project research can be regarded as a kind of system superior to any that could consciously be devised to advance preordained goals. The government supports "science . . . in terms of its own goals because experience has taught that this is one way you achieve social goals. . . . And . . . this may be a more economical and more effective way for certain goals."

Turning philosophical, a university scientist warmly endorsed Eric Ashby's conception that a university is and properly should be an institution in which initiative essentially comes from below[1]—that is, from the faculty. But, the scientist proceeded, "This is the tradition of the Euro-

[1] See Ashby, in *Technology and the Academics* (Macmillan & Co., 1959), particularly chap. 5, "Postscript on Self-Government in Civic Universities." One pertinent passage follows: "Modern universities differ greatly as to the number of items of business which flow from below upwards. . . . By and large it is true to say that the main direction of flow of new ideas and proposals is from below upwards and not in the reverse direction.

"In a university where the flow of business is upwards and not downwards through the hierarchy, members of the academic staff are able to determine their own policies and to manage their own affairs, notwithstanding the fact that sovereignty formally resides in a governing body composed predominantly of laymen" (p. 101).

pean university. It is not as strong at the American university, but I think it is strongest in the best American universities. . . ." As the project system bolsters faculty initiative, he suggested, it helps, in the American context, to preserve the essence of a university. ". . . [T]o carry the institutional control of funds [via institutional grants] to the point where this tradition [of faculty initiative] was destroyed . . . would really be a disaster for American education."

However, another university representative, who likewise saw project grants as strengthening faculty independence, stressed that this independence helped to maintain the structural *differences* between the American and the European university: ". . . [T]his is the fundamental strength of the American academic system that distinguishes it from the one-Herr-Professor-system in a department in a German university and from the [British] University Grants Committee, which parcels money out and gives no initiative whatever to me [that is, to the individual scholar]."

Some limit was placed upon the seeming anarchy of individual faculty interests by the fact that "after all, the collective faculty does determine who gets appointed [to the university], and this is the most important decision." At times, "a good department chairman and a faculty that works together can really make do just as well with individual project grants as with institutional grants—but this is a rare situation."

Overall, it seemed desirable to increase the proportion of federal funds going in broader departmental and institutional forms as a central institutional "counterpoise" to individually financed faculty projects. The reasons adduced for providing such a counterpoise may be summarized under three headings: administrative, scientific, and institutional.

Administrative Grounds for Broader Grants

The function of accounting for (or as it was put less discretely, "policing") public funds is likely to be performed better if universities receive some funds for their own allocation and thereby have a direct financial stake in economizing. ". . . [A]s long as university administrations think that the conduct of research under project grants is really only the business of the individual investigator, they will not try to police it, even to the limited extent that . . . they ought to police it."

Simplification of administration was, a government official indicated, one of the two principal reasons advanced in the Federal Council for Science and Technology for the National Science Foundation's initial institutional grants. (The other was restoration to the institution of greater control over its research destiny.) Though another official questioned this explanation, substituting a different one to which we will later allude, he did not question the need to simplify the complexities of project funding and, as a matter of fact, went on to outline a way of doing so:

[The National Science Foundation has] been thinking a little bit in the last eighteen months about how you could get around this terrible problem of so many pieces of paper, so many . . . grants going to . . . an institution . . . [and even to the same man. The foundation] ought to be able to send one piece of paper to the institution. . . .

There is no theoretical reason, at any rate, why Harvard, or Mississippi, ought not to be able, in its own wisdom, between deans, president, and faculty, to sit down and, somewhere in its budget cycle, figure out what kind of support it would normally ask of the National Science Foundation, and once in the semester or quarter system come to the Foundation with an omnibus proposal. . . .

I don't know whether [NSF] . . . could get away with this with the [Budget] Bureau or the Congress—or the university faculties—but it is worth talking about.

For whose benefit are you doing this?

The whole spectrum of people who are involved. This would mean faculty would stop writing so many proposals. It would mean that deans would not review so many proposals. It would mean that so many accounts that are now set up could be reduced to one account in the business office. It could mean that [the foundation] . . . could have fewer panel meetings.

The similarity of this proposal to the basic research agreement subsequently recommended by the Bureau of the Budget may be noted.[2]

The foregoing indicates one dimension—the reduction of paperwork—in which broader funding should prove administratively more efficient. A second dimension was also pointed out: the greater likelihood that institutional funds will be put to good use and their readier reallocability. This was attested by the experience of one university to

[2] The Bureau of the Budget has called for the preparation of a master agreement covering the administrative conditions of basic research projects financed by all government agencies at a single university; task orders specifying the objectives and budgetary level of individual projects would then replace present contracts and grants (see Bureau of the Budget, *The Administration of Government Supported Research at Universities* [March 1966], pp. 3, 21–23). The seminar idea clearly embraces the master agreement–task order pattern but goes beyond it in advocating institution-wide proposals timed to the academic year cycle and comprehensive financial commitments by federal agencies.

which a substantial grant had been given by a private foundation for research in a broad field, in lieu of project grants: ". . . [I]nstead of forty
or fifty little pockets of [project] money, each one of which sits there,
whether it is being used or not, year by year the [university] president
reviews the whole thing and, if it is not being spent . . . it will be used
for something else."

Scientific Grounds for Broader Funding

Institutional grants would facilitate the conduct of research that falls between the disciplinary and project lines of current federal financing. A
relatively small amount of money uncommitted to prescribed purposes
can accomplish relatively more than a larger volume of restricted grants.
". . . [W]hat I really sweat to do," one dean declared,

> is . . . to get from a private foundation some unrestricted money for sup-
> port of research and experimental efforts in teaching. And with this money,
> not in the aggregate 20 percent of the total of these project grants, I have
> done things in shaping the program of . . . [the] school that would never
> have been accomplished by any stretch of the imagination if I had waited
> for individual faculty members to bring the money in.

In addition, it was claimed that as institutional funds would be used
only for research meeting the intellectual standards of the institution
(which, it was plainly said, were often higher than those of government
agencies) they would raise the quality of research. By contrast, in the
project system,

> . . . there is really a great range in the degree . . . and kind of quality
> criteria that are made. So, to be very blunt, a man who couldn't possibly get
> a grant from the National Science Foundation can go to the Wright Air
> Development Center and get a grant five times the size. It is very difficult,
> because of this sort of range in the way that quality judgments are made . . .
> for the university to control the situation. . . .

This argument reverses the more common contention that grants
awarded nationally on the basis of judgments by professional peers are
likely to maintain higher quality standards than grants awarded locally
by institutions. It may reflect either the speaker's disdain for the quality
or the academic relevance of certain federal programs or a confidence
that his university, if not some other institutions, can maintain high standards.

Other participants doubted that a relatively small rise in institutional support would restrain some professors from accepting projects that their colleagues judged to be of poor quality or academically unsuitable. It was unrealistic to imagine that a little institutional money could rectify "the evils of the faculty entrepreneur."

The most detailed defense of the scientific usefulness of small institutional grants was given by an official who offered the following explanation of the origin of the National Science Foundation's program of modest institutional grants:

> . . . [I]n travelling around the country . . . it was very obvious there were certain kinds of problems that were unique to given institutions. One might need some help in renovating a laboratory, or one might need some help in furnishing more science [books] to libraries. . . . Some of these other problems were . . . more pressing than some of the projects . . . [the foundation was] supporting. So . . . [NSF] invented the institutional grant . . . [which institutions could use] however they want . . . to solve the problem they had individually. You couldn't invent as many programs as there were problems. And this is the way the concept arose at the 10 percent [of NSF project grants] level, because the [National Science] Board wouldn't accept any higher percentage.

Institutional Grounds for Broader Funding

The reasons grouped together as "institutional" ranged from the concrete objective of strengthening the hand of academic authorities against the power of distant men in Washington to broader and, in a measure, perhaps utopian aspirations of promoting harmony and a sense of common purpose among faculty members.

" . . . [T]he crux of the matter is," a government official asserted, ". . . unlike anything else we have done in the nation, we have centralized . . . scientific decision-making [in the hands of panels, committees, and staff in Washington]. Essentially, the root of the decision is national. It is not possible under the present system to . . . make divergent local decisions and strengthen thereby the truly unusual capability that may be residing in a local institution." To correct the situation, a dean suggested, it would be desirable to have relatively more money for "the disposition of the department as a whole, to be controlled by its senior members, not just by the chairman or the dean. . . ." Another dean carried the argument beyond the bounds of the department to the collective faculty:

The faculty collectively cannot sufficiently influence the direction in which the university's program is going. . . . I think it is much better to speak of the collective faculty vs. the individual faculty, because there are real differences between the two. You give a faculty committee a responsibility and it will come up with an entirely different answer than if you ask the members of the faculty committee individually what should be done. This is really the dichotomy that you ought to make in the universities. It is the difference between the collective faculty and the individual faculty.

The argument was summarized and mayhap clarified by a scientist: ". . . [I]n the present system of making judgments, there are wise judgments made by professional groups nationally, and there are perhaps wise proposals or ideas that come from individuals . . . , but something that is left out . . . is the collective judgment of faculties. . . ."

While the outlook of the collective faculty remains ill charted, the individual scientist is known to favor the project system and to resist moves toward broader—particularly, institutional—forms of research support:

> The greatest resistance . . . comes from the scientists themselves. . . . The science community is apathetic to strong, local institutional support. It does not want controls put upon the scientist by his own institution. On the other hand, if that is not done, we weaken the institution. . . . The scientific community itself does not want strong local institutions. . . .

A simple explanation of the scientist's attitude was offered by a dean. ". . . [T]hey know good and well that a panel of advisers to NSF or NIH or whatever, drawn from among the leaders of their special field, know more about their business and understand them better than their dean or their president"—"And they are absolutely right," interrupted a government scientist; and the dean readily concurred. A university representative recounted an episode that not only confirmed the opposition of professors to institutional grants but suggested that university deans and presidents may not all be as enamored of them as is generally imagined.

> Several years ago, the ———— Foundation got in touch with the president and the dean . . . at ———— and said, "We are being pestered to death by all your people coming up individually and asking for money in the field of ————. We are not going to give you any more on this basis. Give us a five-year proposal from the university as a whole for ————."
>
> Oh, boy, what a headache that was! It meant three or four faculties had to get together, five or six departments. A great package was put together and presented to the foundation; the foundation cut it down and sent it back and said, "Distribute this total any way you like, but you take the responsibility."

Well, my experience in this teaches me something about why professors don't like this, deans hate it, and university presidents absolutely consider it murder—because, for the first time, they have to make the nasty judgments saying who can't have the money and can't put it off on the foundation officers.

The Balance between Institutional and Project Funding

The question of what proportion of federal science money should go into general grants and what into specific projects was discussed at some length. The discussion started with the proposition of one university participant that, if all relevant government funds were lumped together and considered a "science budget for universities" institutional grants should comprise 25 percent, "personal" grants (that is, fellowships and traineeships) another 25 percent, and research projects 50 percent. This was offered as an "order of magnitude" target for the next five years, the current distribution being estimated at "about 12 percent institutional, most of which is NIH, about 14 percent personal, and the rest projects."

Asked for the criteria that yielded the 25 percent figure for institutional grants—"Why not 30 percent?"—its proponent conceded that there were none. "I don't think you can make a quantitative criterion. This is just my best judgment from having seen the system operate." After an interval, he tried to explain his reasoning. "Looking at the present system, I think it is overbalanced on the side of project grants . . . , and I think, therefore, we ought to experiment with moving further in the other direction. I am not willing to move further than 25 percent [initially], because I am not wise enough to predict what the effects will be." Acknowledging the difficulty and, to some extent, the arbitrariness of setting an absolute percentage, one participant recalled that the problem had arisen when National Science Foundation institutional grants were initiated. ". . . [S]hould it be 5 percent, 10 percent [of total project grants], what should be the order of magnitude . . . ? I don't think anybody has ever had any brief or rationale for a particular level. . . ." Another participant suggested that the 25 percent target for institutional grants represented a realistic assessment of what the political traffic might bear:

One man at NSF said to me, "We are going crazy in making all these quality judgments," and obviously this is a way of simplifying that; and the political element is very simple: twice [the 12 percent of federal funds now going in institutional grants], or something more than at present, is realistic. To say "five times as much" becomes unrealistic, it is too much of a jump. . . .

The Problem of Invidious Choice

The 25 percent goal—or, at any rate, some increase—for institutional funding seemed to be generally accepted by the seminar. How institutional funds should be allocated, however, was far less clear. The discussion lapped around the issue without ever quite enveloping it. The group, it seems fair to say, favored allocations that, in one way or another, were based on some judgment or appraisal of institutional quality rather than a mathematical formula (unless that formula were based, in turn, on quality judgments, as in NSF institutional grants). However, the political difficulty of a public agency's making invidious judgments about the quality of educational institutions was recognized. Indeed, it was recalled that a private agency, the Ford Foundation, also found this difficult when it first sought to make institutional grants.

> When the Ford Foundation decided to get rid of a lot of money in general endowment grants to universities, it came smack up against . . . this question. If you make grants for research projects, you are not passing judgment on the relative merits of universities. And so your judgments are not affronts to individual universities. . . .
>
> But, if you are going to give unrestricted money to universities, you cannot possibly escape this invidious task. It amounts to rating the universities, and universities have never wanted anybody to rate them. The very minimum business is accreditation and that is only a floor . . . ; it is very difficult to get below it. . . . [T]he predominant judgment at the Ford Foundation . . . was that it was absolutely impossible to do this on any other than a formula basis, even for a private foundation. . . . You know which side the formula was weighted on, in some cases, but it was still a formula. . . . the Ford Foundation five or six years later decided it had to bite the bullet and make these general judgments, and it didn't prove to be as impossible as they thought . . . and I . . . [think] the time . . . [has] come for government agencies to face up to this too. . . . [3]

[3] The first reference is to the $260 million appropriated in fiscal years 1955 and 1956 by the trustees of the Ford Foundation, for distribution as endowment grants to all 630 regionally accredited, private four-year colleges and universities granting degrees in the liberal arts and sciences and allied professional fields; the largest grant to any institution was some $5 million. Grants approximated each institution's 1954–55 payroll for teachers of undergraduate programs and of graduate programs in the arts and sciences; an

Whereupon several persons rapidly observed that NASA institutional grants and NSF science development grants had not encountered these problems; the objectives of increasing the number of "capable institutions" were politically not merely acceptable but delectable. Grants to upgrade an institution's scientific capacity in an area officially designated as nationally important (such as health or space) have been made in recent years without furore. The Defense Department's Advanced Research Project Agency had "smooth sailing" with its materials sciences grants, because its justification was that it was "buying research results," and the same logic worked well in other defense programs:

> A number of letters I have drafted for the Secretary of Defense, saying, "We are not here to stimulate the general economy or to take care of relief or to advance higher education; we are here for the defense of the country, and on that criteria we stand, and we ain't going to put a plant in Mississippi." You have to do this, and it is the Defense Department's only defense.
>
> *What do you think the President said on September 13? . . . That mission-oriented agencies should "as far as possible within their missions" do exactly what we were just hearing they shouldn't do.*[4]

additional "accomplishment grant" of about half this sum went to 126 of the schools, which had significantly raised faculty salaries since World War II. In explaining the latter awards, "the Foundation's Advisory Committee emphasized that it had not attempted to evaluate the *caliber* of the colleges, or their general excellence or reputation. 'Indeed,' it said, 'our study confirms the belief so widely held that variety of excellence is a healthy aspect of our entire system of higher education, whether publicly or privately supported. This variety cannot readily be reduced to mathematical comparisons or scores' " (*The Ford Foundation Annual Report* [1955], p. 4).

The second reference is to the Special Program in Education initiated by the Ford Foundation in 1960 with grants totaling $46 million to five private universities—Stanford, Denver, Notre Dame, Vanderbilt, and Johns Hopkins. The program (which is discussed further on pp. 116–18) was characterized as "an experiment in excellence. The universities were carefully selected on the basis of location, leadership, past performance, and future plans. . . . The program seeks to raise their sights even higher" (*The Ford Foundation Annual Report* [1960], p. 16).

[4] A "Memorandum from the President to the Heads of Departments and Agencies," September 14, 1965, stated, in part, "All Federal agencies with substantial research and development programs have an interest and need to develop academic capabilities for research and scientific education as a part of their research missions.

"To the fullest extent compatible with their primary interests in specific fields of science, their basic statutes, and their needs for research results in [*sic*] high quality, all Federal agencies should act so as to: . . . Contribute to the improvement of potentially strong universities through measures such as: . . . Assisting such institutions or parts of institutions in strengthening themselves while performing research relevant to agency missions, by such means as establishing university-administered programs in specialized areas relevant to the missions of the agencies."

The point was hardly resolved for all time, but some in the group, at least, were clearly seeking a politically and administratively practicable formula for bestowing general funds on one institution without damning another that did not receive any. "... [I]t is much less invidious to choose between two universities on the grounds, 'This is going to help the space program,' ... than to say, 'This is a good university generally, and better than this one.' " Neither of NSF's two major institutional grant programs really overcame the problem. The NSF "science development" formula was limited in duration and in the number of eligible institutions, while its "institutional grants" were more a modest override on project awards than an independent program with its own criteria for institutional evaluation. Could a new program be devised which united the breadth and number of the latter grants with the magnitude and qualitative discrimination of the former and which rewarded both existing and potential excellence? Such a program might be either visionary or illusory; its character was not delineated further, beyond a suggestion that the criteria for institutional choice remain "a matter of administrative discretion based on the best advice that could be mustered . . . this is awfully tough to do, but . . . it is what the situation requires." (After the meeting, this thought was elaborated into a proposal for a system as comparable to that of the British University Grants Committee as could be devised in an American setting, with a distinguished group of disinterested persons, such as the presidents of the Ford and Carnegie foundations, the Bell Laboratories, and the National Academy of Sciences, that would make the judgments as to which institutions should receive substantial grants of unfettered public funds.)

The Quality of Federal Personnel

At one point in the evening, allusion was made to the fear of "government control"—mainly to mark its passing:

> Perhaps I am getting old [the speaker was 58], but I am astounded by the educators and university people present changing their ideas so dramatically—in how many years? [In] 1939 . . . or 1938 . . . it would be completely unthinkable to take these grants. Now you are saying: How much do I get, how do I divide it up? This is from the government, which is going to—not in my opinion, but in some people's opinions—control your future.

May I have some of the educators speak on this subject of taking grants
. . . and what it means in the long-term future?

"In thirty years you can change your mind," an educator responded. The
point so lightly dismissed led, however, to a consideration of the caliber of the civil service, in whose hands rested so much responsibility for
the protection of the freedom of educational institutions: ". . . [T]he
only guarantee of your freedom is to have [in the government] first-class
people who will respect private institutions and not consider themselves
rivals to them. . . ." Concern was expressed that excessive use of outside
advisers in making project awards was impairing the development of
such a high-class civil service. Although tribute was paid to this system
of outside advice (which was termed "a great invention . . . the best
possible way to help the government make decisions that turn on the
scientific aspects of scientific projects"), the problems that science agencies faced were no longer (if they ever had been) confined to technical
choices that technical experts were qualified to make but extended to
"fundamental strategy questions" about broader issues.

What should be the balance of government scientific expenditures between "mission-oriented" agencies and the National Science Foundation,
between project and broader grants, between institutions of existing and
potential excellence, between research and education? Questions of this
order cannot, seminar members felt, be delegated to narrow specialists
but should be answered by men with a great breadth of administrative
and political experience and judgment, more of whom must be attracted
to government service:

> . . . [W]e have desocialized the government so much more than we have
> socialized the universities. . . . [W]e load the dice here, and . . . there are
> higher odds that a first-rate man in his early thirties in the government will
> leave it and go to private employment than vice versa. . . .
>
> Certainly, I am not saying I don't want private advisers to have their fin-
> gers in government pies. I would feel very hurt if I had never had a chance
> to put my finger in occasionally, and I would hope many of my colleagues
> would continue to do the same. But, on balance . . . there are some things
> that outside advisers cannot do and outside research cannot accomplish, and
> . . . nothing but a very great strengthening of the internal machinery will
> do it.

At this juncture, the two threads of discussion (the proportion of government science funds that should be assigned to institutional grants,
and the character of the men who should decide such an issue) were
drawn together:

In two respects we have extended the mechanism of . . . a grant evaluated by a panel of outside advisers. One is in having the grant cover a greater variety of things, so that now . . . it covers graduate students, faculty salaries, things of this sort. . . . [T]he second . . . [is in] using essentially the same mechanism for developmental grants, for blocks of fellowships under the Office of Education's NDEA [National Defense Education Act] law, and things of that sort.

Is there any hope to approach both the problem of strengthening the governmental staff and also the problem of reaching some kind of rational basis for these percentage distributions between one kind of support and another . . . not in terms of dollars but . . . [in terms] of function? If the universities' hard-core money—maybe some of it coming from formula grants, or individually allocated grants, on the basis of the best judgment of the relevant government agencies—provided for graduate student support, . . . for faculty salaries, . . . [and] some minimum level for research, . . . [while] individual projects evaluated by the traditional mechanism [remained] available as a supplement for particularly meritorious or particularly expensive [work] or things that somehow or other just did not get funded through the first kind of mechanism? Is this a line of possible change toward which we ought to be giving some exploratory thinking?

As the discussion drew toward a close, a government administrator remarked that the improvement of government programs at universities does not depend only on the government but also on the university. ". . . [S]ome of us have been puzzled and even disappointed at the lack of initiative, imagination, and leadership within the university administration to try to do some of these things better. Simply changing the process at this end is not likely to correct all of these evils. . . ." Another official took him to task, believing that "evils" put it far too strongly. ". . . [W]e really only have to correct some errors . . . and . . . we do that not by overturning a system that is working, basically, pretty soundly. . . ." But the response to this was that

> . . . it somewhat understates the difficulty of our problem. . . . [W]e . . . have backed into a system in which the relationship between the government and the universities is . . . more profound and complicated and deeply rooted now than the average citizen understands, and the political misunderstandings of this can be very easy . . . and very dangerous, because, unless there is a clearer realization of how much depends on this profoundly new system, in the development of . . . higher education, . . . I don't think we will summon up the energy to deal with the problem.

The $64 question, which turned out to be the last of the evening, was asked by a congressman:

I find here tonight a great number of provocative ideas, most of them leaning . . . toward a better distribution of funds by the use of the institutional method. . . . [H]owever, as we take testimony . . . and ask what ought to be done . . . people say, "No, don't take moneys away from the project programs; what you must do is . . . get more money to take care of all of these . . . other points. . . ." Many members of Congress feel that their areas are not getting enough of this money, so therefore they lean toward the formula technique . . . , and everyone in Congress believes . . . [in building] up more centers of excellence throughout the country. So we have a whole panorama of programs before us, . . . and most of the solutions boil down to how much can we appropriate to take care of these requirements, and how do we get the best adjustment.

. . . Are we in such a position . . . that we ought to radically change the project programs at the moment and do more in the institutional area . . . , or are we talking about doing it some time down the road—[in] three or four or five years? . . . So, the major decision necessarily being ours [the Congress'], we cannot very well hold firm to something . . . when we hear strong voices sounding in all directions. . . . If we do more in another direction, then we must, if there is a shortage of funds, do less in those directions where funds are now going.

Which said, as clearly as possible: the universities want an increase in both project *and* institutional funding; but if they cannot have both, which do they prefer?

Unfortunately, or perhaps fortunately since thereby no one had to commit himself to an answer, the chairman chose this moment to close the discussion. Continuing the exchange after the gong despite the Queensberry rules, a member offered the congressman his opinion that, if necessary, the group would have voted for an increase in institutional funding at the cost of some reduction in project funding. Don Price had already gone on record elsewhere with a similar answer: "If there were to be no increase from this time on in the total level of support [for university science], I would reduce the project grants. But I don't think that should be necessary to accomplish the purpose."[5]

[5] In *Conflicts between the Federal Research Programs and the Nation's Goals for Higher Education*, Hearings before a Subcommittee of the House Committee on Government Operations, 89 Cong. 1 sess. (June 14, 15, and 17, 1965), p. 56.

HARVEY BROOKS

The Future Growth
of Academic Research:
Criteria and Needs

HOW TO DETERMINE our national investment in re-
search and its rate of growth in the future has come to be referred to as
"science policy." Only in the last five years has public policy become
concerned with science as such. Until recently, federal support of science
has been determined almost entirely as an incidental by-product of other
federal missions such as health, national defense, and agriculture. Since
the pursuit of these missions has been the responsibility of designated
agencies and departments, their expenditures for research have been
largely determined in competition with their expenditures for other activities and functions.

Since the end of World War II, explicit "planning" for science as a
whole has been considered of relatively little importance because the
overall rate of expenditures for scientific activities has been growing rapidly enough to permit a large margin for new enterprises and the entry
of new scientific investigators into the system. Nevertheless, as the totality of research and development activities has grown, there has been an
increasing demand for integrated planning even in basic research. Such a
demand for planning tends to be repugnant to basic scientists, who look
on the scientific endeavor as a sort of free enterprise system of ideas.
However, the leveling off in the growth of research budgets since 1963
has convinced the scientific community that a more systematic confronta-

53

tion of alternatives will probably be necessary even within basic science.

There is increasing public and political acceptance of the fact that basic science cannot be planned in detail, except possibly for the construction of very large and expensive research tools such as space vehicles or accelerators. Scientific planning is concerned not with the central direction of science itself but with the *resources* for scientific research and technology. In fact, the dialogue between the scientific and political communities is concerned in large measure with the question of just what the appropriate areas for planning *are*.

What are the alternatives to be confronted? Planning is inevitably concerned with aggregates, usually expressed as financial obligations for the support of research, which are the summation of many diverse individual activities having some property in common. The politician and the administrator are often bewildered by the categorizations of scientific activity, which are multidimensional in character. Yet the appropriateness of the various possible characterizations of aggregates lies at the heart of the planning problem and the determination of criteria for choice. Of course, this multidimensional character is not entirely unique to science. Few federal activities can be defined by a single purpose; and once an activity serves many purposes, the problem arises of how to combine the different purposes into a single objective function, since, in the last analysis, choices are unidimensional and the ordering of alternatives is a scalar function.

In the United States system, programming for scientific activities begins, or should begin, more at the bottom than at the top. One does not start with an a priori allocation to broad categories of scientific activity and then suballocate to projects within them. Instead, specific projects originate at many levels within the federal and nonfederal structure and are gradually selected as they move up through the decision-making process. There is no government-wide allocation for basic research, or for physics or chemistry as such; rather, each federal agency tends to balance all of its activities within its own budgetary ceiling. Of course, the ceilings assigned to agencies are influenced by their scientific responsibilities as well as their other missions. The budget of the Atomic Energy Commission, for example, is not determined independently of the fact that it has a responsibility for high energy physics, and an increase in its high energy physics expenditures does put pressure on all its other activities.

Several factors, however, have led to increased scrutiny of research and development activities as an aggregate. The most important of these is the sheer magnitude of the total—of the same order as total sales of the automobile industry, for example. A second factor is the increasing budgetary importance of independent agencies whose mission is mainly defined in terms of science or technology itself—notably, the National Aeronautics and Space Administration, the National Science Foundation, and, to a lesser extent, the Atomic Energy Commission. A third factor is the growing public attention to higher education and belief in the close connection between academic science, graduate education, and regional development.

Alternative Classifications for Science

If planning for the totality of national scientific and technical resources is to proceed on a more rational basis than at present, the first step must be a better understanding of alternative classifications of science and their implications. Whereas development, which constitutes about two-thirds of federal support of technical activities, tends to be concentrated in a relatively small number of large projects, research, with which this paper is primarily concerned, is distributed among tens of thousands of individual projects. To aggregate these projects or expenditures for planning purposes is meaningful only to the extent that they have some significant property in common which is related to a national objective. Otherwise, the classification tends merely to confuse discussion.

For example, it is not clear what significance the category "basic research" has when it includes activities ranging all the way from the proof of a theorem in topology to a huge engineering and logistic effort such as a space probe to Mars or a Mohole project. Yet these disparate activities are included in that category by the National Science Foundation in its reporting of federal research and development expenditures. I am not questioning the validity of the category for its limited statistical purposes but only its significance for broader decisions about the level of federal expenditures for basic research. Is there any proper sense in which such disparate "basic research" activities should be regarded as competitive, or is the Mars space probe more properly competitive with, for example, the national highway program, the maritime subsidy, or the supersonic transport?

In the discussion of scientific activities, a number of classifications have been used: (1) the degree of fundamentality or applicability—basic research, applied research, development; (2) the scientific discipline —physics, chemistry, biology; (3) the social purpose or function of the research—health, defense, natural resources; (4) the character of the institution conducting the research—university, research institute, industry, government laboratory; (5) the scale or style of the research—"big" science versus "little" science; (6) the object of study—oceans, atmosphere, space. Although subjects such as oceanography, meteorology, and space science are often confused with scientific disciplines in common parlance, they are actually multidisciplinary studies applied to a single object or feature of the environment.

Since there are different ways of classifying the same activities, they overlap to a large extent, and certain classification schemes will be more appropriate for some purposes than others. For example, the more basic or fundamental a research activity is, the more appropriate it is, usually, to classify the activity in terms of scientific disciplines. Similarly, a disciplinary classification is more appropriate for academic research than for research in industrial or governmental laboratories.

It is also important to understand the limitations and ambiguities in each of the classification schemes listed above. In the basic-applied spectrum, for example, the same research project may be regarded as "applied" by one investigator and "basic" by another, depending on the institutional environment in which he is working. Two research projects which start from the same point and ask the same questions may develop along entirely different lines as a result of the outlook of the researcher and the nature of the scientific communication network within which he works.

Furthermore, the basic-applied classification is constantly changing. Last year's basic research is often this year's applied research. Not only are applications found for new discoveries, but new applications often generate new questions for basic research or new technologies that can be applied as tools in basic investigations. The basic research of one field may be the technology of another. Whether research is regarded as basic or applied depends on the time horizon within which one views it. It has been argued with some justification that all research in biology and biochemistry should be regarded as applied. Our understanding of fundamental life processes is still so rudimentary that almost any advance in understanding is likely to find applications rather quickly in medicine or agriculture. One of the least applicable of all branches of physics—elementary particle physics—nevertheless places extreme demands on advanced technology. Thus many techniques developed as an incidental by-product of elementary particle research have had an important impact on technology and on other fields of science, even though the concepts and theories of the field itself are little related to presently foreseeable applications.

The disciplinary classification is equally limited. This has become increasingly obvious as advances in understanding have extended the use of physical science concepts and techniques to other disciplines. The growth of science in the postwar era has been characterized by the spectacular expansion of hybrid disciplines such as geophysics, geochemistry, biochemistry, chemical physics, computer science, and systems analysis. Techniques such as radiocarbon dating, the use of radioactive tracers, paper and gas chromatography, microwave and nuclear resonance spectroscopy, and X-ray diffraction have spread rapidly. Interdisciplinary subjects such as oceanography, atmospheric sciences, and space science draw on all of the more classical disciplines, and it is difficult to tell at what point they do or should be considered disciplines in their own right. Whole areas of research often move from one discipline to another. For example, atomic spectroscopy, which used to be a major branch of physics, has now moved almost entirely into astronomy. Similarly, molecular spectroscopy has largely moved from physics into chemistry. The study of cosmic rays has largely moved from physics into a branch of space science. The theory of low energy nuclear reactions has become an important aspect of astrophysics. It becomes increasingly difficult to define a discipline except by the organizational framework within which it is pursued—for example, physics is what is done currently in academic physics departments.

The classification of research by social function encounters similar difficulties. Missions such as defense and space are so broad that they require a large amount of general purpose research which is equally relevant to other missions. Both, for example, are heavily dependent on electronics, which in turn depends increasingly on advances in solid state physics and on a number of basic engineering disciplines such as information theory. Yet, unless this general purpose research is carried out in connection with the defense or space missions, it may not find application to them. On the one hand, the volume of general purpose research in a given area that should be supported by the Defense Department is dependent on the volume of similar research supported by other agencies, including the National Science Foundation. On the other hand, no mission-oriented agency can afford to depend for its general purpose research entirely on other agencies, since each area of application requires a slightly different emphasis. Such general purpose research blends continuously into more specifically relevant activities, and no simple rule can serve to distinguish the two. Furthermore, several important areas of research cut across the social purposes defined by present federal organization. They are vital to the mission of a given agency but also transcend it and constitute a new social mission in their own right. One of the best examples is oceanography; another is information technology.

To what extent should the support of research as part of missions be "counted" in evaluating the total activity in a discipline? This difficulty was encountered in acute form by the Physics Survey Committee of the National Academy of Sciences–National Research Council (NAS-NRC) in its attempt to estimate federal expenditures for physics and astronomy.[1] It found that gross reclassifications of National Aeronautics and Space Administration (NASA) expenditures resulted in radical changes in the total picture for physics and astronomy. Similar questions arose in determining National Institutes of Health support of chemistry for the NAS-NRC Committee on the Survey of Chemistry.[2] This type of difficulty has arisen in almost every field where an important mission of a federal agency has been extensively dependent on a particular scientific discipline and yet where the agency's organization and goals differ from those of the discipline. For example, there is a question as to the extent to which in-house physical research in NASA related to ion propulsion should be counted as physics.

A great deal of attention has been given recently to the classification of science into "big" and "little."[3] The limitations of this approach have been clearly discussed by Panofsky in a later chapter.[4] A principal difficulty with such a classification lies in the fact that there is a continuous spectrum of activities between big and little science ranging from a

---

[1] National Academy of Sciences–National Research Council, Physics Survey Committee, *Physics: Survey and Outlook,* A Report on the Present State of U.S. Physics and Its Requirements for Future Growth (NAS-NRC, 1966); see chap. 6, pp. 81–90, esp. figs. 4 and 5 (p. 87).

[2] National Academy of Sciences–National Research Council, Committee for the Survey of Chemistry, *Chemistry: Opportunities and Needs,* A Report on Basic Research in U.S. Chemistry (NAS-NRC, 1965); see chap. 12, pp. 163–81.

[3] National Academy of Sciences, *Basic Research and National Goals,* A Report to the House Committee on Science and Astronautics by the National Academy of Sciences, 89 Cong. 1 sess. (March 1965); see esp. essays by G. B. Kistiakowsky and Harvey Brooks.

[4] See pp. 189–201.

scientific space probe to the work of an individual professor in his laboratory with two or three graduate students. Clearly, a strong argument can be made for some segregation of the logistic costs of certain types of scientific research requiring expensive equipment or large-scale institutionalization. Otherwise, there is a serious danger that these costs will consume a disproportionate share of the total funds available to support science. This has apparently happened, at least for short periods, in the case of nuclear structure physics and oceanography. Nevertheless, it is also true that many big science activities have some of the same characteristics and educational functions as little science. Therefore, there are also real dangers both to the health of a research field and to the health of graduate education in treating big science—and especially that part in which graduate students and professors are involved—as too "different."

Institutional Classification of Research

Probably the most convenient and meaningful classification of research is in terms of the primary purpose of the institution in which it is conducted or of the institution's organizational subdivisions. This approach has several advantages.

1) Resources devoted to research in each kind of institution can be much more objectively identified than resources devoted to categories such as "basic research" or to various social purposes.

2) The institutional environment, or the communication network in which it is performed, and the movement of scientists between different institutional networks strongly condition the contribution of research to society.

3) Once the institutional framework is defined, other research classifications are easier to use. For example, the classification by scientific discipline is much more meaningful in academic than in industrial or government laboratories. Contrariwise, the classification by social purpose tends to be much more meaningful in government laboratories or contract research centers than in universities.

4) The institutional framework clarifies considerably the relationships between big and little science. In general, big science is conducted in institutions especially created for the purpose, whereas little science is a primary function of the normal university structure. Even within the university, separate organizations tend to be created to carry on big sci-

ence. However, although a large volume of little science may be conducted within federal agencies or laboratories, it does not generally constitute their *raison d'être*.

5) The institutional framework also clarifies the relationship between basic and applied research. As already mentioned, the line between basic and applied research tends to be determined by the environment in which it is conducted. Thus, what may be regarded as "basic" in an academic context may be regarded as "applied" in an industrial one. In short, activities classified as basic and applied, physics and chemistry, big science and little science, tend to differ according to their different institutional contexts.

For the purpose of discussing the problem of resource allocation in scientific research, I have found the following classifications most useful:

Nonacademic fundamental research: basic, and very fundamental applied, research performed in institutions whose missions are defined in terms of nonscientific objectives such as health, technical standards, defense, and agriculture. These are functional missions, where the term "functional" may denote either a specific end product or service or the cultivation of a general technological area related to the overall mission of the parent agency. This classification includes all industrial basic research plus basic research conducted in most government laboratories, in federal contract laboratories, and in nonprofit technological institutes.

National center basic research: research that is primarily institutional in character, like the preceding, but defined in terms of an area of science rather than a technological or social objective. In most cases, national center research is clearly related to, and supportive of, university research and may be regarded as an extension of academic research. Some national centers, such as the Cambridge Electron Accelerator or the Lawrence Radiation Laboratory at Berkeley, are actually located on campus and administered by a university. Others, such as Brookhaven, the National Radio Astronomy Observatory, the Kitt Peak National Observatory, the National Center for Atmospheric Research, and the Woods Hole Oceanographic Institution, are located off campus and administered by nonprofit organizations. Fundamental research conducted at Lincoln Laboratory, the National Bureau of Standards, the Naval Research Laboratory, or the Livermore Radiation Laboratory should not be regarded as "national center basic research" but as "nonacademic fundamental research" because these laboratories are primarily oriented toward technology or a particular mission rather than toward science or a discipline. National center research usually involves a component of big science, but it may involve only a "supercritical" interdisciplinary organization of scientists. Such research is characterized by a larger number of supporting engineering and service personnel than normal academic research (often including professionals with training and experience equivalent to that of scientists) and hence a higher ratio of supporting personnel to independent research investigators.

Academic research, both basic and applied: research conducted within the framework of graduate education and faculty activity, most often within academic departments organized by scientific discipline. For most purposes, the term "academic research" is congruent with the category "research in educational institutions proper" used by the National Science Foundation in reporting on research expenditures.[5] Characteristically, it is little science, with a low ratio of supporting personnel to independent investigators and apprentice researchers. One may distinguish two subtypes of academic research according to their relationships to their external sponsors. One is mission-oriented academic research, which is supported primarily for the sake of research results that will be of interest to a nonscientific mission or purpose or for the training of people who may ultimately contribute to such a mission. This subtype includes essentially all research sponsored by government agencies other than the National Science Foundation. It may also include certain basic research activities (such as the elementary particle physics program of the Atomic Energy Commission) which a mission-oriented agency has undertaken as a national responsibility beyond that which was strictly justified by its assigned social mission. The second subtype is nonmission-oriented academic research, the primary motivation of which is the education of scientists and an increase in the store of human knowledge, with potential applications only a secondary consideration. Most of the basic research supported by the National Science Foundation at universities falls in this category, even in engineering.[6]

[5] See National Science Foundation, *Federal Funds for Research, Development, and Other Scientific Activities, Fiscal Years 1963–65,* vol. 13 (1965), pp. 92–96, for general definitions including classes of performers, and pp. 104–5 for a list of federal contract research centers; the definition of "colleges and universities proper" is given on p. 95.

[6] The term "basic research in engineering" causes a great deal of confusion, since engineering is ordinarily thought of as, by definition, "applied." Nevertheless, a number of basic scientific disciplines have become traditionally associated with engineering in universities. These are pursued largely for their own sake and are just as fundamental as the disciplines associated with the natural sciences. The basic sciences associated with

Like any other, the above classification scheme has limitations, and its value will depend strongly on the purpose for which it is used. This paper is primarily concerned with criteria for the growth of academic research in the aggregate, and my general thesis is that academic research is the only *aggregate* for which it is reasonable to have some policy for support. Other aggregates should emerge only as by-products of decisions regarding the creation of specific institutions and capital facilities, as outlined in my paper "Future Needs for the Support of Basic Research."[7] In other words, academic research is the only aggregate of research and development expenditures that should be considered separately competitive with other federal expenditures. Federal expenditures for other kinds of science and technology should be considered primarily on the merits of the individual activities in competition with nonscientific expenditures, not on an aggregate basis.

One difficulty with this classification scheme arises from those national center activities that provide support for graduate students and faculties. In the disciplinary studies by the National Academy of Sciences, the classification of national center research has tended to vary. For example, the Physics Survey Committee counted as "academic research" 80 percent of the elementary particle research in national centers such as Brookhaven.[8] This had the effect of yielding a figure for physics research nearly double that given by the National Science Foundation for "educational institutions proper." The justification for this assessment was that 80 percent of the machine time at the national centers is devoted to experiments conceived by and carried out in collaboration with faculty members and graduate students and only 20 percent is controlled primarily by resident research staff. A similar situation prevails in the case of national center research in optical and radio astronomy.[9]

On the other hand, the NAS-NRC chemistry panel included in its

---

engineering are primarily those concerned with the behavior of man-made systems—information theory, the theory of structures, the theory of feedback and control systems, computer and systems theory—but they are nonetheless fundamental. Moreover, subjects such as fluid mechanics, solid mechanics, and thermodynamics—what might be called macroscopic or classical physics—have been largely taken over as basic engineering sciences. All these engineering sciences are distinct from engineering as the art of applying the mathematical and physical sciences to human needs, but their vigorous cultivation is essential to the progress of engineering's primary purpose.

[7] In National Academy of Sciences, *Basic Research and National Goals*, pp. 77–110.
[8] See *Physics: Survey and Outlook*, p. 104, Table 14, note *b*.
[9] *Ibid.*, pp. 91–92.

figures only about 20 percent of the chemical research undertaken at such on-campus centers as the Atomic Energy Commission's Berkeley and Ames laboratories and none of the basic chemistry at such off-campus centers as Brookhaven, Argonne, or Oak Ridge. The figure for Ames and Berkeley was arrived at by assigning these laboratories the same cost for each graduate student and faculty member working at these centers as the average for research in the chemistry department of each university. The panel report entirely excluded the operating cost of AEC-financed university reactors and accelerators, which are extensively used by chemists for research in nuclear chemistry. Indeed, for the most part the machine costs for nuclear chemistry research were allocated to nuclear structure or elementary particle physics.[10]

A good case can be made for the differences in procedure followed by the two panels, but they make it necessary to be extremely cautious in drawing conclusions about the comparative levels of support for university chemistry and physics. A further complication is that whereas the chemistry panel defined chemistry support as that going only to university departments of chemistry, excluding biochemistry departments and basic science departments in medical schools, the physics panel counted as physics a number of activities supported in engineering and chemistry departments.[11]

Another problem in aggregating research support arises from the restriction of most statistics to what the chemistry panel termed "explicit support." There is also a large component of what the panel termed "hidden support," which includes, for example, the salaries paid by universities for the time faculty devote to research, fellowships, amortization of facilities, and unreimbursed indirect costs. Because of these hidden costs, the panel concluded that explicit federal support provided only 55 percent of the total costs of academic chemistry research.[12] Hardly any information of this sort is available for other fields of science, and yet such statistics will be essential if the aggregate costs of academic research are to constitute a basis for science policy.

The remainder of this paper will be concerned primarily with academic research and with such research outside of university departments —mainly in national centers—as can be classified as academically related.

[10] See *Chemistry: Opportunities and Needs*, p. 217, note *b*, and also p. 171.
[11] *Ibid.*, p. 151, and *Physics: Survey and Outlook*, p. 103.
[12] *Chemistry: Opportunities and Needs*, pp. 169–71.

The Function of the University

It is impossible to discuss the support of academic research without some assumptions about the purposes and functions of the modern university in American society. During the last fifty years there has been a dramatic change in what society expects of universities. From institutions whose function was primarily to teach a fixed body of knowledge to students, they have been transformed into "multiversities" and expected to be omnicompetent. Public and political attitudes have not uniformly caught up with this transformation, nor have the universities themselves always been able to define their own functions and recognize their own limitations. No single institution or structure of internal communication can serve all the purposes for which scientific work is performed. The very characteristics which make universities effective performers of most types of basic science often make them rather ineffective in the application of science to well-defined short-term goals.

I would list the primary functions of the university as follows: (1) to add through research and scholarship to man's understanding of himself and the world in which he lives; (2) to integrate newly acquired knowledge into our total intellectual structure, to systematize and organize knowledge for each generation; (3) to communicate existing understanding and knowledge through formal teaching, writing, and other kinds of communication to the intellectual public and to train the next generation of scholars through apprenticeship; (4) to be the custodian of the intellectual standards of society and to maintain intellectual leadership in the major fields of human knowledge and its long-term applications.

Research is essential to all of these functions but especially to the maintenance of intellectual leadership. The universities must be able to attract and hold a fair proportion of the best minds in each generation in each major intellectual field. Universities should be concerned with the application of knowledge only insofar as it enriches their entire intellectual enterprise and contributes to the proper training of future leaders in the professions. Hence, their natural organization is along disciplinary lines, and the very word "discipline" carries the connotation of standards. A discipline is a certain mode of approach to the acquisition of knowledge and understanding. By its very nature it is partial; to some extent it sacrifices breadth for depth. This is not to say that interdisciplinary activities are unimportant; they provide the seed from which new disciplines may spring and are particularly important in training people to apply the fruits of learning to the needs of society.

Characteristically, universities are individualistic and at their best when they try to exploit the freedom of the individual intellect. Separate institutions or "establishments" are best for programmed research and for a well-coordinated multidisciplinary approach to problem areas, as opposed to disciplines. The application of research findings to technological or other uses is naturally accorded more prestige at nonacademic institutions. Academic institutions have pioneered in the early stages of certain technologies, such as that of computers, when the primary need was for new ideas and concepts which could be developed by small groups. But universities lack the continuity of effort required for concrete applications of ideas and for systems development and the organizational discipline necessary to channel the work of many people toward a planned, large-scale goal. There is no proper place in their social structure for the necessary supporting engineering or service personnel. Historically, when the intellectual incentives were strong enough, they have occasionally been able to accommodate their structure in an ad hoc fashion to big science enterprises, but this is not natural and generally produces internal strains. Examples of the social problem are the difficulty of attracting chemistry faculty to a supporting role in solid state physics research, the difficulty of interesting physicists and engineers in problems of medical research and instrumentation, and the lack of interest among engineering faculties and students in the design and construction of complex research instruments for scientists in other disciplines, despite the fact that this would appear to be a logical activity for engineers within a university.

Nevertheless, the kinds of research conducted at nonacademic institutions, national research centers, and university departments are by no means mutually exclusive. Nonacademic institutions and national centers may be expected to conduct much research that is indistinguishable from the academic variety, but their reason for existence disappears if *all* their activity is of this type. Similarly, highly applied research (such as short-range process or product improvement, service to a particular customer, or work requiring the permanent employment of numerous personnel or a high degree of planning and programming) may as an expedient be done occasionally at universities but is inappropriately located if it becomes a significant fraction of university research.

Basis of Policy for Academic Research

The general guiding principles which, in my opinion, should govern policy for the support of academic research in the next several years are set forth below. Obviously, the level of expenditures will depend on the magnitude of the federal budget. This section will deal with relevant qualitative factors and a later section with certain quantitative factors.

At their best, good teaching and good research are inseparable. Each should reinforce the other. Research is necessary to keep faculty intellectually alive, but the continual effort to synthesize and present existing understanding to less specialized students also helps the faculty member to illuminate his own research activities and to open up new lines of inquiry. Ideally, students should be exposed to a variety of specialists, so that they can stand intellectually on the shoulders of several disciplines or specialties. Thus, for example, today's graduate student in physics or electrical engineering should learn more abstract mathematics than his physics or engineering professors know, and the student of biology should learn more physics and chemistry than most of his biology professors know. It is partly by this synthesis of many specialties that each new generation of apprentice researchers is able to penetrate more deeply than its teachers.

It should be national policy to help create a university environment to which some of the best minds of each generation will be attracted. No significant intellectual discipline or line of basic research should remain unrepresented at the universities; and, in general, universities should be encouraged to maintain the balance of intellectual leadership in all important fields. Leadership does not necessarily imply a numerical preponderance of research workers or funds, but it does imply enough funds to maintain some investigators at the cutting edge of every major field within the university system as a whole. Thus, when national decisions are taken to pursue new lines of research or expand existing efforts, priority should be given to universities, and new programs should be undertaken outside universities only if, for reasons outlined earlier, other types of institutions are better fitted to execute them. In other words, the burden of proof should lie with nonacademic research institutions.

It is now a goal of national policy to make available to all American youth, regardless of their financial ability, the maximum educational opportunities they are capable of absorbing. This is not only a matter of social justice but also a sound social investment from the standpoint of economic growth and a better society, since it ensures selection of the ablest people from the largest possible pool of students.

The number of Ph.D.'s awarded in science and engineering has been rising at about 7 percent a year since 1900. There is no indication of, or reason to expect, a downward departure from this trend in the next fifteen years; the more recent trend of over 10 percent a year is likely to continue for several years but will probably drop back to the long-term trend line after that period. The level of support for academic research should ensure the availability of a high-quality educational experience within this trend. It is important to remember that this upward trend in Ph.D production is not unique to science and engineering. In fact, despite structural changes in American society, the distribution of Ph.D.'s among the major areas of learning has remained surprisingly constant over a period of sixty years.[13]

The sociology of our educational system will tend to change in such a way that, as the size of the enterprise grows, we will be able to maintain approximately the present degree of selectivity among students and research projects. This assumption is based on evidence that at present, because of economic, class, and geographical disabilities, a large proportion of elementary and secondary school students do not come close to realizing their full educational potential. The maintenance of selectivity ob-

[13] The percentage of awards in science and engineering was 54.9 in 1964 and has varied by less than 1 percent since 1900. Similarly, the proportion of bachelor's degrees in science and engineering has remained constant at 24.5 percent of the total since 1920. Between 1950 and 1963, the number of scientists and engineers increased by 91 percent, as compared with an 85 percent increase in "professional, technical, and kindred" workers of all types. Scientists and engineers constituted 16.5 percent of the professional work force in 1963. The annual growth in the professional work force is about 4.8 percent, as compared with 1.2 percent for the labor force as a whole. At this rate, the professional category will grow only from 10.4 to about 17.7 percent of the total labor force in the next fifteen years, and scientists and engineers will grow from about 1.7 to 3 percent of the total. Although the rise in the proportion of technical people will obviously have to level off before the end of the century, such a leveling does not appear to be imminent and will probably not affect the projections discussed in this paper.

viously depends on accelerated efforts in curriculum development and science education at all levels, not just on academic research.

The rate of incorporation of technical people into our economy is limited primarily by supply rather than demand, and this will continue to be so. In other words, despite short-term fluctuations in supply and demand, the availability of scientific and engineering manpower acts as a spur to development over the long term rather than the economy acting as a pull on the manpower supply. The supply tends to generate its own demand by opening up new opportunities, as demonstrated by the continuing immigration of foreign scientists and professionals into the United States.

A pluralistic system of decision-making for academic research will optimize the distribution of funds. Each organizational subunit in the system—for example, a plurality of federal agencies with different missions, panels of scientific peers, institutions, fellowship panels, and individual researchers—should control some funds with which significant choices can be made. Policy should also be designed to encourage the expansion of private and nonfederal support to match approximately the expansion of federal support. In practice, this appears to have happened in the past, although federal research support has expanded somewhat faster than national expenditures for higher education from all sources.

Everyone trained in basic research should not be expected to stay in basic research. On the contrary, the output of Ph.D.'s in a discipline should normally exceed the needs of universities for scientists in that discipline. Part of the social value of basic-science training stems from the migration of scientists into other fields and into applied science and technology.

A study of a sample of 1955–60 Ph.D.'s from the National Register indicates that, in 1962, only 35 percent of those in the physical sciences were employed at colleges and universities, whereas 45 percent were in government and industry. Only 30 percent of the 1960 cohort of chemists remained at colleges and universities.[14] In the life sciences, however, nearly 60 percent remained, because universities (through medical and agricultural schools) are much more heavily engaged in the applications of the life sciences than of the physical sciences. The Physics Survey Committee found that each major subfield of physics absorbs fewer Ph.D.'s than it produces. I believe that this is a healthy situation; but it

[14] National Academy of Sciences–National Research Council, *Profiles of Ph.D.'s in the Sciences,* Publication 1293 (1965).

would be unhealthy if, over a long period, there were too few outlets within universities for the Ph.D.'s trained in any field.

Policy should aim to diffuse the geographic and institutional distribution of basic research capability but not at the expense of dismantling existing excellence or creating too many subcritical or substandard activities. Past trends in academic research support have resulted in a gradual but steady decentralization of academic research and graduate education, and the most rapid growth of support has taken place at institutions with no previous tradition of graduate education.[15] This trend should be continued and, if sufficient funds are available, accelerated. Current emphasis on traineeships, institutional grants, and development grants should accelerate the trends of the 1950's. However, redistribution should take place by differential growth rather than by reallocation.

Criteria for Support of Academic Research

As implied in the previous discussion, the adequacy of the level of academic research support should be judged in relation to the growth of graduate education and the production of Ph.D.'s in science and engineering. However, academic research should not be supported exclusively for educational reasons. It must be good research as judged either

---

[15] This is factually true despite some considerable folklore to the contrary. Examples of relevant statistics follow. In fiscal years 1948, 1949, and 1950, 11 universities accounted for 50 percent of federal research funds; by 1963, 20 universities accounted for 50 percent. Similarly, 65 universities received 90 percent of the funds in the early period, whereas 100 received 90 percent of the funds in 1963. Between 1945 and 1959, 10 institutions awarded 46 percent of the Ph.D.'s in the natural sciences; by 1961, the leading 10 institutions awarded only 35 percent and, by 1964, less than 30 percent. Between 1940–49 and 1960–61, the two regions of the country showing the greatest gains in Ph.D. production relative to population were the South Central and Mountain states; the two regions showing the greatest relative decline were the Northeast and the Pacific. The maximum spread between regions dropped from a factor of 14 in the early period to only 4 in the later period and to less than 3.5 by 1964. Thus, all evidence points to an accelerating trend toward the dispersion of research and graduate education brought about by federal support of academic research.

See Office of Science and Technology, "The Impact of Federal Research Programs on Higher Education," in *Conflicts between the Federal Research Programs and the Nation's Goals for Higher Education,* Hearings before a Subcommittee of the House Committee on Government Operations, June 14, 15, and 17, 1965, 89 Cong. 1 sess., pp. 94–104; and National Science Foundation, "NSF Funds for Academic Science: Statistical Analysis," Prepared for the House Committee on Science and Astronautics, pt. 2 (October 1965).

by standards intrinsic to a scientific discipline or by criteria of social usefulness. If this is not the case, the university's role in maintaining the intellectual standards of society will be eroded. The guiding principle of national policy should be to support research in conjunction with higher education whenever the research is appropriate for an academic institution and when a realistic choice is available between academic and nonacademic support. Even when the character of the research is considered inappropriate, an effort should be made to conduct it near a university. Within the university, however, the fields that receive support should be determined more by the judgment of individual scientists about what is important than by a priori and centrally determined judgments of national needs. In the terminology of A. M. Weinberg, scientific merit should be given greater weight than social merit in the support of academic research, in contrast to nonacademic and national center research, where social merit and impact on technology are of greater importance.

Academic research should be biased toward national needs only indirectly, by publicizing and analyzing such needs and consequent career opportunities. As far as possible, the government should depend on this "market" information to generate new ideas and research proposals from faculties and fellowship applications from students. This policy takes maximum advantage of the individualistic and freewheeling character of academic science and is best designed to maximize its contribution to the long-run needs of society. Where a more highly programmed effort is desirable or the social need is so urgent that some technical effort is required, even though no very promising new approaches are evident, it should probably be centered at nonacademic institutions, with academic participation only when interest or new ideas appear spontaneously from the academic community.

Forward planning for academic research is needed primarily in the area of facilities and equipment, including new national centers, not in the allocation of resources among basic research fields of little science. In general, allocations to little science should not be made a priori among scientific disciplines but should be based on the promise of individual projects, programs, or research groups. This suggestion is based on the assumption, which I believe to be true, that the variation of quality between individual projects or investigators within a discipline is far greater than the variations between disciplines. I do not mean to imply that the role of supporting agencies should be purely passive, waiting for good ideas to come in, but that the main direction of academic research should be set at the level of the working scientist rather than by central decisions of program officers, committees of scientists, or politicians. The role of supporting, and especially mission-oriented, agencies should be to make the academic community aware of new problems and needs and to foster communication among disciplines and problem areas through special meetings and other mechanisms but not to "direct" research or "force feed" certain areas and starve others on the basis of a priori judgments of relative importance.

Criteria which should be considered in judging individual reseach proposals may be summarized as follows:

1. What is the promise of significant scientific results from the proposed project? The evaluation of such promise implicitly involves the past accomplishment of the investigator and the judgment of his competence and originality by peers, either nationally or locally. The term "significant" may refer either to scientific significance or to potential applicability, but it implies some degree of fundamentality and generality.

2. How novel is the work proposed? To what degree does it break new ground? To what extent does it exploit a new technique or unexplored research methodology? Does it provide a meaningful test of current theory and understanding in its field?

3. To what extent are the probable results of the proposed work likely to influence other work either in the same field or in related or even distant fields?

4. What is the probable educational value of the research, based on the quality and number of students or other trainees in relation to the cost of the project, the record of success of the investigator's students, and the general academic environment in which the work is to be done?

5. What is the potential relevance of the work to possible future applications, especially to existing national goals? This question is of particular relevance in judging engineering research and applied research in health, agriculture, environmental pollution, or similar areas.

Quantitative Growth Requirements

A 15 percent increase in the total support for academic science, including both explicit and hidden costs, appears to be the minimum necessary to keep up with the increase in graduate students and faculty and at the same time not lower quality standards or change drastically the present distribution among fields. Obviously, there are wide variations in the cost of producing a Ph.D. in different fields, and the growing student population could, in principle, be accommodated by shifting present research support from more expensive fields such as nuclear physics and astronomy to cheaper fields such as pure mathematics or chemistry. Possibly, marginal adjustments of this sort should be considered if the present stagnation of academic research budgets continues, but there are many other nonacademic federal technical activities which ought to be carefully scrutinized before any such drastic step is taken for academic science.

Furthermore, the 15 percent requirement is really predicated on expanding research activity in approximately its present institutional pattern. To the extent that wider dispersion accompanies expansion, additional funds will be required to accelerate the development of the research capabilities of weaker institutions. So far, there are no convincing estimates of what this differential is. A rough rule of thumb seems to be that, on the average, it costs about twice as much in the first year to start a research project in little science in a new location as to support a project where work is already going on in the same or a closely related field. At present, institutional development grants such as those of the National Science Foundation are really designed to provide this differential. The extra federal cost may be partly offset by the unusually high leverage on nonfederal sources of funds apparently possessed by competitive development grants.

The introduction of new technology into basic research makes for further uncertainty about costs. Experience in biomedical research suggests that a research field can absorb very large annual increments of money without sacrificing scientific quality if sophisticated and reliable instrumentation is available commercially. For example, the application of computers to almost all phases of research, including the social sciences, has produced a large element of uncertainty in projecting future research requirements. Computer usage at universities has been increasing at an annual rate of about 40–45 percent since 1962, and the imminent introduction of time-sharing and conversational modes of computer usage is likely to accelerate both usage and costs.[16] Hitherto manufacturers' discounts and subsidies from university funds have kept down explicit charges to research. However, as computer charges rapidly become an increasing fraction of both university and research budgets, it is unlikely that the costs can be covered by such "hidden" sources. Manufacturers' discounts have largely disappeared, and normal university budgets are no

[16] National Academy of Sciences–National Research Council, *Digital Computers in Universities and Colleges,* A Report of the Committee on Uses of Computers (1966).

longer able to absorb as large a fraction of the costs, because they represent a higher proportion of the total university budget. Computer techniques so alter the character of research and the scope of the problems that can be successfully attacked in many fields that competitive pressures are likely to spread the demand for this new capability (for teaching as well as research) much faster than has been the case with other types of more specialized instrumentation.

At current levels of support, a 15 percent annual expansion implies about $200 million in increased support annually, including support for fellowships, traineeships, training grants, and various forms of institutional or departmental aid as well as for research.[17] This is only a statistical average based on past experience and should not be interpreted as implying an equal allocation among investigators or institutions. Using such an average as a standard against which to measure the adequacy of project support is not the same thing as distributing the increment according to some formula based on the numbers of students or faculty or a similar mechanical criterion. The maintenance of selectivity among projects and investigators is essential to the maintenance of quality standards in the system as a whole. Furthermore, different projects have legitimately differing costs even within a field, let alone between fields. For example, a study by the National Academy of Sciences' chemistry panel of the annual research grants in chemistry departments showed that nearly half of the *potential* investigators (that is, faculty members capable of supervising graduate students) received less than half the *average* annual grant support of $20,000, and 27 percent of the potential investigators received no federal grant support. This is despite the fact that, according to another finding of the chemistry panel, "the federal support per graduate student per year in chemistry is fairly uniform throughout the United States, averaging about $6,000, almost without

---

[17] Academic research has expanded from about 10 to 13 percent of higher education expenditures in the last ten years, and this trend is likely to continue as graduate education expands relative to undergraduate; Ph.D. awards in science and engineering have risen from 4.4 to 8.0 percent of B.S. awards during the same period. The total costs of higher education are now expanding at an annual rate of about 12 percent. Considering the more rapid rate of expansion of Ph.D. than of B.S. output, the suggested figure of 15 percent for academic research seems, if anything, rather conservative. See National Science Foundation, *Scientific and Technical Manpower Resources: Summary Information on Employment, Characteristics, Supply, and Training* (1964), p. 6. Recent statistics from the Office of Education indicate that the percentage of all educational support, federal and nonfederal, devoted to organized research in educational institutions proper declined slightly from 1960 to 1965.

regard to the size or the scientific tradition of the university in which the student is enrolled."[18] This uniformity is probably unique to chemistry because of its little science character. A study of the size of National Science Foundation basic research grants in 1963 showed that roughly 12 percent of the funds were expended in 1.4 percent of the grants, and 60 percent of the money was expended in about 25 percent of the grants.[19] As another illustration, estimates of the average cost in federal research support of producing a Ph.D. in the various subfields of physics and in chemistry as a whole are given below:[20]

Elementary particle physics	$910,000
Astrophysics, solar system physics, cosmic rays	500,000
Nuclear physics	234,000
Plasma physics	230,000
Solid state and condensed matter	160,000
Atomic and molecular physics	93,000
Chemistry	39,000

It is possible, of course, to question many of the assumptions on which the above projections are based. For example, one may question whether a research degree is really essential for undergraduate college teaching, whether in fact it imparts an appropriate set of values to the potential undergraduate teacher, especially in liberal arts colleges. The same question might be raised with respect to potential industrial scientists and engineers. Indeed, the Physics Survey Committee explicitly considered the desirability of an intermediate graduate degree more appropriate for physicists who would not be engaged primarily in basic research. It is certainly true that graduate students who fail to complete their research often become valuable college teachers and that they are nearly as successful in industry as those who obtain their Ph.D.'s. If the Ph.D. were made a much more elite degree, the necessary investment in academic research purely for educational purposes could be reduced. It must not be overlooked, however, that such a policy would decrease the attractiveness of university faculty positions, and it is doubtful whether universities could retain intellectual leadership in society under these conditions. Few people would wish to take the risk of such a drastic departure from the past pattern in higher education.

[18] *Chemistry: Opportunities and Needs,* p. 168.

[19] Unpublished analysis of National Science Foundation fiscal year 1963 grants.

[20] These figures are for fiscal 1963. Estimates include grants and contracts only at what the National Science Foundation has defined as "universities proper" (which excludes major university-managed research centers).

It might also be argued that not all federally supported academic research is essential to the training of graduate students or that the large numbers of postdoctoral research workers in university science departments are luxuries that the academic research budget can no longer afford. These are complex issues with no simple answers. One obstacle to a simple answer is the importance in graduate training of the total environment of the university—of the research atmosphere created by the presence of individuals at various levels of training. Even professors who do not supervise graduate students may make an important contribution to the educational environment through their influence on colleagues who do teach. Most postdoctoral students stay for only a short time and then move into regular employment on or off campus. There is little evidence for the existence of a large career research population in universities divorced from the rest of their intellectual function, although this matter requires further attention from the universities themselves. Clearly, the competitive nature of basic research forces all researchers to demand a similar standard with respect to both postdoctoral associates and sophisticated instrumentation. On the other hand, not only other universities but nonacademic institutions set the competitive standard. Indeed, the level of industrial and governmental research inevitably sets the standard for academic research so far as logistic support and experimental sophistication are concerned. On the face of it, it appears unwise to stint on academic research, when it accounts for only 7 percent of national expenditures for research and development and only 32 percent of federal expenditures for basic research, especially if intellectual leadership in learning, as well as the mere production of Ph.D.'s, is taken seriously as a primary social function of universities.

If academic research budgets continue to level off, grave questions of policy will be posed. The vigor of a scientific field seems to depend on a continuing injection of new investigators with fresh ideas and on sufficient funds to exploit new ideas and replace outmoded equipment. Controlled thermonuclear research provides an interesting model of what happens in a field in which support has stagnated. In a few short years, the United States has lost the commanding leadership it enjoyed in high temperature plasma research. A principal reason was the lack of funds for new investigators and new experiments. The bad effects of this stagnation might have been reduced if the results of cuts in funds had been foreseen. Although other factors, such as isolation from the general physics community and the absence of a university base, also contributed to the stagnation of this field, the fact remains that there are few if any examples of fields which have managed to retain their vigor and intellectual vitality in the face of level or declining support. In the absence of new funding, it will be necessary to invent new mechanisms of funding which will permit greater concentration and specialization of effort. Only by such concentration can strong growing points be maintained in the absence of new funds. To spread the same funds more and more thinly over a growing number of investigators, institutions, and students would be a prescription for the slow strangulation of science in the United States.

Unfortunately, techniques for maintaining quality and progress under conditions of level funding and rising costs would involve policies that would be politically unpopular. They would run directly counter to present pressures to spread federal support more widely and uniformly. In addition to fostering greater concentration of effort in a few places, these policies would probably have to encourage deliberate gambling on new ideas, new approaches, and new investigators at the expense of approaches or investigators whose previous record of accomplishment was high but predictable. If the evolution of science is not to be slowed by the declining growth of academic research, it will be necessary to try to compensate by gambling on mutations. The problem of maintaining the quality and momentum of science in the face of slackening growth has little precedent and probably represents the most serious crisis faced by the United States scientific community in many years.

DISCUSSION

The Wisdom of Capriciousness

Dael Wolfle, who was asked to prepare comments on Brooks's paper, opened the discussion as follows.

THE CRITERIA that one tries to use in making decisions about expenditures for research serve different purposes and are applied at different times. Harvey Brooks has talked about the importance of dealing in a nonaggregative fashion with expenditures for basic research. But in thinking about these problems, one does try, from time to time, to deal with them in an aggregative fashion.

When Warren Weaver wrote his chapter of *Goals for Americans,* he proposed a rather quick increase from the then level [of $800–$900 million] to approximately the present level and then proposed, as others have, that further growth be tied to the gross national product or some other economic measure.[1]

In an oversimplified sense, the "15 percent formula" [for the annual increase in federal science expenditures at universities] associated sometimes with Harvey Brooks is another kind of measure.

I would like first to agree with Brooks's emphasis that most aggregative approaches are generally a much less useful way of establishing proper levels of support than are homogeneous categories. The categories of basic and applied research and development, or disciplinary categories, have been tried periodically. Tonight we had a good exposition of the reasons for institutional categories.

The line of thinking developed in his paper leads to the conclusion that the proper total (if there is a proper total) for academic research and basic research has to be arrived at as a summation of a lot of individual decisions each made in terms of its own appropriate criteria—that you can't start with any lump sum. Obviously, that conclusion makes difficulties for the budget makers, because at any particular time there isn't an unlimited amount of money that can be allocated in terms of these criteria; there are limits.

In relation to the topic that we talked of last time ["The Allocation of Federal Support among Scientific Fields"—see chapter 5], it seemed to me that the group came to the consensus that it is impossible, on the basis of anything other than such operational devices as proposal pressure, to make distinctions or divisions in the levels of support among fields of science. And, probably, it is also impossible to make arbitrary or generally agreed upon divisions in funding among other categories, such as applied and basic research or different kinds of research institutions.

I think we decided this at the last meeting. But the decision wasn't

---

[1] "The increase from $800–$900 million for basic research to about $1500 million should occur as promptly as personnel and physical facilities will permit—say in three years at the most. And in addition to this corrective increase in the fraction of our GNP which we devote to basic research, there should of course be a continuing increase to keep pace with our growing economy" (Warren Weaver, "A Great Age for Science," in *Goals for Americans,* The Report of the President's Commission on National Goals, American Assembly [1960], p. 120).

implemented, because we do in fact make such comparisons repeatedly. We do it at present by the total of a lot of decisions made in a very pluralistic system, with many advocates of different kinds of work, many sources of funds, and several levels of decision within each of these sources. At intervals, we have special reports that analyze the needs in a particular area. Recently, we have had—chiefly from the National Academy of Sciences—studies of the needs in oceanography, ground-based astronomy, high energy physics, and the most recent one of all, chemistry, which is perhaps the best of this series.[2]

If we continue with this system, which seems to be the moral of what the speaker has said, the "proper total" at any one time will be the sum of whatever the advocates for the various competitive areas can persuade the supporters of research to give, and the proper distribution will be the distribution emerging from that pluralism of decision.

This is something we have been living with, and there is certainly much good, much diversity, in this system and the guarantee of a second chance for the review of an idea. It has both the advantage of a great many loci of decisions and the danger that decisions can be made because of the particular persuasiveness or power of an individual. Yet it always results in an ex post facto division—that is, we have for 1965 and 1964 allotted so much to ground-based astronomy, so much to chemistry and meterology, so much to academic institutions, and so on.

I know of no group of scientists that has seriously been willing to try to institutionalize their decisions. Some planners think that we ought to be able to develop a better system that in the long run would look at the high energy physics report, and the chemistry report, and some others and say, "Well, chemistry has been underplayed and we ought to be able now to put some special emphasis on it," or "We want to be sure that academic resarch grows at a 15 percent rate," or make other policy decisions of this kind.

We don't, at present, have any institutionalized level or arrangement for making this kind of decision. Perhaps it is impossible, perhaps no people are wise enough to make it, or perhaps it is only that our democracy isn't willing to trust any group of people who might be given that

---

[2] See *Economic Benefits from Oceanographic Research* (1964); *Ground-based Astronomy: A Ten-Year Program* (1964); and *Chemistry: Opportunities and Needs* (1965), all published by the National Academy of Sciences; and *Report of the Panel of High Energy Accelerator Physics of the General Advisory Committee to the Atomic Energy Commission and the President's Science Advisory Committee* (the Ramsey report), published by the Atomic Energy Commission (April 1963).

responsibility. And yet, I conclude with a dissatisfied feeling that the system that we have, or the system that Brooks has advocated, leaves a gap.

". . . [O]n the basis of my own transcendental experience with the problems, I couldn't agree more," remarked a social scientist who had actually had considerable experience with budgeting for science.

> It is a most capricious kind of activity. . . . [A]nyone who has studied even superficially the processes by which we have arrived at the present level of outlays on medical research has varying degrees of dissatisfaction or even outrage at the kind of capriciousness and the primitiveness of the standards we have used.
>
> But, then, you ask a question of the same person who is unhappy about the methods we have used . . . : "Are we better off today in medical research than we would be if there were no Congressman Fogarty?" you have an embarrassed silence, because I think most people come up with the decision that we are better off for having had Congressman Fogarty.[3]

In other words, the chance location and convictions of a few individuals had an awful lot to do with government science budgets—but were the consequences so awful?

To this unchallenged observation two other observations were added. First, the power an individual exercised because of his position could not always be distinguished from that which he exercised "as the spokesman for some deep-felt national interest. . . . [I]f Congressman Fogarty had not existed . . . the opportunities would have been there for some Congressman to rise to this occasion and do precisely the same thing." And second, was the "pluralistic, complicated decision-making process" of arriving at budgets for science and technology so different from the budgetary process in other programs?

"What Is a Mistake in High Energy Physics?"

Yes, it *was* different, at least in the area of basic research, a physicist rejoined. ". . . [W]hen you make an investment in something like the Poverty Program, you know more or less what you are investing in, whereas in . . . basic science, you don't. . . ." An economist agreed:

[3] Congressman John Fogarty of Rhode Island was, of course, for many years chairman of the subcommittee of the House Committee on Appropriations responsible for the National Institutes of Health appropriations; together with Senator Lister Hill, chairman of the comparable Senate appropriations subcommittee, he has generally been given much credit for the generosity of Congress toward medical research, particularly since 1956.

. . . [I]f you take the average situation in the nonscience part of the budget . . . the nature of the benefits you are dealing with tend to be somewhat more commensurable than they are in the average situation in the science part. . . . We don't know . . . a lot now about what we will get out of the Poverty Program, because the thing is hardly airborne, but as a matter of simple reporting there are today, in operation, quite sophisticated efforts to measure the benefits of various parts of the Poverty Program . . . [for example, by measuring] the improvement in the earning power of Job Corps members whose skills are upgraded. There are all kinds of things which can be measured and quantified.

To be sure, the physicist volunteered, "You can measure things in basic science, but they are not measures which anybody else will accept. . . . [For example,] basic research publications have increased in accordance [with] the money that has gone into it." However, the public does not want to produce more scientific publications but some demonstrable and measurable national good, and it is easier to determine whether such a technological, economic, or social good resulted from applied research than from basic research. In applied research, there is a perceptible target, so that one can say whether it has been hit or missed; whereas in basic research, the target—"the advance of knowledge"—is so broad, could it ever be missed? "What is a mistake in high energy physics? What is a mistake?"

To that aggravating question, one physicist replied, ". . . [I]f you had built the MURA machine and not built the 200 Bev accelerator (assuming we do), that would have been a mistake,"[4] but another physicist immediately interpolated, "You couldn't prove it until some time after the machine was built." "What I know about high energy physics you could easily pack into the bottom of a thimble," a social scientist said with no trace of remorse, "but I have . . . talked with a lot of experts and I have yet to hear any expert give me any reason why x amount spent on high energy physics is better than $2x$ or $1\frac{1}{2}x$." "Or put in another field," added an engineer.

"One of the bravest things" that Harvey Brooks has done, commented another social scientist, was his statement about the scientific fields in

[4] The "MURA machine" was a 12.5 Bev accelerator, whose construction had been proposed by the Midwestern Universities Research Association, with headquarters in Madison, Wis. The proposal was endorsed by a high-level panel of physicists (the Ramsey panel, whose April 1963 report is cited in note 2) on the express condition that it not delay authorization of the higher energy 200 Bev accelerator. As it developed, funds for the MURA machine were dropped from President Johnson's first budget (the fiscal year 1965 budget, announced in January 1964).

which he would reduce expenditures. "It was one of the rarest para-
graphs I have ever read."[5]

SOCIAL SCIENTIST A: There were two reductions; one field that should
be stabilized, and about a dozen that should be increased.

SOCIAL SCIENTIST B: . . . I was very pleased to see even two [reductions].
That is two more than I have ever seen before.

SOCIAL SCIENTIST C: I would be interested in the criteria. . . .

AGENCY SCIENTIST D: This is what I describe as a "gut" feeling.

SOCIAL SCIENTIST B: . . . [N]obody ever makes these statements in public.

SCIENTIST E: [Such a] . . . statement on nuclear structure physics [was
made] to the Bureau of the Budget two years ago. . . .

SOCIAL SCIENTIST B: [Can the] Bureau of the Budget people . . . report
themselves deluged with such comment on fields that should be cut?

BUDGET BUREAU TYPE: No.

AGENCY MAN: But this isn't quite fair. . . . Before it ever gets to [the
bureau] . . . there are some agency look-sees in which there is quite a bit of
[cutting]——

BUDGET BUREAU TYPE: . . . [Y]our agency did something courageous,
almost positively heroic in doing a conscientious job of assigning priorities.

AGENCY MAN: And it didn't come easy. . . .

SCIENTIST E: I must confess I find it much easier to do this in applied fields
than in basic fields. . . . [I]t is very hard . . . when you know very little
about the field [to say] that your wisdom is superior to that of a lot of
other people who do know a lot about the field.

Isn't there some way, a government administrator wondered, to overcome sectarian disciplinary interests by getting "the total judgment of a
university" about the important areas of common national and academic
concern, a judgment to which all disciplines—history, economics, and
philosophy as well as the sciences—would contribute? Something of this
kind is being attempted at Harvard, it was suggested, in the program
conducted under a $5 million IBM grant, in which all interested sectors
of the university are being involved in an effort "to get some wisdom"
on the interrelations of technological and social change. But "it takes a
long time to mobilize intellectual effort in a university . . . around an
area of concern." (Not, it was interpolated, in professional schools such
as medicine or agriculture.) An institute might be formed within the

[5] This is a reference to Harvey Brooks's "Reply to Six Questions," in the course of
which he advocated reduced expenditures for "low energy nuclear physics, especially
nuclear spectroscopy" and for "research in agriculture oriented toward products and
utilization of products" (pp. 149, 150).

university for the purpose, but such institutes tend to be created around an individual; "an institute . . . is really never university-wide. . . ." The administrator preferred a genuinely "university-wide approach" organized and monitored "by the senior spirits of the university. . . ."

Of Time and the United States Budget

Part of the weakness of present science allocations, a government participant suggested, is attributable to the inexorable deadlines of the government budgeting system.

> . . . [I]f somehow you could slow down the present system you would improve it considerably. I have reviewed what I consider to be either errors in decision or decisions which were not quite as good as they might otherwise have been . . . , and I think invariably . . . every one of these is characterized by the fact that a decision had to be reached with respect to an annual budget cycle. . . . [The] characteristic situation is, if it doesn't get into the budget this year, it has to wait until next year: and if it once gets into the budget, then you never get it out. If you miss it in the Congressional presentation this year, it is there in the record and you go back to the same thing again. The inflexibility and the necessity to make a decision in a very short time span . . . is totally unnecessary, really, and very bad [for basic research programs]. . . .
>
> I am talking about capital programs and new programs . . . , departures into new program areas, which . . . might have taken a quite different form entirely if we had time really to sit down and perhaps get more argumentation on them, more contact with the people who are involved . . . , when . . . a very strong pressure group from a high-level status outfit comes down the street and says, "We want to go on this right away." Under those circumstances, and under the circumstances of an annual budget cycle, the pressure to get something in is so much greater than the pressure to hold back and think it through.

One of the best things about the early days of the National Science Foundation, someone recalled, was that "we didn't have a lot of money and we had more time to think—I am not saying we don't need more money now." "—I never heard a suggestion before that the government was not slow enough!" remarked an incredulous participant.

> OFFICIAL: The cycle is too fast. Getting it through several cycles is very slow sometimes, but you are always . . . either preparing a budget, spending a budget, or defending a budget. . . . Universities are not time-bound in their substantive characteristics. They are timeless. We are operating in an

interface with the university constituency; yet we are operating on a budget cycle which is terribly time-bound. . . .

CITIZEN A: . . . [O]ne of the implications of the new planning-program-ming-budgeting system is to provide a longer digestion process. But the other side of the story, of course, is [that] if you were not time-bound you would probably never make a decision. . . . One of the things that ought to be said in support of the annual budget is that it forces decisions. Sev-enty-five percent of the decisions which are made in the budget . . . would not be made if they didn't have to be made. . . .

OFFICIAL: . . . I don't think the total national budget has to be on an annual cycle.

CITIZEN B: Can you make a practical suggestion: Would you break free several billion dollars . . . from the normal budget cycle?

OFFICIAL: . . . We could go for a budget part of which is on a two year base. . . .

CITIZEN C: . . . [M]ost people in the agencies don't have time to think ahead . . . because they are so busy solving tomorrow's problems. They never really have time to sit down and put their feet on the table and think about problems two or three years from now.

CITIZEN D: What you are really saying is that the world should slow down.

Pluralism and Politics Are Good

The best system for allocating funds to basic science, a scientist declared, is "the pluralistic system in which you make decisions compete with each other in as many different ways as possible." (The system that he had in mind is evidently very much like the system, or lack of system, that now prevails.)

> You give some money to the institution to decide how it is going to spend it, and you give some money to disciplinary panels to decide how they are going to spend it within a discipline, and you give some money to individ-ual scientists to decide how they are going to spend their time—that is, the fellowship. And this . . . pluralistic way of forcing people to make choices ends . . . up with better choices than any single method of making choices.

A government official was somewhat less sanguine about present ar-rangements. One possible improvement, he thought, would be to invite the twenty-five institutions receiving the largest volume of R&D funds to submit institution-wide proposals covering all, or most, of their present activities. The notion that all wisdom resided in Washington staff and panels, while only "prejudices and stupidity and bias and infighting" could be expected from decisions made locally on each campus, was "rather paradoxical," he suggested, since "these . . . institutions grew up and got to greatness largely on the basis of these local decisions. . . . [Local decisions] can't be so bad and have resulted in a Harvard and a Chicago and a Berkeley and a Stanford. . . ."

OFFICIAL A: What is valid for the Harvards and the Berkeleys . . . might be the reverse for the weak institutions. . . .

OFFICIAL B: If you don't allow them to make the decisions, they will stay that way.

Institutional grants should be enlarged, a university spokesman agreed; but carried to an extreme, they would lead to "a frittering away of funds over a lot of mediocre institutions that don't have any [scientific] potential and probably never will. . . ." The government could pass qualitative judgments on the merit of individual scientists, via the project system, but it could never do so on the merit of institutions without severe political repercussions, because "there is no institution . . . [whose] alumni do not think it is a pretty great place." Furthermore, institutional grants would give further encouragement to the wasteful "university syndrome" under the influence of which every college wants to become a university.

Is it so impossible to evaluate objectively an institution's research achievement? it was asked. A NASA review board assessed the performance of General Electric and other major contractors each month, as a basis for determining their incentive fee. Could not this kind of evaluation be approximated at universities?

Obviously there is a lot of politics in the present system of scientific allocations, said a participant from Capitol Hill, but what is wrong with that? Politics is the way by which important needs and interests get recognized and financed.

If I had to . . . choose between the politicking that would go on . . . in the universities or in the executive branch and the politicking that goes on on the Hill, I [would] choose the politicking that goes on on the Hill. . . . [T]his political process . . . is a way of allocating resources based upon practical considerations, . . . upon persuasion. . . .

. . . [T]his process . . . works out pretty well. Nobody here has found a better one, and maybe it is impossible to find a better one. Or maybe the solution is semantic, in that you take the same thing and translate it into other terms and think you have a solution. I don't think there is any other solution to the process of allocating [resources]. . . . Because what you would do is merely move politics from the arena in which they are experts in it into the arena in which they make fools of themselves.

The utter admirability of our present system of allocations was challenged by an economist. "We like to believe everything works out all right in the end, but I think there is too much evidence to the contrary." An example of poor allocation is the more than $100 million a year that has gone into agriculture production research for as long as anyone can remember.

> I think it is pretty readily demonstrable that the benefits yielded by this research are not only small but negative. If we spent the money on anything else we would be better off. . . .
>
> . . . [T]he benefits of agricultural production research—I wasn't talking about utilization, but production research—are currently negative in the following sense: the relationship between the growth of demand for agricultural output, which is reasonably slow, the growth of productivity in agriculture, which is spectacularly rapid, and the immobility of productive research out of agriculture, which is very low, is such that any increase in the rate of productivity in agriculture will have its effect simply in creating underemployment . . . in agriculture. Not [in] increasing our standard of living or lowering food cost but simply increasing the number of unemployed in agriculture.

POLITICAL SCIENTIST: You say this even though two-thirds of the world is hungry?

ECONOMIST: Yes. That is another, quite different, problem. That really is a red herring. . . .

PHYSICIST: . . . [W]hat you are saying . . . isn't that agricultural research is not productive; in fact, your complaint is that it is too productive. This, then, is a political judgment. . . .

ECONOMIST: No. It is an economic judgment. To put it in its simplest form: . . . [I]s it productive in a manufacturing process when you introduce improved technology which now makes it possible to produce twice as much per worker as it did before, if the demand for the product doesn't increase and the workers displaced can do nothing else but sit at the machines and do nothing? This is a good parallel to agriculture. I say this is not a productive application of research funds.

PHYSICIST: I think this is a defect in the rest of the society.

ENGINEER: . . . [I]n most applied technology, that kind of decision . . . can be made on fairly rational grounds. It is not true in the basic [research field].

ECONOMIST: I would agree. . . .

SOCIOLOGIST: . . . [E]ven basic science is socially rooted; whether you are talking about high energy physics or what . . . you expect some benefits, and . . . you are not just fiddling around. . . . We do have some very absurd allocations. . . . I mean, the gross distortion between physical science and technology, and social science. If you went around this table and asked where the really critical problems are that are making for unhappiness . . .

[T]his defense of a laissez faire scheme [contains] the conclusion which ineptly follows that we are living in the best of all possible worlds. Otherwise, if you don't think that, you think you can improve the system. . . .

PHYSICIST : . . . You have to look at the social need, and you have to look at the probability of success. I just don't think it pays to spend millions of dollars pushing worms into the ground, as Herb York says. If you can really show opportunities that we are missing in the social sciences—specific opportunities where, by spending more money on specific projects, we can advance the social sciences faster, I will be the first man to back you up.

SOCIOLOGIST : I am not arguing that more money would produce better results. I think that is a fallacy behind the Foundation for the Humanities and the Arts.[6] I, frankly, am dubious about what [that] may lead to. But, I think the fragmented approach . . . is a part of our transportation problem in this country. You have the automotive people looking at automobiles, and the railroad people the railroads, and so on, but not a total approach to the system. I think you have to look at the educational system, not just by institutions, but as a total system, and determine what it is you want to produce. . . .

PSYCHOLOGIST : . . . I agree. . . . If we don't see any way to improve the present system, then we are implying that this is the best of all systems. . . . Or that we are ignorant or unimaginative; and my own conclusion, so far, is the latter. I don't think this is the best system, but I don't know how to improve it.

Earlier, there had been a confident allusion to the self-correcting nature of the "pluralistic system." Thus, many chemists had complained about the inadequacy of funds for research in chemistry, but, as a result, "something has been done about chemistry. . . . [T]hese kind of restorative forces do exist in the pluralistic system." Last year (presumably July 1964–June 1965, in the Washington idiom!), it struck a government participant, the greatest increases in research expenditures were for research on education, crime, the origins of poverty, regional economics, and hospital medical technology; taken together, these represented "radical changes" in response to changing national needs. As for the social sciences, "true, the total support is small, but the social sciences have been the fastest growing field now for ten years. . . ." ("This makes me

---

[6] That is, the National Foundation on the Arts and the Humanities.

think of Russian economic statistics," interpolated an economist.) Accordingly, it could reasonably be said that although the system of allocations "isn't perfect," it is "responsive. . . ."

Others remained skeptical. Such flexibility as can be observed, they felt, applies only to small science. "It clearly does not apply to capital science, which is almost by definition inflexible." And the current demands of small science may be only a reflection of how university resources were allocated twenty-five or fifty years ago. One political scientist, at least, did not share the faith of other participants "that there is an invisible hand operating which is going to lead to the maximization of decisions."

". . . [Y]ou have to proceed in this business by increments, and not by allocating from scratch," a scientist concluded. ". . . [T]oo much of the whole business of scientific planning is discussed from the point of view that you are starting with a *tabula rasa*. . . . That isn't the way the process works."

CHRISTIAN K. ARNOLD

The Government
and University Science:
Purchase or Investment?

ALMOST REVOLUTIONARY advances have been achieved in American science since World War II. These advances are substantially attributable to the expenditure of federal funds for research and development and especially for basic research carried out by faculty members at our institutions of higher education. There can be no serious doubt about the wisdom—or even the necessity—of these expenditures. Research productivity has become a matter not simply of national concern but of national survival. The extension and application of knowledge have become a necessary condition of human welfare and even of the preservation of human dignity and freedom. In this situation, the subvention of research, and of the education of people capable of conducting it, becomes a necessary function of the central government. We have discharged this function with distinction. Further, it is also clear that these federal expenditures have greatly strengthened both the research and the instructional capacities of those institutions participating in the federal programs, particularly at the graduate level.

Most of these funds have been channeled from federal agencies to colleges and universities through the project grant or contract system developed, but not invented, during World War II. At the beginning of our involvement in the war, our military technology and machinery were almost hopelessly inadequate and obsolete. Therefore, the military agencies did what they had to do—they bought the information, engineering, and "hardware" they needed by negotiating contracts with organizations and individuals that seemed most likely to do the best job for them.

With the ending of the war, national research priorities shifted fundamentally. No longer were we in such a crisis situation, notwithstanding the subsequent shock to our national pride at the success of the first Russian Sputnik. During the war, we had ruthlessly exploited the existing supply of scientific and technological knowledge; now we needed to invest substantially in its renewal and expansion. Despite the shift in priorities, however, the government's administrative philosophy and the project mechanism by which it was implemented remained essentially unchanged; federal agencies continued to purchase what they needed by awarding grants and contracts for specific purposes. This combination —the shifting of priorities along with the continuation of almost sole reliance on the purchase-of-service mechanism and philosophy—has created serious problems both for the universities and for the federal agencies. These problems have been compounded by the vast increase in the amount of funds available.

The project system served us well in meeting the vital urgencies of the war, and it continues to serve us well in funding those types of activities for which it was designed. As President Lee A. DuBridge, of the California Institute of Technology, has said, ". . . [T]he contract or grant funds, of necessity, are highly restricted to meet the needs of particular projects."[1] In other words, the project system is designed to meet the needs of the unusual, the special, the extraordinary. It is well adapted, for instance, to supporting the work of an extraordinarily brilliant scientist, or to financing definable, short-term "one-shot" ventures, or to establishing a unique national research facility. It is well adapted to attacking problems that arise suddenly or to capitalizing rapidly on a basic new discovery.

Limitations of the Project System

By its nature, however, the system is less well suited to the long-term development and maintenance of an enhanced national competence in

---

[1] *Panel on Science and Technology, Seventh Meeting: Government, Science, and Public Policy,* Proceedings before the House Committee on Science and Astronautics, 89 Cong. 2 sess. (January 25, 26, and 27, 1966), p. 45.

science and to the preservation and strengthening of those characteristics that make our colleges and universities uniquely valuable national assets.

A major difficulty lies in the tendency of the project system to concentrate federal funds in a relatively small number of institutions. This tendency is inherent in the system. When research grants and contracts are awarded to the more competent scientists, the competence of their institutions is increased by their accumulation of additional scientists, better facilities, improved fiscal and supporting services, and the like. At the same time, the competence of the other institutions is relatively weakened by the loss of capable scientists and the lack of the newer, more sophisticated, and more expensive facilities. At some point, the growing prestige of the grant-receiving institution and its improved facilities and services help the scientist to get grants (rather than the grants helping to improve the institution, as may have been true initially), and the institution's competitive position in the scientific market place is even further strengthened. To the extent that proposals are in fact judged on the single basis of merit, this tendency to institutional concentration is inexorable. We do not need the example (one among many) of the simultaneous announcement by a large, prestigious west coast university of its receipt of a multimillion dollar grant and of its importation, to run the program, of a distinguished department head from a small northern plains university to prove the point.

These facts have been known for a long time. Raising the question in 1960 of how federal research funds should be distributed, President Eric A. Walker, of Pennsylvania State University, replied with another question:

> To those institutions and individuals most likely to produce the best results? These funds are already concentrated in a relatively small number of institutions, and this policy would surely lead to an even greater concentration. This further concentration would lead to an even greater disparity in research competence and to an even greater degree of concentration, with the possible result that these institutions might become, in time, huge research centers with little connection with the instructional function, at least at the undergraduate level.[2]

The effects of concentration are also felt by communities and regions. The growth of strong research universities tends symbiotically to encourage the growth of science-oriented industry nearby. A further concentra-

---

[2] *Proceedings of the National Association of State Universities and Land-Grant Colleges,* 74th Annual Convention, Washington, D.C., Nov. 13–16, 1960 (the Association, 1961), p. 44.

tion of professional and technical manpower, facilities, administrative competence, and supporting services results, leading to a further improvement in the competitive position of the region, and so on. It barely matters which comes first: the more chickens there are, the more eggs; the more eggs, the more chickens.

This tendency toward concentration, of course, most seriously affects those institutions and regions that have been unable to participate substantially in federal grant programs and to make their full potential contribution to the achievement of national aims and goals. But the agency-to-individual relationship enforced by the project system has also created problems for institutions participating heavily in federal programs. All the basic decisions in a project award—the nature of the proposed research, the size of the budget, the duration of the project, and so on—are made by the university scientist and the officials of the agency to which the proposal is submitted. In this process, the responsible administrative officers of the university are largely bypassed, retaining for all practical purposes only veto power, which, if exercised, can—and often does, especially at less prestigious institutions—result in the scientist's leaving the institution and taking *his* grant (and the equipment purchased with it) to another institution.

Combined with the short-term nature of the funding and the fact that federal funds now support up to 80 or 90 percent of physical science research at colleges and universities, this relationship clearly erodes the ability of institutions to plan and execute cohesive long-range development programs in the sciences. Just as clearly, it shifts control of large segments of the university programs from university officers to federal officials. (At "have" institutions, half or more of the total institutional budget may come from federal sources.)

Despite this erosion of its decision-making power, the university remains legally responsible for the conduct of the research and for the expenditure of funds in connection with it. At the same time, the project system denies the institution the authority to discharge this responsibility effectively. Furthermore, the effective control over projects exercised by agency administrators raises serious threats to the independence and freedom of inquiry of the institutions and their grant-supported faculty. As *Scientific American* publisher Gerard Piel told the House Committee on Science and Astronautics in January 1966, "With such a high percentage of the total activity hanging upon project-by-project support, the independence of the university scientist would seem to be heavily compromised."[3] So also is the autonomy of the institutions involved.

It has become fairly commonplace, lately, first to recognize the need to give universities a greater degree of fiscal and management control over research projects and, then, to suggest that university administrations must be strengthened before such control can be given.[4] Seldom is it pointed out, however, that the project system by its nature, mitigates against the development of responsible university administration.

The project system also creates difficulties for government agencies. As the amount of money and the number of special-purpose programs, investigators, review panels, and participating institutions and agencies multiply, effective management becomes almost impossible despite herculean efforts by the increasing number of conscientious, well-qualified federal administrators. The highly centralized system simply is not designed for the volume of business now being thrust upon it.

Further, the fact that the system is being increasingly used for purposes for which it is not well designed has created some annoying problems to which satisfactory solutions have not been, and perhaps cannot be, found. One of these problems has already been suggested: how to provide the stability and continuity needed for sound progress in basic research through short-term grants and contracts, each of which is justified in terms of its contribution to an agency's statutory mission and to the demands of a particular division or program within that agency. Though agency officials, university administrators, and individual scientists may accept a moral obligation to provide program and financial stability, it is difficult for them to discharge it without subterfuge.

The sticky problems of overhead and of cost sharing also rise in connection with grants. In commercial practice, when a purchase is made, the buyer normally pays the full costs including those of lighting, heating, and sweeping out the shop, plus a profit. This practice is also followed without much difficulty in government-financed research purchased by contract. On the other hand, when undiluted support funds are granted, as in a pension to an artist, they are expected to be used for groceries and heat as well as for paint brushes. We follow this model without difficulty, for the most part, in public appropriations to state

[3] *Panel on Science and Technology, Seventh Meeting,* p. 50.
[4] See, for example, Bureau of the Budget, *The Administration of Government Supported Research at Universities* (March 1966).

universities, where the concept of cost sharing is irrelevant. However, by attempting, through research grants, to serve a support function through a purchase mechanism and philosophy, a situation is created in which endless squabbling is likely about the proper degree of cost sharing and the payment of indirect costs.

Mounting pressures intensify the difficulties of the project system. These pressures come from all directions: from the "have" and "near have" institutions and regions competing for the larger, more prestigious awards such as the National Science Foundation's science development grants; from the "have-not" institutions and regions seeking an "equitable share" of the public funds being expended; from spokesmen and advocates of disciplines, professional areas, and services for which federal support programs have not yet been devised; and even from federal agencies that have not yet been able to develop their own support programs.

Such pressures should surprise no one. Competition is built into the system, and the amount of federal funds received by an individual or institution has become a powerful, if unofficial, *ad hoc* rating device. As the amount of funds and the costs of research rise, and as the university's other financial resources become stretched to the breaking point by competing but vital functions such as undergraduate instruction, it becomes steadily more difficult for any institution to develop and maintain strong research and educational programs in the sciences *without* federal aid. The institutions really have no choice: they *must* compete for grants. With the cards stacked against most of them by the nature of the system, the competition leads to pressure.

These difficulties have been recognized. The 1964 report of the National Academy of Sciences' Committee on Science and Public Policy, *Federal Support of Basic Research in Institutions of Higher Learning,* mentioned most of them, but minimized their importance. They have been discussed, at least in part, by such major scientific spokesmen as Donald Hornig, the President's science adviser; Leland Haworth, director of the National Science Foundation; James Shannon, director of the National Institutes of Health; Frederick Seitz, president of the National Academy of Sciences; Don Price, president of the American Association for the Advancement of Science; *Scientific American* publisher Gerard Piel; *Science* editor Philip Abelson; and others. Of special importance was President Johnson's September 14, 1965, statement aimed "to insure that our programs for Federal support of research in colleges and universities contribute more to the long run strengthening of the universities and colleges so that these institutions can best serve the nation in the years ahead." Directing each agency "to reexamine its practices in the financing of research," the President declared, "I want to be sure that, consistent with agency missions and objectives, all practical measures are taken to strengthen the institutions where research now goes on, and to help additional institutions to become more effective centers for teaching and research."[5]

Ameliorative Measures

Not only have these difficulties been recognized, but substantial steps have been taken to alleviate them. Programs that provide essentially unrestricted grants for broad purposes have been established by both the National Science Foundation (Institutional Grants Program) and the National Institutes of Health (General Research Support Program and the Biomedical Sciences Support Program). The "step-funding" innovation of the National Aeronautics and Space Administration provides a new degree of continuity and stability for project grants. The National Institutes of Health (NIH) is experimenting with a plan to give institutions greater management and fiscal control over projects. The National Science Foundation, NIH, the Office of Education, and NASA have all begun programs to counter the institutional concentration of graduate students that results from free-choice fellowship programs by providing grants for fellowships or traineeships to the institutions instead.

The National Science Foundation has instituted Science Development grants to provide large sums over limited periods of time to selected institutions to force-feed the development of additional "centers of excellence," and the program will soon be extended to provide more modest grants to smaller institutions for the same purpose. In the spring of 1966, NIH followed suit with its Health Science Advancement awards. Many federal agencies are tending to fund whole programs, laboratories, and centers en bloc in an effort, among other purposes, to reduce the management problems posed both to them and to educational institutions by the proliferation of project awards. New kinds of programs (such as the NSF secondary- and elementary-school teacher and re-

[5] "Memorandum from the President to the Heads of Departments and Agencies," The White House, September 14, 1965.

search-participation programs) have enlarged the number of institutions whose scientific activities are eligible for federal support.

These developments are helpful, but their thrust remains that of an attempt to modify a vehicle designed for one purpose to serve a basically different purpose. We would hardly attempt to modify an Indianapolis racer for use as a family car, but that is essentially what these types of modifications amount to. Science development grants may create new "centers of excellence," but if used to pirate faculty, they will weaken the competitive position of other institutions. Helpful as present institutional grants to recipient institutions are, they do not serve to increase the number of institutions participating in federal programs. The multiplication of programs creates bewildering information and management problems, especially for institutions that have not received substantial grants and have not, therefore, had the opportunity to develop effective liaison with federal agencies.

The modifications in the project system are compromises that give recognition to the difficulties without providing basic relief from them. "Grantsmanship" is thereby encouraged, as well as a growing cynicism that seriously threatens to limit the usefulness of the system even for its original purposes. Thus, for instance, when considerations of "equitable geographical distribution" are superimposed upon considerations of merit in the selection or funding of projects, the integrity of the system is weakened. As experience bears out the adage that "the squeaky wheel gets the grease," have-not institutions grow more aggressive. Regional organizations such as the Midwest Resources Association are formed with congressional backing because, as Senator Roman Hruska of Nebraska put it, "only by uniting the Midwest would we be able to compete with the more populous and better financed states."[6] Washington-based commercial organizations solicit clients among colleges, universities, communities, and states. When 80 to 90 percent of the proposals submitted by the faculties of some institutions are funded, more than humor can be found in the remark, "While you're up, get me a grant."

A More Basic Solution

Patently, the basic solution to most of these problems is to supplement project awards by substantial and widespread *institutional* grants explic-

---

[6] *Congressional Record,* daily ed., March 2, 1966, p. 4493.

itly designed to undergird the strength of colleges and universities. To be effective and to prevent abuse, such awards must be based on measurable indices of institutional need and "productivity." Together with project grants, government programs could then begin to meet the objectives enunciated by Don Price: ". . . [T]o support an educational and scientific establishment, including private as well as public institutions, without either destroying its freedom or leaving it in a position of privileged irresponsibility . . . [and] to take account of the need for balanced national development while building up our existing centers of high scientific quality."[7]

Recognizing this need, the National Association of State Universities and Land-Grant Colleges, in cooperation with the Association of State Colleges and Universities, designed a national institutional grants program,[8] and in March 1966, Representative George Miller of California, chairman of the House Committee on Science and Astronautics, introduced a bill (H.R. 13786) to establish such a program.[9] The bill has been reintroduced in the Ninetieth Congress (as H.R. 875) by Representative Miller and others and has been endorsed by the Association of American Universities and also by NSF Director Leland Haworth.

It calls for the distribution of $150 million annually for research and education in the physical, biological, and social sciences, engineering, and mathematics, in proportion to the level of each institution's activities in research and teaching. One-third of the funds would be distributed as a graduated percentage of the volume of research grants received from NSF, NIH, and the Office of Education, along the lines of NSF institutional grants. Another third would be allocated first among the states according to the relative number of their high-school graduates and then to each institution within the state in proportion to the number of its undergraduate semester credit-hours in the natural and social sciences. The final third would be distributed in proportion to the number of masters' and doctors' degrees awarded by each institution in the sciences, including degrees that qualify graduates to teach science and mathematics courses in the schools. The only restriction on the grants would be a post-audit to insure that funds were spent for research or education in the natural or social sciences, and institutions would be en-

[7] See p. 38 in this volume.

[8] The proposal is detailed in *Recommendations for National Action Affecting Higher Education by the National Association of State Universities and Land-Grant Colleges* (the Association, January 1966), pp. 7–9.

[9] See *Congressional Record,* daily ed., March 17, 1966, p. 5987.

couraged to anticipate funding in order to design long-range development programs.

This is not the only and perhaps not the best program of institutional grants that can be designed, but it illustrates the *type* of program needed to supplement project awards. Its specific proposals provide a concrete focus for public discussion to clarify national policy toward science in universities and the national action that should follow to implement it.

The charge of "pork barrel" and "logrolling" will be brought against any such program. During the debates leading to the establishment of the National Science Foundation, similar charges killed a proposal advanced by the then Association of Land-Grant Colleges and Universities that a portion—perhaps as much as 25 percent—of the funds appropriated to the foundation be distributed on a formula basis. The answer to these charges given in 1946 is still applicable today. Speaking for the association, the late Edmund E. Day, then president of Cornell, and Reuben G. Gustavson, then chancellor of the University of Nebraska, noted the "political pressures to which the operations of the National Science Foundation are certain to be subject" and went on to say,

> The wisest way to protect the Foundation from such political pressures is to provide in the Act itself for a partial allocation of funds to the states. If this is done, the Foundation can reasonably take the position that the requirements of nation-wide distribution of the Foundation's support of basic research have been provided for in . . . the Act itself. The officers of the Foundation can then concentrate their activities largely on the promotion of specific projects and programs which are thought to meet the most exacting requirements of immediate scientific promise and significance.[10]

"Pork barrel" is generally understood to mean a process of "divvying up" projects supported by government funds on the basis of political influence and regional, state, and local pressures. The charge of pork barrel or politics is almost invariably raised by those who sit in the seats of power in the politics of science and cry out against the intrusion of politics in science. As has been noted, the project system is not exactly immune to political pressures. The best way to ensure open and severe partisan, regional, and institutional pressures for scientific funds is to foster the impression that such pressures play a major role in fund allocations. The best way to reduce such political pressures is to employ an objective, easily determinable method of supporting scientific research and educa-

---

[10] Unpublished memorandum dated April 1, 1947, by Day and Gustavson to Presidents of Land-Grant Colleges and Universities, reprinted in Circular Letter No. 33, of the Association of State Universities and Land-Grant Colleges, Oct. 31, 1963.

tion in all parts of the country, in all institutions, and for the benefit of all students. This is the antithesis of pork barrel. Meeting a legitimate need directly would substantially reduce, and in many instances eliminate, pressures to meet it through political channels, pitting institution against institution, region against region, state against state.

It will be charged, also, that inferior work would be supported under such a program. Doubtless, some of the resultant research would be less efficient and perhaps less productive than that which would be conducted were the funds allocated under the project system. However, a formula grant would also enable an institution to strengthen its faculty, undergraduate instruction, and long-range development, which cannot usually be done with project grants. Its principal purpose is not to "purchase" science, but to increase the nation's competence in scientific research and instruction, to invest in the development of a national resource. In making an investment, we are interested in the development of a resource. In making a purchase, we are basically interested in its exploitation. The two are not the same things, and expenditures for them should not be judged by the same standards.

As a supplement to existing programs, such a program cannot possibly weaken our present efforts or fail to raise their quality in the future. There is much talk about the danger of "leveling down" but little about the equal danger of not "leveling up." No man ever made himself taller by pushing down those around him, but each generation of Americans has grown taller by steadily improving the nutrition and health of all.

Finally, some will argue that it is unwise to "take from the rich and give to the poor"—to weaken strong institutions in order to strengthen weak ones. No one has suggested, or is suggesting, that this be done. The stringencies of the federal budget in 1966 and 1967, due to the Vietnam war, should not obscure the fact that normally we can make a larger investment *both* in mission-oriented research *and* in a broad program to strengthen the national capacity and competence in science. Normally, federal revenues increase $6 billion or more a year through the growth of the economy—growth to which "value added by education" is a substantial contributor. Some of the congressional reluctance to increase science support clearly stems from concern over the inequitable character of the present system. If this concern is dispelled, the probability of increased support will be greater.

There are, of course, many precedents for the formula distribution of federal funds. Perhaps the best are the agricultural research awards which have gone to land-grant institutions since 1887 with highly successful results. Here the funds are apportioned on a formula basis, and although continuity of support is assured, institutional programs are submitted annually for review and approval. A comprehensive file is maintained of all ongoing research (state or federally supported), as well as research conducted or supported by the U.S. Department of Agriculture. Thus, the government has a regular opportunity to call attention to possible duplication, to suggest which lines of work should be pursued and which might be discontinued, and so forth. This system has yielded many outstanding examples of basic and applied research. While the quality and strength of the university research centers under this program vary widely, even the smaller and less well financed research stations have a high productivity record of undergraduates who go on to complete their doctoral work, particularly in the life sciences.

As Paul M. Gross, then chairman of the board of the American Association for the Advancement of Science, has pointed out, a considerable part of the argument about the geographic distribution of research funds "has been confused and is confusing because we have been trying to use the same money for objectives that in the short run are mutually contradictory. . . . [A]rriving at a better adjustment between the immediate, short-term research goals and the long-term goals of attaining a broadened national educational and research competence . . . [is] one of the most fundamental and important problems in the area of Government-science relations."[11]

Congressman Miller's bill represents one attempt to solve this problem. Formula grants of this type could make as basic a contribution to the future of American science and higher education as did the Morrill Land-Grant Act of 1862.

[11] *Government and Science,* Hearings before the Subcommittee on Science, Research, and Development of the House Committee on Science and Astronautics, October and November 1963, 88 Cong. 1 sess. (1964), no. 8, pp. 144–45.

HOWARD E. PAGE

The Science Development Program

DESPITE THE outstanding successes of the land-grant colleges and of the long-established formula-grant program of the U.S. Department of Agriculture under the Hatch Act, some recent programs of institutional support for scientific research and education have come into being only after a great deal of agonizing appraisal—in the federal science agencies, on Capitol Hill, and in conclaves of educational associations. The National Science Foundation's Science Development Program is one of these. Because it has received so much attention from scientists, leaders in higher education, and framers of governmental policy and action, and because it has seemed such a new and daring departure for a federal agency, I should like to describe its genesis and formation. And, since the program seems especially indicative of a new kind of partnership that is emerging between the campus and the Capitol, I also want to indicate something of what the current grants involve and to assess the implications of the program for educational institutions and the federal government.

If any single document can be said to have stimulated the thinking that finally produced the Science Development Program, it was the November 15, 1960, statement by the President's Science Advisory

Parts of this paper are adaptations of a speech delivered at the annual meeting of the National Council of University Research Administrators, October 28, 1965, at the Mayflower Hotel, Washington, D.C.

Committee.[1] This statement, usually referred to as the "Seaborg Report," called attention to the need for more university "centers of excellence" in science and estimated that there were then only fifteen or twenty such centers. "Over the next fifteen years," the report recommended, "the United States should seek to double the number of universities doing generally excellent work in basic research and graduate education."[2] This document, so cogent in its analysis and in its program for action, gave rise to a new parlor game among Washington bureaucrats of listing the "top twenty" academic centers of science and, more difficult, the "second twenty" which might be aspirants to the title "center of excellence." But how could excellence be objectively measured? How could relative potential for achieving excellence be assessed? Should the target be twenty universities with graduate programs in science, or should it be a much larger number which included undergraduate institutions? And how could a public agency, even one that bore the title of "foundation," design and put into operation a program to select a fortunate few institutions for the massive support that might lift them rapidly to the summit of academic prestige?

Exploratory Visits

Despite the difficulties of the task, the goal was so compelling that the National Science Foundation and the National Science Board undertook to achieve it. On June 22, 1962, after discussions within the foundation for nearly a year, the board approved in principle the idea of a science development program; and by September 1962, NSF staff had agreed upon steps to be followed in designing the program. The first step was a series of exploratory visits to twelve colleges and universities representative of a broad range of institutional types. These visits were planned, a staff paper stated, "to encourage a mutual exchange of information and views about the needs, plans, opportunities, and obstacles confronting the institutions; to discuss present NSF programs, any difficulties or handicaps they might impose on the institutions, and how these programs could be improved . . . and to discuss institutional needs that are not now being met through the Foundation's present programs and the possibilities of finding effective ways of broadening its support."

[1] *Scientific Progress, the Universities, and the Federal Government* (The White House, November 15, 1960).

[2] *Ibid.,* p. 28.

The teams visiting the dozen institutions represented all divisions of the foundation. From the beginning the Science Development Program has involved the active participation of all foundation divisions, even though its administration is lodged in the Division of Institutional Programs. The visits were intended to provide the understanding essential for implementing a national program that would have general repercussions upon all American higher education, not only upon those institutions ultimately receiving grants. Furthermore, they were intended to teach foundation officials how to think about institutions as complex organisms rather than simply as places where individual scientists did research or teaching or where particular science departments were strong or weak.

Heretofore, NSF programs had been concerned mainly with the development of individual scientists, the expansion of scientific knowledge, and the building of research laboratories. Valuable as these programs were, their aim was to strengthen science per se; they did not necessarily aim at strengthening the institutions that furnish the home for science. To think institutionally meant to think more broadly than the foundation had done before. An institutional program must provide a means of integrating the various components of the customary kinds of support into an organic unit. Activities in natural science and engineering must be viewed in relation to those in the humanities and social sciences; the ways by which an institution's educational and research policies are determined and administered must be understood; the present and potential sources of the institution's financial support must be known; and the hopes and plans of the institution, its special culture, and its relation to its social and intellectual environment must be perceived. In other words, a foundation official must put himself behind the desk of the college or university president, at the same time remembering that, as a guardian of federal tax funds, he is concerned about the general health of science rather than the advancement of one institution alone.

The twelve institutions visited by NSF staff in the fall and winter of 1962–63 were a diverse group; each had unique problems and opportunities.[3] Nevertheless, common factors established the need and the justification for a science development program. All twelve had institutional plans for development. In some, planning was a continuing process. Al-

[3] Stanford, University of Colorado, Grinnell College, Purdue, Case Institute of Technology, Western Reserve, Wesleyan University, City College of New York, University of Maryland, University of Louisville, Fisk, and Florida State.

though those interviewed at all institutions thought that existing NSF programs of research and education should be continued and strengthened, they felt a need for more flexible funds that could be used for broad institutional purposes in science, especially for strengthening areas neglected by compartmented types of support. All institutions had plans for major improvements and changes that could not be undertaken through existing NSF programs.

The experience gained by the Science Development Committee on these exploratory visits and subsequent discussions led, as had been hoped, to a new dimension in the foundation's thinking. The belief that a science development program was needed was confirmed. At the same time, conflicting viewpoints within the foundation and the National Science Board were gradually tempered and accommodated. This was a slow process, lasting all through 1963. What resulted was a foundation-wide consensus upon the major points at issue and concurrence by the National Science Board.

The consensus is expressed in an announcement dated March 1964.[4]

> The major objective of the Science Development Program is to increase the number of institutions of recognized excellence in research and education in the sciences. The grants are not intended to replace or consolidate existing NSF support to these institutions. The program's primary purpose is to accelerate improvement in science through the provision of funds to be expended in accordance with carefully developed plans designed to produce significant upgrading in the quality of the institution's science activities. Grants will be made to institutions judged to have the greatest possibility of moving upward to a higher level of scientific quality and to have sound plans for maintaining this quality.

The program was open to *all* institutions granting baccalaureate or higher degrees in science or engineering—not just to a small number of universities. Institutions already considered excellent in science were discouraged from applying. So were those which did not have substantial strength upon which to build excellence, although it was anticipated that many of the weaker institutions would consider the program especially intended for them. The maximum grant was expected not to exceed $5 million for a three-year period. Applying institutions were asked to present their plans for a five-year period of growth, and the possibility of supplementary support from NSF during the fourth and fifth years of

---

[4] National Science Foundation, *Science Development Program for Colleges and Universities, 1964 and 1965* (1964).

development was mentioned. They were also asked to submit the following information concerning their development plans:

 a. The proposed five-year plan for science development, including an explanation of how it fits into the overall development plans for the institution.

 b. The purposes for which foundation support would be used during three years of the five-year plan.

 c. The major changes that can be expected if the proposed plan is achieved —specifically, the programs that are to be upgraded.

 d. The estimated budget for the five-year plan, showing the amount requested from NSF and the amount to be obtained from other sources.

Meanwhile, Congress had examined the foundation's plans and allocated $3 million to the Science Development Program for fiscal year 1964. Another $25 million was appropriated for fiscal 1965, and $37 million more should be available during fiscal 1966.[5]

The review process involves, in addition to evaluation by the foundation staff, the participation of qualified persons drawn from industry, government, and academic institutions. They offer their judgment on a wide variety of questions, such as the feasibility of the proposed plan, the quality of the institution's existing scientific capability, the extent of expected improvement, the ability of the institution to sustain continued growth in scientific potential, the existing and potential effectiveness of the institution's science programs in serving the needs of surrounding regions, and the institution's ability to attract outstanding undergraduate and graduate students in the region.

As of December 1, 1965, the foundation had completed evaluation of 46 proposals, which involved site visits by more than 100 foundation employees and 132 university personnel. The latter group has been widely representative of both top administrators (including 19 college and university presidents) and the scientific community. All have given gladly of their time and have made a difficult administrative task a pleasant undertaking.

 [5] During fiscal year 1966 $36.4 million was actually available for the program and during fiscal 1967 $35.6 million. It is expected that about $25 million will be available for fiscal 1968. The budget reduction is offset by a planned allocation in fiscal years 1967 and 1968 of about $22 million for the Departmental Science Development Program. Following the initiation in January 1967 of the College Science Improvement Program for institutions granting science baccalaureates, the former Science Development Program was redesignated the University Science Development Program and eligibility was limited to institutions granting Ph.D.'s.

The First Thirteen Grants

Since the program was announced in March 1964, the foundation staff has had conferences with representatives of nearly 200 different colleges and universities. By November 15, 1965, 76 proposals requesting $311 million had been received and, by the end of 1965, 13 grants totaling $47.3 million had been awarded for the following purposes:

Western Reserve University and *Case Institute of Technology* each received awards of $3.5 million and will coordinate their science development efforts to serve the maximum benefits of both institutions. Interdisciplinary centers in the living and condensed states will be developed at Western Reserve, and the development of chemistry, physics, and materials science will be emphasized at Case Institute. The two schools will cooperate in a joint program in high energy physics. [In January 1967, the trustees of Western Reserve and Case approved the merger of the two institutions into Case Western Reserve University.—Editor.]

Washington University was awarded $3.9 million to improve certain facilities, purchase new equipment, accelerate faculty development, and support graduate students. Departments participating are chemistry, physics, and zoology in the Faculty of Arts and Science and several others in the School of Engineering and Applied Science.

The University of Oregon received $4 million to reinforce the number of top quality science faculty and to obtain a more powerful computer and additional equipment and space.

Rice University was awarded $2.4 million to help initiate a program of systems research and engineering, including appointments of new professors, provision of stipends for graduate students of science and engineering, construction of a mathematics building, and purchase of an analog computer.

The University of Arizona was granted $4 million to strengthen the physical sciences by developing the departments of astronomy, which will construct a major new telescope on Kitt Peak; chemistry, which will add equipment; mathematics, which will increase its space; and physics, which will obtain a Van de Graff facility.

The University of Southern California award of $4.5 million will pay for half of a new solid-states science building and provide for new appointments and basic research equipment in the fields of electrical engineering, physics, chemistry, materials science, mathematics, aerospace engineering, and geology.

Polytechnic Institute of Brooklyn was awarded $3.3 million to support chemistry and electronics, through new professorships, visiting professorships, and faculty development.

Louisiana State University received $3.8 million to support chemistry, geology, mathematics, and physics.

The University of Colorado was awarded $3.7 million principally for new appointments in the fields of physics, chemistry, mathematics, and psychology in the Institute of Behavioral Sciences, and in three engineering departments. The award will also help construct a facility for graduate research and teaching in physics.

The University of Rochester was given $2.5 million to finance about half the cost of constructing and equipping a new chemistry building and to appoint new staff members, particularly in inorganic chemistry, physical biochemistry, and physical chemistry.

The University of Virginia's $3.8 million grant will support the establishment of a center for advanced studies in the sciences, the appointment of a number of outstanding scholars to the faculty and to the center, and the costs of their research. The areas to be emphasized initially are astronomy, developmental biology and genetics, and the physical and chemical properties of matter.

The University of Florida was awarded $4.2 million to acquire personnel and equipment in the physical sciences and engineering, particularly in the areas of radiation, kinetics, and the microstructure of matter.[6]

Table 1 indicates the disciplines receiving support in the first 13 grants. Chemistry ranks first, with more than 25 percent of the funds, while the social sciences have played only a minor role in development plans supported so far. This is of some concern to the foundation as are the limited requests and support provided for the biological sciences. Some $19.4 million, or 41 percent of the first 13 grants, was to be used for personnel (including not only faculty but graduate and postdoctoral students, technicians, and training programs); $14.2 million, or 30 percent, for facilities; and $13.7 or 29 percent, for equipment.

The foundation has stressed the need for long-range planning for science development. Institutions have been asked to submit five-year plans and to indicate their own financial contributions to them. Some $55.5 million over and above expenditures for regular ongoing programs is to be contributed from institutional sources to augment the $47.3 million provided by NSF for the first three years of the five-year development plans. For the fourth and fifth years, the 13 institutions plan to spend an

---

[6] As of June 1967, an additional 12 grants had been made as follows: Carnegie Institute of Technology, $4.3 million; Duke University, $2.5 million; Indiana University, $3.8 million; University of Maryland, $3.7 million; University of North Carolina at Chapel Hill, $4.9 million; North Carolina State University at Raleigh, $3.5 million; University of Notre Dame, $4.8 million; Purdue University, $3.6 million; Rutgers, The State University, $3.7 million; University of Tennessee, $5 million; Tulane University, $3.7 million; Vanderbilt University, $4 million.

TABLE 1. *Distribution of the First Thirteen Development Grants by Field*

Field	Millions of dollars	Percent
Physical sciences	29.8	63.0
Chemistry	12.0	25.4
Physics	9.5	20.1
Mathematics	5.2	11.0
Astronomy	1.9	4.0
Geology	1.2	2.5
Engineering[a]	8.7	18.4
Biological sciences	1.8	3.8
Social sciences	1.0	2.1
Multidisciplinary	6.0	12.7
Total	47.3	100.0

[a] Includes materials science.

additional $94 million, which—although it is more than 2.5 times their annual contributions to the first three years of the plans—will be insufficient for the continued growth that they are planning. The foundation, however, has indicated a willingness to consider supplemental requests for the later stages of development if institutional funds prove inadequate.

Evaluating Proposals

The foundation's experience in evaluating proposals has been so overwhelming that it is hard to gain the perspective required for meaningful generalizations. Nevertheless, I will try to assess this experience.

Many colleges and universities welcomed the program enthusiastically and had enough confidence in the possibility of their success to undertake the arduous preparation of detailed proposals. A number of institutions have said that the preparation involved a look into the future that was invaluable to them whatever the outcome of their proposals. The resultant institutional planning, specifically for science but related to broader institutional objectives, is probably one of the program's important repercussions upon higher education.

Most institutions submitting plans have been able to pick out their areas of strength and weakness, although they frequently overestimate the former and usually underestimate the latter. Sometimes the plans for overcoming weakness seem likely to be ineffectual, not sufficiently ruthless. Academic leaders, like Americans in general, often have a tender regard for the feelings of the unfortunate, especially when they are members of the family. In any event, institutional self-evaluation and self-criticism, like institutional planning, have been important results of the preparation of science development proposals.

It is sometimes a disappointment that institutional planning, while sound and rigorous, is usually conventional. Institutional plans are usually projections of present actualities, not imaginative ventures into unknown academic frontiers. Development is usually taken to mean quantitative growth, greater thoroughness, increased coverage—all desirable in themselves, all needing impetus for early achievement, but all predictable. One university critic of the program has said (in a private communication) that the institutions are requesting funds "to do more of what is already being done"; their proposals show "a great confusion between excellence and institutional size" and are wanting in new and imaginative ideas. Perhaps the lack of innovation in most proposals reflects a suspicion that a government agency would shy away from anything that was not tried and true. It certainly reflects the basic conservatism of higher education management.

As was expected, the proposals reveal a good deal of confusion about the meaning of "excellence." Another critic of the program has said, "Pretense at excellence is a fatal flaw." He calls the program "vague, because it has no objective criteria. . . ." A "center of excellence," as he says, "usually requires some tradition and certainly requires a sufficient concentration (a 'critical mass') of first-rate scientists."[7] But traditions, even in our hurrying time, are not built overnight and the number of first-rate scientists is definitely limited. This criticism was expected by NSF when it launched the program. Admittedly, "excellence" is a fuzzy word, but it has conveyed to applying institutions, as it did for the Seaborg panel, certain goals and connotations that the foundation shares. The foundation knows that "objective criteria" are inadequate for measuring excellence, a fact especially bothersome to scientists; nevertheless, they have managed to get over that hurdle and have begun to think like humanists.

If the foundation has had cause to feel general, but qualified, satisfac-

[7] Saunders MacLane, "Leadership and Quality in Science," in *Basic Research and National Goals,* A Report to the House Committee on Science and Astronautics by the National Academy of Sciences, 89 Cong. 1 sess. (March 1965), p. 200.

tion with the proposals thus far, the college and university world has probably had a similar experience with the Science Development Program. As previously indicated, many institutional spokesmen expressed gratitude for the outside stimulus to planning and self-criticism, and some have also said that the criticisms of their programs resulting from site visits have been valuable to them. There may be reasons, though, for some disappointment with the Science Development Program.

For one thing, I am sure some academic administrators and scientists regard NSF as too conservative when it doubts their capacity to achieve and maintain "excellence." The process of evaluation has been extremely careful and traditional, as one would expect of a new and untried governmental program. After all, universities themselves are divided as to both the need and the mechanisms for accrediting graduate education! Perhaps the evaluators have wanted assurances that institutional administrators could not give. Similarly, evaluators have often looked for a kind of "quality" that is extremely limited and to be found in abundance in only a very few institutions; they are apt to be thinking of the "top twenty" universities even when examining a proposal from an undergraduate college. Even though the program was not restricted to any particular group of institutions, other than those offering at least the baccalaureate degree, it has appeared to some that it was aimed only at the "second twenty."

The fact that, to date, all of the grants have gone to universities with graduate programs may cause undergraduate colleges to wonder if the invitation for them to apply was genuine. The foundation itself seems confused on this issue; it is now searching for a means of evaluating liberal arts colleges in competition with one another rather than with universities. And a number of admittedly weak institutions have applied for grants on the basis that there are special circumstances which justify their application and good grounds for believing that they can achieve "excellence" within their particular class or region.

Those who expected the program to "redistribute the wealth"—which it was not designed to do—may be unhappy that recipient institutions were already faring pretty well in support from federal agencies. Those relatively strong, it is sometimes said, have been made stronger and have been given a "hunting license" to raid the scientific preserves of the less fortunate. This criticism was expected; so far it has been less vocal than had been anticipated.

Grants have been made to universities in "have-not" regions. This was

one of the strong impulses behind the inauguration of the program, as
stated forcefully by President Kennedy when he said there should be an
outstanding university in every major region of the country.[8] Perhaps it
is just as imperative that there be first-rate undergraduate colleges in
every state or subregion, since undergraduates are far less mobile than
graduate students, but *so far* the Science Development Program has not
faced up to this problem. It is likely that the demand for *equality* of
educational opportunity (which must also mean opportunity for an education of *quality*) will bring increasing pressures upon the federal government to satisfy this goal. While the Office of Education would have
primary responsibility for that goal, the foundation's Science Development Program might also contribute to it.

Strengthening Institutional Autonomy and Initiative

Institutional support has many implications, and I have touched only on
a few. In the Science Development Program, as in other federal forms
of institutional support, it is essential that there be careful and continuous planning which encompasses the institution's entire educational and
research program and takes into account the ways in which that program
will be financed. Where an academic anarchy of autonomous departments and colleges prevails, an institution will have to bring order, if it
is to preserve autonomy and control the direction of its development.
The president and his top lieutenants must exert more authority in setting policy and seeing to its execution. Resistance from faculty members
who have been free agents and whose institutional loyalty has been less
than their loyalty to their field of specialization must be expected. In
many respects, a loss of departmental autonomy may seem unfortunate,
but a complex social organism that functions as an effective unit cannot
exist in a primitive state. Presidents cannot be mere channels through
which government research grants flow to faculty scientists from their
professional colleagues in Washington. Presidents must be more than in-
termediaries or conciliators of opposing views. They alone are charged
with responsibility for the administration of the entire institution, and
they cannot discharge that responsibility effectively without controls
which many have let slip away in recent years. Correspondingly, faculty

[8] *Public Papers of the Presidents of the United States, John F. Kennedy, 1963* (Government Printing Office, 1964), p. 111.

members must start thinking institutionally, and academic administrators will have to help them to do so.

If institutional support implies a loss of autonomy for individual professors, it also implies a far greater degree of autonomy for the faculty as a whole. Federal programs of institutional support are based upon the conviction that strong institutions of higher education are essential. They cannot be strong without the freedom to move toward goals of their own choice. As the Committee on Science and Public Policy of the National Academy of Sciences has said,

> The object of federal support is not only increasing scientific knowledge but also strengthening of the universities themselves. The trained men and strong institutions produced by federal support are in themselves a major national resource in peace or war. Thus, the production of future scientists and strong, independent universities broadens both the opportunities and the problems of federal support beyond the bounds of basic research and related graduate education.[9]

Heretofore, both private foundations and federal agencies have thought mainly of particular kinds of categories of national or institutional need, not of the colleges and universities themselves. Academic innovation has come about largely as a result of such external influences. It can be hoped that institutional support will lead the universities themselves to assume more initiative in responding vigorously to new social needs. President James Perkins of Cornell has stated:

> If innovation is left to outside organizations, then initiative for change will have by-passed the university, and where initiative is not exercised, decisions will not be made. And where decisions are not made the case of institutional autonomy is gravely weakened.[10]

Broad flexible support from government challenges institutions to make the most of opportunities presented to them. There is no reason to believe that they will fail to respond to this challenge in a responsible way. Certainly, the large number of colleges and universities receiving Institutional Grants for Science from NSF have used those funds wisely and accounted for them adequately. They have realized that greater freedom in the use of federal funds entails greater responsibility and accountability for them. At the same time, the foundation has resisted pressures to tie institutions down or entangle them in a network of de-

[9] National Academy of Sciences' Committee on Science and Public Policy, *Federal Support of Basic Research in Institutions of Higher Learning* (NAS, March 1964), p. 72.

[10] Logan Wilson (ed.), *Emerging Patterns in American Higher Education* (American Council on Education, 1965), p. 15.

tailed regulations. John W. Gardner has stated clearly what has, from
the first, been NSF's policy in its programs of institutional support:

> The aim is to give government agencies access to the creative potentiali-
> ties of the universities, and the universities access to the resources of Gov-
> ernment. Conditions of the relationship must be so defined that irresponsi-
> ble (or careless) elements in the university community will not show a
> wanton disregard for the taxpayer's dollar and, at the same time, that the
> responsible elements in the university community will not be paralyzed by
> Government red tape.[11]

Despite the seeming conflict between these two aims, they are not necessarily incompatible. Certainly, the long-run interest of the government is
best served by free universities, and the universities' long-run interest is
responsibility to the society that supports them.

DISCUSSION

A Public and a Private Route to "Excellence"

THE DISCUSSION commenced with an amplification
of the experience of the National Science Foundation's Science Development Program and a consideration of the Ford Foundation's challenge
grant program, which had served in many ways as a model for NSF.

The Process of Review

As of January 1966, about seventy-five proposals had been received. Ap-
plicant institutions ran the gamut from near wealth to impoverishment
and from the good-but-not-excellent to schools that could not realistically be expected to become outstanding graduate science centers in five
years. NSF staff have been struggling with the problem of how to help
institutions to which grants could not be given. Few applications had ac-

---

[11] See August 3, 1965, testimony of John Gardner, in *Government and Science: Review
of the National Science Foundation,* Hearings before the Subcommittee on Science, Research, and Development of the House Committee on Science and Astronautics, 89 Cong.
1 sess. (1965), no. 6, vol. 2, p. 1401.

tually been declined, but, in many cases, NSF staff had held lengthy and "brutally frank" discussions with institutional representatives explaining why their proposal was weak or incomplete and inviting them to withdraw it.

Two kinds of institutions posed special problems: those falling into the second hundred (in quality) of the two hundred or so institutions awarding science doctorates, and liberal arts colleges. The foundation hopes eventually to establish special programs for each group.[1]

As proposals often represented months or years of effort by a sizable university group, it would doubtless have been desirable to confine applications to schools with a realistically good chance for a grant. The Ford challenge grant program had been able to do this, since application was by invitation only; but it was more difficult for a public agency. Ideally, a commission, broadly representative of the higher education and scientific communities might be set up to nominate periodically about twice as many institutions as could receive grants, leaving the remaining task of selection to the foundation. NSF staff were at least successful in discouraging some applications during informal exploratory inquiries from more than two hundred institutions.

Foundation staff engaged in an intensive process of evaluation before making their final choices, and the best staff were assigned to work on the most difficult proposals. To assess the financial contribution an institution proposed to make, the year in which the proposal was submitted was adopted as the budgetary base, additional expenditures being reckoned as the institution's contribution to the new program; admittedly, this was a generous procedure because it made no disallowance for normal budgetary growth.

Only a limited portion of the evaluation could rest on quantifiable criteria—such as degrees awarded, average class score on college entrance tests, the volume of federal funds received, and so forth—although a

---

[1] In October 1966, the foundation announced two new programs: (1) a College Science Improvement Program offering grants of up to $100,000 a year for as many as three years "to accelerate development of the science capabilities of predominantly undergraduate institutions"; and (2) a Departmental Science Development Program offering grants of up to $600,000 for a three-year period to upgrade selected areas of science and engineering at graduate level institutions which had neither received general science development awards nor been "already recognized as being outstanding in science . . ." (see announcements with the above program titles issued by NSF in 1966). At the same time, the Science Development Program described in Page's paper was redesignated the University Science Development Program.

great deal of statistical information was usually requested and provided. Ultimately, decisions rested to a considerable extent on personal judgments: judgments of the capability of the institution's president and, if necessary, his hardness—his ability to cut out professorial deadwood; of the distinction of department chairmen; of a state's willingness to support its universities; of the faculty's standing, salary structure, and recruitment plans; of the quality of equipment and facilities; and so on.

NSF did not prescribe how university science programs *should* develop. For example, the foundation did not even indicate whether it was better for an institution to improve the quality of education and research across a broad spectrum of science or to concentrate on a single field. Most exasperating were the (fortunately, few) administrators who came in and said, "What are your specifications? You give me your specifications and I can write a proposal that will compete favorably."

The program did exclude proposals from the unnamed and unnamable institutions in the magical circle of the "top twenty."[2] For example, a proposal to establish a doctoral program in anthropology at the Massachusetts Institute of Technology or an engineering school at the University of Chicago would not be entertained, on the grounds that these institutions could request assistance from other public and private sources. No list of institutions disqualified because of their distinction was ever prepared.[3] One way of preparing such a list would be to take the twenty institutions presently receiving the largest amount of federal funds for science. (Another criterion of quality was attributed to Alvin Weinberg: "An excellent school is one I will send my son to, and a good school is one I will send my nephew to.") One participant declared, "I would bet if you passed a piece of paper around to each one of the people sitting at the table and asked them to name the top twenty they will be almost unanimous on fifteen and you will quibble over the other five." "But," responded another, "if you passed a piece of paper around a certain number of years ago and asked whether the world was flat or round, you

[2] The foundation's program announcement stated, "Since the goal is to increase the number of strong academic centers in science, institutions already recognized as being outstanding in science should continue to depend on existing programs for assistance" (*Science Development Program for Colleges and Universities, 1964 and 1965* [National Science Foundation, 1964], pp. 1–2).

[3] Senior officials of federal science programs at universities, who lunched together informally once a month for a period to discuss common problems, reputedly tried to see if they could agree on the "top twenty," "and there were more than fifteen that coincided. . . ."

would have gotten a strong consensus that it was flat." In evaluating proposals, NSF staff concentrated on four points:

1. *The Plan.* Was it realistic and well defined? Would it significantly improve the status of the institution's science? Will the new quality level be maintained? How is the science plan related to broader institutional development plans?

2. *The Academic Base.* Do existing scientific resources furnish an adequate base for the proposed development? What attention has been given to improving curriculums, faculty, the library, computer services?

3. *The Administrative Base.* How effective are the university's top administrators and scientists, and how closely are they involved in preparing and implementing the plan?

4. *The Financial Base.* Will alumni, trustees, the state legislature, local citizens, other federal agencies back the plan? Can the new level of funding be sustained after the grant is used up?

Ford Challenge Grants

It is instructive to compare the science development grants with the Ford Foundation challenge grants, upon which the NSF program was partly modeled. The first Ford grants were made to universities in the fall of 1960 and to colleges in the spring of 1961. Some ran up to $25 million (as against NSF's $5 million ceiling) at universities and from $1 million to $2.5 million at liberal arts colleges.[4] Ford grants, which were confined to private institutions, were completely invitational—applications were not permitted—whereas, as noted, NSF was burdened with too many applications which, as a public agency, it had not been able openly to discourage or subsequently to decline without much labor. Both programs awarded grants for periods of three to five years and both carried matching provisions. Ford required matching ratios of 2.5 or 3.0 to 1, and did not count federal funds in the matching sums. As of January 1966, Ford had given $277 million to 13 universities and 57 colleges, which had pledged more than $1 billion in matching funds.[5] (An additional $13 million had also been awarded to 13 predominantly Negro institutions in a special program with no matching provisions.) No institution has yet failed to meet its pledge, but some private gifts have evidently been withheld until they could be credited against the grant.

[4] Grants in the recently announced NSF college science improvement program are unlikely to exceed $300,000.

[5] This special program of matching grants for the general support of selected academic institutions was suspended early in 1967.

Like NSF, Ford did not try to tell an institution how to develop but examined plans to see if they were realistic and convincing; unlike NSF, of course, Ford funds were available to the entire institution, not just its scientific departments. Both programs put great emphasis on the quality of an institution's leadership—particularly, in the case of Ford, of the president and trustees; and both sought a broad geographic dispersion of grants.

How were the Ford institutions selected? Staff were constantly visiting institutions; and available information served to eliminate many institutions without a visit (although no president was ever told that his institution would never receive an award, since circumstances do change). Racially segregated institutions were ineligible. The quality of faculty and students was important; and the "matching" provision that was a key feature of the program attached special weight to the magnitude of an institution's private financial resources. But "objective" information of this sort went only so far and, in the last analysis, many awards were based upon judgments about the character of an institution's leaders.

In considering whether a liberal arts college merited an award, Ford tried to determine what was special about it and its plan that set it apart from hundreds of other possible claimants. Among universities, Ford eliminated not the top twenty but the top six "international leaders"— and especially Harvard, Princeton, and Yale. When one participant questioned the elimination of Yale—he was an alumnus—which he ranked well below the top ten or fifteen "in my time there," the issue of quality was not directly joined. It seemed, however, that, like NSF, Ford kept careful tabs on the schools which received most of its money, and Yale could be eliminated on that score.

Where did the faculty come from to upgrade schools receiving NSF or Ford grants? Neither agency has any explicit policy against using a grant to "pirate" faculty from prominent institutions; but they do not believe that this is the only way to get first-class men. In any event, no more than a third of the junior faculty at a place like Yale receive tenure, so that even the best institutions could normally provide a ready source of younger faculty without disrupting their normal pattern of movement "up or out." (At a succeeding seminar, it was reported that an analysis of the source of faculty brought into the first thirteen institutions receiving NSF development grants had shown that roughly a third came from other educational institutions, a third from other national sources, and a third from abroad.)

Both Ford and NSF staff, it appeared, have some regrets that the word "excellence" was ever used to designate the objectives of their program. The word, and even more the phrase "center of excellence," suggests a goal that is somewhat too glowing and, accordingly, too unrealistic. A "major upgrading" is, in fact, the more common usage within the foundation.

In Union There Is Not Strength

Were the same institutions being built up collectively by NSF, the Office of Education, the National Institutes of Health, and other federal agencies, or did each agency go its own way, unmindful of the others? No clear answer was given. It appeared that it was easier to exchange information than to concert policies at interagency meetings. One senior agency official was rather optimistic; where the President had asked science agencies, or a particular official, to attend to a particular problem, it had generally been disposed of pretty well and cooperatively. Others were more dubious about the extent or even the desirability of such coordination. ". . . [T]his central coordination thing can be overdone," an administrator said. "Our customers oftentimes do a better job of coordinating our activities than we do. If they know that they need a bit from this agency and a piece from that agency . . . to make the thing click, they coordinate us extremely well." "As a former university official," another participant recalled, "I once put out . . . a statement about institutional freedom, which was: a play on the interstices between government agencies. . . ."

The evaluation of the effects of development grants was recognized as important but difficult. (One official declared forcefully that the government and the research community were more interested in spending money than in carefully evaluating what had been accomplished by money already spent. "Now, the government is spending $15 billion a year in RDT&E . . . , [and] how much of that is going into an analysis of how our RDT&E is done? Peanuts." "If they knew what they were achieving," it was suggested sarcastically, "they might spend less and that is an argument for not knowing.") Some marks of failure—such as a university president's moving on to another job after securing the grant or putting all of his free money into buildings rather than people —were more evident than signs of success. Progress was not, by itself, proof that it had been caused by the grant, as many schools receiving grants were on the upswing and would have improved in any event. Furthermore, a good plan, prepared not just by the president's office (as was too common with the poorer plans) but by the genuine involvement of a broad group of faculty, might be as responsible for an institution's progress as the grant itself, an NSF representative pointed out:

> I am not at all sure that we won't find as much forward progress at some of these institutions we did not give the grants to as we will at the institutions [receiving grants]. . . . There is no question about [their] . . . benefiting by seeing how outsiders look at their institution.
>
> The mere fact that the president and faculty have committed themselves to a plan for the growth and development of science almost commits the president to do something about this whether he gets a grant or not.

"The government's problem," a participant concluded, "is one of spreading fertilizer without having a clear idea as to what you want to grow. You want the institution to have a sense of what ought to be grown. Isn't that true?" Probably it was, as it was and is very much in the spirit of the National Science Foundation not to dictate what is good for science but to respond to the good ideas freely proposed by scientists. Whether the plans of administrators can be evaluated as clearly as the ideas of scientists is something that time will determine.

PART II

Allocations among Scientific Fields

HENDRIK W. BODE

Allocation of Federal Support among Scientific Fields

I HAVE BEEN asked to consider how federal support for university research should be divided or, to express it differently, on what principles funds should be allocated among the different fields of science.

As I review my qualifications for such a job, it seems to me that what I bring to it can most charitably be described as detachment. As an engineer I am perhaps closer to mathematics and physics than to other fields, but I can claim no really good entree to any field of science. In addition, since I come from industry, my attitude toward the problems of universities is necessarily one of good will rather than deep understanding. However, detachment does have a few advantages. You will at least be spared the spectacle of a university chemist, let us say, searching his soul and finally having to acknowledge in all honesty that he thinks that research in chemistry is important.

Fortunately, the job I have been asked to do does not call for a large measure of personal contribution. It is rather a reportorial one. It consists, in other words, of an attempt to summarize what has been written on the problem by others. There is a good deal of such material. Some of it has appeared in *Minerva* and *Science* and other magazines of that nature. The natural starting point is probably the paper by Alvin M. Weinberg of the Oak Ridge Laboratory, which appeared in *Minerva* a few years ago.[1] It is likely to become a minor classic. I would like to read the first few sentences of the paper because it identifies what I understand to be my topic:

> As science grows, its demands on our society's resources grow. It seems inevitable that science's demands will eventually be limited by what society can allocate to it. We shall then have to make choices. These choices are of two kinds. We shall have to choose among different, often incommensurable, fields of science—between, for example, high-energy physics and oceanography or between molecular biology and science of metals. We shall also have to choose among the different institutions that receive support for science from the government—among universities, governmental laboratories and industry. The first choice I call scientific choice; the second, institutional choice. My purpose is to suggest criteria for making scientific choices. . . .

A second source of material consists of testimony given before various congressional committees. Of these, the hearings on high energy physics research before the Joint Committee on Atomic Energy are perhaps the most noteworthy.[2] High energy physics, as we all know, poses the problem of relative expenditure for different scientific purposes in acute form because the field is so expensive. It is difficult to contemplate the high energy program without asking what its impact might be on support for other areas.

A third important source is the series of reports emanating from the National Academy of Sciences under the auspices of their Committee on Science and Public Policy. A particularly important reference is the study *Basic Research and National Goals,* which was prepared for the House Committee on Science and Astronautics.[3] This report was in answer to two questions asked by the House committee. The first question dealt with the appropriate level of federal support for basic research generally, and the second asked the study group's judgment on the balance of support to various fields of scientific endeavor. The second will be recognized as essentially the subject under discussion. The seventeen papers in the report did not all deal with this question, but among them there are several attempts to make some headway with it. In addition to this report, the academy has sponsored a number of reviews of special fields of

[1] "Criteria for Scientific Choice," *Minerva,* Winter 1963, pp. 159–71.

[2] *High Energy Physics Research,* Hearings before the Subcommittee on Research, Development, and Radiation of the Joint Committee on Atomic Energy, March 2, 3, 4, and 5, 1965, 89 Cong. 1 sess. (1965), esp. pp. 204–37.

[3] National Academy of Sciences, *Basic Research and National Goals: A Report to the House Committee on Science and Astronautics* (March 1965).

science, which attempt to indicate the level of support that seems appropriate to each field's research promise over the next several years.[4]

Stimulating, but Not Practical, Ideas

If one reviews this mass of material one finds, I think, that it contains many interesting and stimulating ideas. On the other hand, it must be acknowledged that very little of it would give an administrator trying to make practical decisions much comfort. It provides many broad ways of looking at the problem, but not many of them are definite enough to lead easily to concrete conclusions.

Why is the problem so intractable? There are many reasons. Some are consequences of the way in which the national scientific and technological effort is organized. Weinberg speaks of the problem of "institutional choice" but avoids discussing it in his paper. I will also try to avoid it, and with it the very thorny problem of geographic choice. However, in a real sense the problem won't stay dead. More than half of all federal funds for basic research are not spent in universities proper but in the other ways that Weinberg mentions. Obviously, one cannot really come to grips with the way in which the government supports basic research in universities, with its right hand, so to speak, without knowing what it is doing with its left hand.

A similar set of complications appears when one turns to the details of support within the university sphere. Most, but by no means all, of such support comes from the federal government. A substantial fraction still comes from university funds or from industry. Moreover, even within the government's contribution, the greater portion comes through the mission-oriented agencies and thus necessarily reflects broadly their purposes and constraints. Only a minority comes through the National Science Foundation and can be thought of as an effort to support basic science for its own sake. Clearly, the various constraints and limitations that come about from the multiple sources of funding need to be thought about carefully if we are to deal realistically with the way in which support should be allocated among the various fields of science.

---

[4] Among these reports have been *Ground-Based Astronomy: A Ten-Year Program* (1964); *Solid-Earth Geophysics: Survey and Outlook* (1964); *Chemistry: Opportunities and Needs* (1965); *Physics: Survey and Outlook* (1966); and *The Plant Sciences Now and in the Coming Decade* (1966).

Another set of difficulties is inherent in the problem. Thus, the categorization of university research by major scientific fields is not really adequate for many purposes; a much finer structure is required. Fields like physics, for example, contain so many special areas which pose individual problems of support that few generalizations will hold throughout. Thus, the problems of high energy physics are as different from those of solid state physics as they are from the problems of chemistry. In addition, many subjects, like molecular biology, occupy an intermediate area between classical fields; they are not quite subdivisions of any one field, and particularly in their early phases, their boundaries may be quite fluid.

These remarks apply to what might be called the vertical subdivisions of science. But if we are to pay attention to the ultimate impact of science on our society, we must also consider a sort of horizontal stratification. We must, in other words, consider all the gradations between the purest research and the final engineering application. Obviously, this raises many questions beyond that of appropriate levels of support for the primary scientific fields.

The Handicap of Politeness

These problems of categorization are exacerbated by a certain reluctance in the scientific community generally to think about the problem of scientific quality in any broad sense. In some ways, scientists tend to be very polite to each other. They say, in effect, that only members of each specialized field are capable of appreciating or judging the work of others in that field. Weinberg, for example, after listing two so-called internal criteria for scientific choice—(1) whether the field is ready for exploitation, and (2) whether the scientists in the field are really competent —goes on to say that only experts who know the field and the people in it intimately can apply them. This approach is similar to the one underlying the panel system used by the National Science Foundation on a day-by-day basis to evaluate proposals. It has many virtues but also some possible weaknesses. I include in the latter an obvious tendency to ingrownness and also a possible flattening out of estimates of scientific quality. In any case, it is clearly not a suitable way to make the sorts of comparative estimates we are concerned with here. For these reasons,

Weinberg goes on to propose external criteria, but I will postpone discussion of these until later.

One further observation seems to be worth making. In the long run, we cannot decide how the budgetary pie is to be cut—how support among various fields of science is to be divided—until we know why the pie exists in the first place or, in other words, why the federal government supports science at all. Thus, if we follow the logical order of questions in the report *Basic Research and National Goals,* the answer to the second question the House committee raised must depend on the answer to the first, on the proper overall level of federal support. In this discussion, I will try to focus on the problem of "scientific choice" (as Weinberg has labeled it), but it will not be possible to avoid the more fundamental issue entirely. The reason the two questions are intertwined so intimately is readily apparent in the language of the first question, which asks for the level of federal support "needed to maintain for the United States a position of leadership through basic research in the advancement of science and technology and their economic, cultural, and military applications." Obviously, a mixture of criteria, both scientific and nonscientific, not readily reduced to a common base, is envisaged. Unless we know which criteria were dominant in setting the overall level of support, we may still be at a loss in solving the problem of choice. We might all decide that the support of basic research should be set at, let us say, a $1 billion or $2 billion level, but if we had based our estimate on different weights for the military, economic, or scientific criteria, we would probably want to cut the pie in different ways.

We can, of course, replace the particular list of criteria advanced by the House committee by some others. Weinberg, for example, speaks of "scientific merit," "technological merit," and "social merit." In these, he includes such considerations as international prestige and the growth of international understanding through cooperative ventures like CERN (the European Organization for Nuclear Research). Whatever the particular words we use, however, the essential difficulty remains. The overall justification for the support of science does depend on a number of different and basically unrelated considerations. We are living in a pluralistic world, and the problem of scientific choice becomes in the long run a problem of nonscientific judgment among these different considerations. The interplay among them can be illustrated by grouping the approaches to this problem into four general classes.

1. The Needs of Individual Fields. In the first group, the authors write as individual scientists, protagonists of the particular field for which support is being asked. Most of the documents prepared for the hearings on high energy physics are in this class. National Academy of Sciences studies, on a larger or smaller scale, provide roughly comparable treatments for chemistry, some areas of biology and the behavioral sciences, astronomy, and so forth. In all cases, the obvious central concern of the authors is, naturally enough, the intrinsic interest of the scientific field under discussion. Normally, however, the treatment also includes an indication of practical results which might follow from the proposed work. In some cases, in biology and chemistry, for example, it is possible to substantiate such an argument quite fully. In other areas, such as high energy physics, it amounts to little more than a profession of faith that all basic research is eventually of some value. In some cases, such as high energy physics again, an additional claim can be made that ancillary benefits, such as the advance of electrical engineering or computer techniques, may also be important.

As I read these documents individually, I find, for myself, that they are quite convincing. Any weakness in the argument for practical value is made up, as far as I am concerned, by that of the intrinsic interest of the fields. Obviously, science offers many promising frontiers. Unfortunately, it is quite clear that no such documents, by themselves, can provide a good way of making relative judgments among different fields. They are all illustrations of a remark by Weinberg that one must get outside a given universe of discourse in order to establish reliable value judgments for that universe in relation to other areas.

2. The Needs of "Big" and "Little" Science. My second category includes papers by "senior statesmen" in universities who are not writing in behalf of single fields of science. I am thinking here, in particular, of the papers by Harvey Brooks and George Kistiakowsky in *Basic Research and National Goals*. Both papers are quite comprehensive and include substantial discussions of the problem of scientific choice, although they do not go so far as to indicate specific fields for support. I shall return to this point later. For the moment, it may be sufficient to say that both men recognize the pluralistic nature of the problem but tend to find the chief justification for federal support of science in its ultimate practical benefits.

The principal contribution of the two papers to the problem of scientific choice, however, is indirect. It is to stress the fact that the total flow of funds to any given field of science is not by itself a sufficient indicator of its overall value for the scientific effort. The exact kinds of activities which will be supported and, sometimes, the administrative channels through which the funds flow must also be considered. For example, Brooks makes sharp distinctions among the effects of individual grants, institutional programs for development support, capital and operating costs of major installations, and the like, on the activities of university scientists.

For present purposes, the principal point of the two papers is probably the distinction between so-called little science and big science. "Little science" is defined as the activities of a single investigator, with a few graduate students, which might be supported by individual grants in the neighborhood of $20,000 to perhaps $50,000 or more a year. "Big science," at the other extreme, refers to enterprises like large accelerators or oceanographic survey ships, which typically call for much larger expenditures and must necessarily be used by a large number of investigators in common. The principal argument, made especially by Kistiakowsky, is that little science deserves priority in national funding. Little science is, in other words, the bread and butter, the staple, of our educational and research process. Big science can be justified because of its inherent interest, for example, or its value for national defense, or because it is so spectacular that it contributes to national prestige. However, it should not be put in direct competition with little science, but should be supported from different budgetary accounts.

3. Comparisons between Fields. A third class of authors are members of the scientific fraternity outside the university structure proper. Examples are furnished by Weinberg and Philip Abelson, who testified on the high energy physics research program before the Joint Committee on Atomic Energy.[5] Here, explicit comparisons between fields are made, based on a list of specific criteria. Weinberg's criteria have already been mentioned. Abelson's approach is much the same. He also begins with a list of criteria. They include the importance of the field of science both to its practitioners and to practitioners in other fields; tangible contributions to the needs of society in such categories as health, defense, and economic welfare; and less tangible philosophical or prestige values.

Both men test these categories by attempting to rate four or five typical fields. Interestingly enough, the ratings of fields which both men con-

[5] See *High Energy Physics Research,* pp. 209–11.

sider turn out to be similar. Molecular biology is at the top in both cases and high energy physics at the bottom. The basic reason is that molecular biology is likely at some time to make practical contributions to human welfare, whereas both men consider this as more doubtful in the case of high energy physics. Abelson's list includes materials science and unmanned space exploration, while Weinberg's includes nuclear energy, the behavioral sciences (as a group), and manned space flight. Of these candidates, materials science and nuclear energy are rated highest, primarily because of their obvious practical values. In any such attempt at creating a composite index, of course, everything depends on the relative weights assigned the individual factors.

4. *Economic Analysis.* The final category consists of comments by people outside the scientific fraternity proper. In the material I have reviewed, the papers are primarily by economists, including the two by Johnson and Kaysen in a report on basic research and one by C. F. Carter in *Minerva.*[6] In contrast to the other approaches, these are strictly monistic. They all take the facts of life in a competitive economy as the point of departure and measure the values of scientific research in terms of its ultimate contribution to a country's economy.

With the exception of a part of Carter's paper, these treatments are addressed to the House committee's first question—to the justification of governmental support for science as a whole—rather than to the problem of choice among scientific fields. They are thus basically outside the scope of this discussion. Nevertheless, their approach sheds light indirectly on the problem of choice. For example, the economic market place as the natural mechanism for adjusting supply and demand among goods of various kinds and qualities has its parallel in the idea of an intellectual market place. Both Brooks and Kistiakowsky stress the fact that able scientists tend to seek out the areas where the prospects of rapid advance are the brightest, thus creating a sort of "proposal pressure" for administrative officers of the funding agencies and, in effect, providing an automatic mechanism for solving the problem of scientific choice, at least in the small. Such an economic commonplace as the relation between the shifting pattern of expenses of a family and its standard of living also has a parallel here. It serves to explain, for example,

[6] Harry G. Johnson, "Federal Support of Basic Research: Some Economic Issues," and Carl Kaysen, "Federal Support of Basic Research," in *Basic Research and National Goals,* pp. 127–41 and 147–67, respectively; and C. F. Carter, "The Distribution of Scientific Effort," *Minerva,* Winter 1963, pp. 172–81.

why the country should look first to little science and then, as its total level of support for science rises, turn increasingly to big science.

The paper by Carter also makes two points which are more directly relevant to the question of scientific choice. One is the need for a large enough spread of scientific interest in any country to give it a reasonable understanding of the broad lines of scientific advance elsewhere in the world. While Carter was writing primarily for national economies, and in particular for Great Britain, the principle is obviously one of broader application. In the United States, it might be applied to geographic areas, individual industries, or even single establishments. One of the important reasons for having some sort of research area in an enterprise devoted otherwise to development or routine engineering is to have a suitable point of contact with the scientific world as a whole. Wherever it applies, the principle obviously suggests a larger spread of effort than might otherwise seem economic.

The other major principle advanced by Carter is that the scientific and technological resources of Britain should be directed as far as possible toward a remedy for its problem of exports. In other words, they should be directed toward raising the level of industrial design in areas where increasing technological growth and a reasonably promising export situation can be forecast. This is justified on the basis that the export problem is the most serious limiting factor in Britain's economy and therefore the one for which technological advances will be of most value. Presumably, a similar limiting factor might be identified for the United States economy and thus serve as a guide for the allocation of our resources.

To someone who is not an economist, at least, this reasoning seems very persuasive. I am not sure, however, that I would know how to apply it. The route from basic scientific research to a particular export commodity may be long and tortuous, involving sophisticated technological and industrial contributions from many directions. In addition, advances in basic science are perhaps more likely to offer society essentially new products, or even new services, than to provide simple improvements in existing products. It takes a flexible and opportunistic management, backed by a strong technological system, to take prompt advantage of these opportunities. Thus, while the export criterion may serve to suggest an emphasis on certain general areas of relatively pure science, such as materials research, its real impact is in underlining the importance of the associated areas of engineering, applied science, and even management for the eventual success of the overall technological effort.

Four major questions seem to need further thought, two of which were mentioned at the beginning of the paper. None is by itself decisive for the issue of scientific choice, but a better understanding of them might simplify the problem.

What Constitutes Scientific Quality?

To begin, it would be helpful if we could reach a better general understanding, both inside and outside the scientific community, about what constitutes basic scientific quality, and, in particular, research quality. Harvey Brooks suggests, for example, that the hard core of very creative research workers may amount to only 5 percent of the total. We would all agree, I think, that in the long run the scientific community as a whole must be the custodian of its own standards of scientific quality. It would be a tragedy if administrators, whether in the universities or government, tried to make detailed decisions about the course of research. However, to the extent that we can broaden the basis for such scientific judgments, perhaps by bringing in neighboring scientific disciplines, the job of allocating resources for scientific research can be made much more straightforward and effective.

My own contribution to the House committee report on basic research includes tentative comments on two possible indicators of scientific quality, which I called "novelty" and "intellectual efficiency."[7] By the first, I meant the original discovery of absolutely new and unexpected phenomena, such as radioactivity, extraterrestrial radio emissions, or nuclear fission. I introduced this concept primarily to stress the importance of little science, which I conceive to be the normal means for opening such new doors. By the second, I meant to suggest generality, or advances which provide insight over broad areas. This expresses my bias for theoretical work, which is cheap and historically has been underemphasized in the United States in contrast to the massive accumulation of specific information, as necessary as this may be in some areas.

There are, of course, many other criteria which one might think of. For example, Weinberg includes in his discussion the important idea that the extent to which a given field contributes to and illuminates its neighboring scientific disciplines over many years can be taken as one measure of

---

[7] Hendrik W. Bode, "Reflections on the Relation between Science and Technology," in *Basic Research and National Goals*, pp. 41–76, esp. p. 74.

its scientific quality. Of course, physics in particular has contributed both many tools and many concepts to other areas. A number of workers have pointed out that current scientific progress in many fields results largely from the exploitation of relatively new tools and instruments drawn from other areas. Other things being equal, a possible indicator that a field may be on the point of making rapid progress, thus qualifying for extra support, is the fact that it has recently fallen heir to significant new experimental instruments. Another indicator of promise might be the recent formation of an interface between two areas, since concepts from one field frequently exert stimulating effects on another. Molecular biology is perhaps the best current example. However, since the junction of two or more fields necessarily involves judgments from the separate areas, this simply brings us back to the starting point, which was that we should try to broaden the base of judgment of scientific merit as much as possible.

What is at stake here in the long run is clearly the unity of science. To the extent that science can be kept a cohesive whole, the problem of scientific choice can probably be handled, but the more science becomes balkanized the less possible this becomes.

What Science Should Mission-Oriented Agencies Support?

A second question revolves around the growth of our understanding of what we should expect, *in toto,* from basic research activities supported by the mission-oriented agencies of the government. I am lumping together here strictly government laboratories, other federally supported establishments, and normal academic research supported by the mission agencies. This subject, introduced earlier, clearly covers a vast area which goes well beyond the limits of the present paper. It is important to mention it here, however, because these activities of mission agencies represent the great bulk of federal expenditures for basic research and because, as a matter of pure logic, we cannot have "mission orientation" without preempting the issue of scientific choice to some extent. Such agency activities thus stand in contrast to academic research supported by the National Science Foundation. Most of the writers on this subject seem to feel that the hard core of federal support for academic research should lie in the foundation rather than in the other agencies and that it needs to be increased moderately.

Beyond this point, there appear to be two ways to go. One, espoused by Weinberg, is to charge all reasonably appropriate research to the special agencies, justifying it on the grounds of its value for the practical missions of these agencies alone rather than its value for the general national support of research. Thus, in effect, the special interests of the Atomic Energy Commission in certain areas of physics, or of the Department of Health, Education, and Welfare in areas of biological and medical research, would tend to disappear from the accounting of scientific support generally. If the principle were construed generously, the logical result, one assumes, would be an increase in the total research effort supported by these agencies. The other road, represented by Harvey Brooks, if I understand him correctly, is more cautious. It lays less emphasis on the purely budgetary issue and instead stresses the importance of applying adequate criteria, including social as well as scientific worth, to the work itself.

Industrial laboratories are, of course, mission-oriented in a broad sense. Thus, industrial experience should have some relevance to these questions, although there is unfortunately no general agreement on what it is. However, at least one school would stress clarity of thought and selectivity in deciding just what a particular mission should justify. As applied to academic research, this might mean in the long run a still greater shift toward reliance on the National Science Foundation. The activities we are considering are so diverse, however, that we should be chary about drawing sweeping conclusions.

What Is the Relation between Scientific and Technological Progress?

The third question which seems to need further thought is the interface between pure science, on the one hand, and engineering and the applications of science generally, on the other. There are two aspects to this question. The first rests on the simple observation—by now quite familiar—that big science is, after all, largely an exercise in engineering. Thus, high energy machines are primarily exercises in electrical engineering. Radio astronomy depends largely on methods and devices which are familiar in the radar field.

It is not clear that these projects always get the thorough planning which would seem natural if they were approached directly as engineering matters. One can question, for example, whether trade-offs between costs and performance are always done as carefully and as thoroughly as they are for modern weapons systems. Trade-offs between costs and time may also be important for big science. In testifying on the high energy issue, for example, Eugene Wigner stated that he had no doubt that high energy phenomena are worth exploring, and eventually would be explored, but that he felt less certain when the exploration should take place. A more thorough engineering study might give us a better understanding of the virtues of delay in such situations, either to allow more time for planning and preliminary testing or for progress in the state of the relevant general technology to bring the overall cost down.

Another aspect of this question, however, is of much greater fundamental importance. This is the existence of apparent gaps in our understanding of the paths by which basic scientific advances come to final, practical utilization. The earlier discussion of Carter's paper was introduced primarily to show how wide these gaps might be. The discussion of the high energy program suggested that there might be incidental direct benefits to technology from big science programs. This is, of course, true but it does not by any means follow that the benefits to technology are at all worth the cost or that they are in directions where advances are most needed. We should study the question of technological advance more broadly and on its own merits. Until we do, we cannot really understand the problem of scientific choice, either among different fields or between pure and applied work.

What Is the Relation between Research and Graduate Education?

The last question has to do with the relation between these problems of research support and the responsibilities of the universities for graduate education in the sciences. This is the side of the problem which is stressed by Kistiakowsky and Brooks, although it is given less attention in most of the other papers. It is probably the simplest way of coming to grips quantitatively with appropriate funding levels for basic research in universities. University graduate schools in science are, of course, our sole source of new men for many purposes—a new generation of research workers, new staff for science teaching in both colleges and universities, and a flow of new recruits for applied science in industry and elsewhere. The needs of teaching and the needs of industry are different in detail but can be united for the purposes of this discussion. With the growth in college enrollments and in our economic system, these needs for trained scientists, of course, mount impressively every year.

The best and cheapest, if not almost the only, way of obtaining this training is by the classical method of little science—a single professor with a small group of graduate students. Thus, the first requisite for federal support of science is adequate support for this sort of little science. Simple calculations based on the known rate of growth of college enrollments are enough to give approximate figures. If we assume that the trends of student interests do not change rapidly, the same sort of calculation gives us a fair indication of the relative requirements of the various fields. Thereby, we can obtain a sort of first order answer to the problem of scientific choice, at least for the near future.

On the other hand, money spent in support of research in other ways may serve to defeat these educational ends. A recent report by the House Committee on Government Operations stresses the fact that overemphasis on research as a continuing occupation provides competition which tends to diminish the number of trained scientists available for university or college teaching.[8] Of course, the same sort of competition also affects the flow of scientists into applied work. And there are other, more subtle effects. The high prestige of pure research tends to denigrate both teaching and applied work. It may also promote attitudes of extreme specialization, particularly among men who cannot otherwise meet competition. But breadth of interest and viewpoint, rather than extreme specialization, is what one wants in a teacher. As it happens, industry and applied science also, on the whole, need men with a broad outlook and substantial versatility.

Thus, research funding can be a two-edged sword. In planning government programs we should give weight to the social consequences as well as to the merits of the proposed programs themselves. Clearly, Harvey Brooks's 5 percent should always have adequate support, but surely there is a happy medium between this standard and one which provides support for everyone capable of doing any research.

[8] See *Conflicts between the Federal Research Programs and the Nation's Goals for Higher Education*, Eighteenth Report of the House Committee on Government Operations, 89 Cong. 1 sess. (October 1965), pp. 15–21.

DISCUSSION

"Understanding Comes before Control"

Bode offered the following additional reflections on his paper.

THE QUESTION of how the government should allocate its expenditures among different fields of basic academic research was one that he could not answer, and what was more, it was, probably, inherently unanswerable. One simple reason was that gross fields such as physics or chemistry did not describe accurately enough the nature of the scientific work that was actually underway. To do so meaningfully, finer subfields had to be employed; but, while more meaningful, these subfields were also more transitory. The desirable level of expenditures for various fields at universities could not, of course, be determined without knowing what was being spent on basic research in these fields at nonacademic institutions and also in related areas of applied research. The statutory missions of the agencies sponsoring research also had to be kept in mind; thus, the Public Health Service was now the largest single sponsor of academic basic research, and naturally enough, most of its expenditures were for research in the life sciences.

The administrative method by which research was supported could be as significant as the volume of support. The project system of little science by which relatively small sums were distributed for the work of many small groups of professors and graduate students should be strongly supported. "This is the church that I go to. . . ." Dollar for dollar, little science was more likely than big science to discover unknown and unexpected phenomena and the novel ideas that are of "utmost importance" to the progress of science. "You don't have big science, generally, unless you know what you are looking for."

Progress also depended upon the "generality and universality" of ideas. ". . . [S]ome scientific principles are broader than others and have greater application, and those are the ones that count. Science is . . . a set of economical rules for mastering an extremely complicated and varied nature, . . . finding . . . critical principles—and the more universal they are, the better." Science is "the opposite of the telephone book," because its essence is not a mass of information but structured and synthesized knowledge. To synthesize masses of information was the function of scientific theory, and what is more, theoretical work was cheap.

Weinberg and Abelson had sought to rate the merit of different scientific fields—that is, the degree to which they warranted government support—on two grounds: *intrinsic* (internal, or purely scientific); and *extrinsic* (external, or socially useful). In federal budgeting, some value should be set on intrinsic criteria—on the truth for its own sake. ". . . [A]stronomy is almost purely decorative . . . but very interesting. What can we afford to pay for [a field] . . . which tells us so much about man's place in nature . . . ?" This kind of question about the value of truth was generally answered "through the side door." It should be confronted directly, for if the value of the truth for its own sake was not acknowledged "science would collapse."

The mere question of allocating funds among various fields assumes "a fragmentation of the body of science . . . to support this field as against that." But you can't "fragment something that wasn't integrated . . . in the first place. . . ." The panel system of using specialists to evaluate the work of other specialists also had the drawback of fragmenting the unitary body of science. The interdisciplinary communicability of scientific knowledge should be stressed. Although inherent in Weinberg's criterion of the amount of light that research in one field could throw on another, Weinberg did not carry the point far enough. To assert the unity of science is to assert that "if you had an ideal science the whole world would be understandable and that [scientific] . . . principles do intermesh. . . ."

Assuredly, an agency with a mission should sponsor basic research; doubtless the Navy had gotten its money's worth from the basic research sponsored by the Office of Naval Research. But if the rewards of pure science are unexpected, it followed that much, if not most, of the practical benefits of the basic research sponsored by mission-oriented agencies would be reaped by others. "If you don't know where a scientific advance is going to have application, neither can you tell from the mission where the scientific advance should be that is in fact going to help it. These are, in a sense, logical schools. . . . [T]he argument for supporting research for the sake of the mission, and that mission only, breaks down sooner than you might think." [End of Bode's remarks.]

Many people seemed to think that scientific fields can somehow be ranked in a hierarchy of "importance" or "quality" which can become a basis for budgetary allocations, a university scientist observed, but he disagreed. ". . . [W]hile there may be some difference in the center of gravity" of two fields, "the difference between individual projects . . . and individual people . . . in a field may be very much more significant than the difference between the fields." At any rate, such differences in quality of work within a field must be kept in mind in little science allocations. He granted that big science posed another problem, because it required a major long-term investment in a particular field.

The most economic policy for the government, suggested another scientist, was "a cream-skimming operation" of supporting the best science regardless of field. This would probably result in a maximum breadth of fields or as great a breadth as was possible "before you begin to . . . spread yourself so thin that nothing is happening." Such a policy was not practicable for an individual laboratory or university, which had to make harder choices about the fields on which it would concentrate. Essentially it was a policy of "insurance," to see that all scientific areas of potential usefulness were covered. And, the group seemed to agree, due to our complex multi-agency pattern of research support if not to any conscious government decision, the United States had actually followed some such policy and was as well "insured" across the breadth of science as any other nation.

Nonetheless, one participant remarked, the multi-agency system could result in gaps or deficiencies in the support of certain fields which "no agency feels [are] sufficiently vital to its own interests to support on the scale which may be in the interests of the government as a whole." There were two ways to deal with this problem: a firmer and more explicit commitment by mission-oriented agencies to support basic research in designated fields, and the allotment to the National Science Foundation of funds to support a larger proportion of federally sponsored basic research.

The Foundation and "Gap-Filling"

If the foundation merely exercised a "gap-filling" role,[1] it could have filled more "gaps" than it has; but NSF has sought both to support all

[1] A resemblance will be noted between this earlier notion of "gap-filling" (which

fields of science and to give special support to selected fields, and, naturally, it has not been able to accomplish both objectives equally well. Should not NSF decide which objective is more important? a participant asked.

The original conception of the foundation, an official replied, "wasn't that of a 'gap-filler,' and you wouldn't have had a piece of legislation written that way. . . . I don't think you can have a live agency with good staff [which] . . . is willing to sit back and essentially say, 'Well, whatever somebody else doesn't do, I'll do,' because you will end up with fields that are in the most fundamental sense the less glamorous of the basic science fields." Nonetheless, because of its small budget, the foundation has been "reasonably selective" in its choice of fields, particularly in the early days. For example, there are areas of physics and agricultural, clinical, and medical research which the foundation chose not to enter.

Within the areas in which NSF has operated, there has been "a certain amount of so-called gap-filling," although it was not thought of in those terms. The foundation has tended to examine "the spectrum of support . . . available from all of the [other] agencies" and then has determined on the basis of this information into what fields its limited funds might best be put. Thus, NSF early resolved to back systematic biology, which had been receiving little support elsewhere, and developed a "first-rate program" in the field; in environmental biology, NSF supported research but not the purchase of equipment, as it did not have enough money for both; and at the outset, NSF supported little or no work in the social sciences. Today the foundation devotes relatively more funds to astronomy, geology, and environmental and atmospheric sciences than the government as a whole. NSF has been more than a passive "gap-filler"; by discriminating choice, it has helped to "conceptualize" certain emergent fields and may thereby have indirectly influenced the structure of some university science departments. Thus, the titling of a new grants program as "molecular biology," then a little known usage, has, it was said, "tremendously" helped the development of that field.

"The question that is unresolved," a participant believed, "is, who takes the lead" in designating gaps—NSF or mission-oriented agencies?

---

seems to derive from dentistry) and the more current notion advanced by a committee of the National Academy of Sciences (which seems to derive rather from watchmaking) that the National Science Foundation should serve as a "balance wheel" in the government's support of academic research.

With regard to academic science, he was told, "no agency takes the lead, but the totality of the scientific community."

That answer did not satisfy everyone. In the expensive field of high energy physics, for example, the Atomic Energy Commission was supposed to serve as executive agent, funding and administering most of the federal program. Why, then, did NSF allocate to the Cornell accelerator millions of dollars from its far smaller budget?

CITIZEN : So far as I have been able to glean . . . , mainly because Cornell worked out a deal with NSF—regardless of any government . . . policy that [high energy physics] . . . was primarily related to the AEC mission.

OFFICIAL A : . . . [W]e are all departing from [the] . . . point of view that this whole business [of allocations] is rational. . . . [I]t isn't rational. If you [adopt] . . . the point of view that this is a schizophrenic . . . rather than a rational world, these things are more understandable.

OFFICIAL B : There is a rationality . . . that . . . has to do with the way money is collected. If you want to call it a fact of life, all right.

CITIZEN : Are you willing to say, in principle, that NSF should not have supported the Cornell machine, but should have used that money for other purposes?

OFFICIAL C : Of course not.

OFFICIAL A : If no other agency had money to support the Cornell accelerator, and it was a good thing to do, and the foundation had some money . . . it should go ahead, and . . . this is what happened.

The Latitude of Mission-Oriented Agencies

A mission-oriented agency's latitude to decide if a marginal field might be relevant to its mission is obviously important in determining the net distribution of federal funds across the spectrum of science and, in turn, the gaps that might emerge. "The thing is, . . . how ingeniously can you spread your effort so that you can reflect all corners of science to accomplish your mission? There will always be gaps, and high energy physics is a perfect case where it doesn't seem to be immediately related to anything the public really wants." The group was of two minds about the breadth of the basic research that major agencies could now support. One official believed that the Department of Defense had supported a very wide range of university research. "Haven't you taken a very broad point of view in the Department of Defense, with respect to the allocation of funds that go to universities . . . ?" he asked a Defense official.

"Haven't you educated the members of the Armed Services Committee and the Appropriations Committee that it is important for you to take a very broad point of view . . . ?" The reply was not quite expected. "Recently they have been asking for a pretty narrow interpretation." "Sir?" "Recently . . . the military committee has been quite narrow. 'NSF is coming along and everybody else is supporting research. Why should you people be spreading money all over the map any more?' "

The university community might now endorse this congressional attitude, an official from a civilian agency thought, since the overhead rates of civilian and military agencies had been equalized. Formerly, a number of "influential people" had preferred military financing, because it had paid full overhead. ". . . [O]verhead rates had a great deal to do with the rate at which the NSF budget expanded over the years. . . ."

P H Y S I C I S T :   Why didn't that affect the NIH budget . . . ?

O F F I C I A L :   Because there weren't as many physical scientists interested in NIH.

P H Y S I C I S T :   You are suggesting that the physical sciences are much more interested in overhead?

O F F I C I A L :   The people representing those areas from those universities, yes.

If this review of the discussion conveys the impression that the group, like Bode, was not convinced of the feasibility or desirability of allocating funds among scientific fields in terms of any of their technical or intellectual aspects, that impression is accurate. Indeed, the group appeared to prefer almost any other mode of allocation to that by scientific field.

The Primacy of Good Ideas

One criterion already mentioned was supporting "any guy with a good idea, and I don't care what you call him, a physicist or what. . . ." And the "you"—the person judging what ideas are "good"—should be as varied as possible. "Essentially, this means that the criteria are independent of the field label. You can come back later on and count up how much you need for the field, but you don't make allocations [by field] to start with." Certainly, this was a utopian criterion that disregarded the practical realities of the budgetary, administrative, academic, and political processes.

In pure science, an official declared, the "ends" (the fields receiving funds) are less important than the "means"—"the mechanisms . . . set up [to determine] who can play the game and [to] help decide all of these interrelated questions . . . [and that either do or do not] permit a feedback so that you can correct error." This vision was quickly rejected by a disconsolate critic. ". . . [A]ll you have done is to translate these questions [of allocation] . . . into the political terms of . . . the . . . representation of physicists, biologists, and social scientists on the key groups and [how] . . . they swing the key committees. . . ."

PHYSICIST: I don't accept the implication that physicists think only in terms of the interests of physics, or biologists think only in terms of interests of biologists.

CRITIC: I wouldn't say *only,* but you are not suggesting that they completely ignore the interests [of their own field]?

PHYSICIST: No, but I think they try . . . to look at the totality of science.

CRITIC: If all scientists do this, then why haven't you had just the opposite representation? Why weren't the social scientists running all the influential groups . . . ? There is no relation at all between the allocation of resources and the . . . people who are doing the allocation?

PHYSICIST: I don't say there is no relation, but I think you are exaggerating. . . . You were implying . . . that this was a completely determinative——

CRITIC: I didn't suggest physicists were not human.

Surely, a university spokesman intruded, the means of allocating funds are secondary to the purposes for which the funds are appropriated. "At a certain point, your physicists and others get in on this, but . . . the allocations to the space program, and so on, go back to broad social-political phenomena. Again, the allocations of the health services . . . [are] determined [less] . . . by the health specialists [than] . . . by the age and prevalence of certain ailments among members of Congress."

On High and Not-So-High Quality Research

One participant was decidedly dissatisfied with the drift of the discussion. The quality of research seemed more important than anything else as a criterion for allocating funds, he remarked, but was not "high quality research" merely the thin end of the wedge justifying expenditures for a vast volume of work that could by no stretch of the imagination be considered high quality? One hundred million dollars might thereby ride on the warrant of $5 million of high quality work.

An industry participant agreed. In fact, in his experience, a ratio of five projects of high quality to ninety-five of ordinary quality was high. ". . . [Y]ou [may] find one out of twenty projects which are economically successful in industrial research . . . , and the surprising thing . . . is that they seem to occur to the same man or group of men. . . ." In opposition, it was stated that industrial research was not basic research, in which the outstanding success of one man rests on the less outstanding work of many other people. However, the man from industry persisted. Despite a tenfold increase in the volume of basic research during the last decade, he observed, there had been "a decreasing ratio of major . . . discoveries. . . ." This was flatly disputed by a university scientist who had recently reviewed the major scientific discoveries of the last seven years. "I was absolutely astounded. What has happened since 1957 or 1958, since the big surge forward in expenditures on science, is just amazing."

A government official sought to resolve the dispute by suggesting that those who spoke of a decline in the quality of research saw the increased volume of lower quality research, while those who spoke of an improvement in quality saw the increased volume of higher quality work; both might well be true. NIH, for example, had "decided in 1957 and told the Secretary and the President that it would . . . support everybody in the field of biology who could contribute. Now, this meant a deliberate decision to go into the area of diminishing returns. So the question is not whether you are in the area of diminishing returns . . . , but, rather, how far should we go [into it]. . . . [I]n all probability, the cost per discovery . . . is going up. . . ."

As the discussion drew to a close, a scientist presented his credo on why basic research was so important: ". . . [Y]ou can do anything, probably, if you can understand it. Understanding comes before control —it is the essential thing. Science, for several hundred years, has been based on the postulate [that] there isn't anything that we can't understand—give us a little time. . . . [W]e don't know how, or how soon, or in what way in detail, of course, but it has been working and it should still work." This was, he acknowledged, "a very optimistic postulate," but "it fits the country, and I think we should live with it. . . ."

The chairman's coda was a sentence drawn from Bode's paper: "We are living in a pluralistic world, and the problem of scientific choice becomes in the long run a problem of nonscientific judgment. . . ."

HARVEY BROOKS

A Reply to Six Questions on the Allocation of Federal Funds

During most of the period reviewed in this volume, each seminar member was presented with a list of agenda questions that, despite the chairmen's valiant efforts, were almost invariably ignored. One exception was so noteworthy that it deserves to be presented to a wider audience. Some days after the discussion of Hendrik Bode's paper (during which participants were, as usual, happily oblivious of the agenda), Harvey Brooks submitted the following reply to the six questions that had been put before the group.

1. Can substantial agreement be reached on one of the critical questions Dr. Bode identifies: What constitutes high quality scientific research?

I believe "yes," but with some modifications. Quality can only be measured on a scale, not by a dichotomy into "high" and "low." By and large, within a specialized area of science, one can get wide consensus on quality judgments of individual pieces of research and research papers. One might classify research quality in the following categories:

A. Outstanding—a significant step forward in insight or understanding, an important new technique or approach, a very careful or critical experiment or analysis, a clearly recognizable advance of wide significance, affecting a considerable area of knowledge.

B. Sound—regarded by workers in the field as interesting and novel, a definite but not highly exciting contribution, not affecting as wide an area of knowledge as *A*. This is the kind of work that would be referred to and used by workers in the outstanding category but would not itself be classified as outstanding; it is work which fully takes into account the best contemporary research in the field, has a degree of generality, and is clearly related to an underlying theoretical structure. It is work which would almost always be acceptable for publication in one of the major journals in the field.

C. *Humdrum*—scientifically reliable, contains no obvious defects in technique or interpretation, but is of rather limited significance. It is usually "gap-filling" work, verifying a result which might have been anticipated with high certainty anyway or reporting a new observation, measurement, or calculation which is not of wide significance or applicability. Though accurate and sound, it is really outside the mainstream of scientific advance and only partially takes into account existing theory or other related work.

D. *Poor*—scientifically unsound or essentially trivial. Unsound work may fail to take into account factors which would disturb the experimental result, the interpretation of the results may contain demonstrable errors, or the work may fail to consider existing experiments or theory in a way that significantly affects the conclusions. Trivial work inspires the reaction "so what?" among the majority of workers in the same field. It may be a slight and insignificant variation or extension of already well-known results. It may consist of a string of isolated facts without adequate interpretation.

To judge the overall quality of the work of a group or individual, one has to assess a number of projects or undertakings according to the criteria listed above. Cumulative impact and significance must be given important weight.

In addition, work cannot always be classified in a single one of the categories. For example, the concept of an experiment or calculation may be exceedingly novel and important, even though it contains defects in execution or in argument. Some of the most important theoretical advances in physics appeared dubious and even illogical when first proposed. But this is the exception. In such cases, which are sufficiently rare that they do not affect the general concept of "quality" in scientific work, subjective judgments are especially important.

It is much harder to evaluate fields than projects or discrete programs or pieces of research. The spectrum of quality within a field is usually wider than the differences in quality between fields. The quality of a field is probably best judged by evaluation of sample projects. Average quality work, however, is often valuable and useful; this will vary with the field and with time. In pure mathematics, for example, average quality work is probably least useful. The same appears to be true, although to a lesser degree, in theoretical physics. Furthermore, a few new seminal ideas in a field can often enhance the value and significance of average experimental work in the field for some time to come.

Victor Weisskopf makes an interesting distinction between "intensive" and "extensive" research.[1] Intensive research includes pure mathematics, elementary particle physics, and molecular biology. It aims at discovering and testing a few very fundamental principles and concepts. Experimental objects and systems are chosen primarily with a view to their suitability for testing these concepts. Extensive research includes most of solid state physics, a large part of biology, a fair fraction of nuclear structure physics, most of applied mathematics. It aims primarily at applying or testing fairly well-established principles and concepts with an ever widening variety of systems, often of increasing complexity—different crystals and compounds in solid state physics, different species or communities in biology, and so forth. One expects to find surprising results and new effects in extensive research, but generally, once discovered, they are fitted fairly quickly into existing understanding and theory. Often, extensive research is concerned with establishing a detailed explanation of a system which is understood in a general way. It aims at uncovering the richness of phenomena which may be fitted into an existing conceptual framework. Usually, average quality work is much more valuable and worth doing in extensive research than in intensive research. Of course, it frequently happens that an accumulation of extensive research results turns up discrepancies and difficulties which eventually lead to the discovery of new principles and concepts of a very fundamental character; so one cannot draw too sharp a distinction between extensive and intensive studies.

I am not impressed with the genius theory of scientific progress. With the present size of the worldwide scientific community, geniuses will appear when the time is ripe. In fact, many individuals and groups are usually on the verge of the same discovery. The step provided by the genius is commonly not the mutation of folklore but a small step which fits together the work of literally hundreds of other people. I think this statement can be documented for almost all the Nobel prizes in physics for the last twenty years. This is not to detract from the contribution of the genius but merely to point out that his contribution is never as isolated or unique as the layman believes. There is an implication in the

---

[1] See Victor Weisskopf, "In Defense of High Energy Physics," in Luke C. L. Yuan (ed.), *The Nature of Matter: Purposes of High Energy Physics* (Brookhaven National Laboratory, 1965), p. 24.

genius theory that if you could only pick out the geniuses you would not need to support the rest of science. The "breakthrough" of a genius usually rests on the lesser but essential contributions of hundreds of other people. Discovery and invention are syntheses, and you have to have something to synthesize.

2. Of the following criteria which have been suggested for evaluating the merit of various fields, are there some to which special weight should be given?
  a) "Intrinsic" criteria
    (1) The quality of scientists, or of research, in a field
    (2) Scientific "ripeness"
    (3) "Proposal pressures"
    (4) Scientific novelty of findings
    (5) Intellectual efficiency or generality—the status of theory
  b) "Extrinsic" criteria
    (1) Contributions of a field to other disciplines
    (2) Relevance to national missions
    (3) Likelihood of ultimate practical (technological or social) returns

The weight of different criteria should probably be different in different fields. One supports some fields because they are fundamental, others because they are useful. Moreover, the criteria listed are not independent. The brightest scientists (a [1]) will tend to gravitate to the "ripest" fields (a [2]). The quality of the scientists in a field, and especially the migration of bright people into it, probably constitutes the most reliable index of ripeness. If one includes quality as well as quantity in the measurement of proposal pressure (which is usually the case), a (3) is not independent of a (1). Novelty, by itself, is not a meaningful criterion (a [4]). It can only be considered in conjunction with generality (a [5]) and intellectual elegance, a kind of aesthetic criterion. Indeed, a new fact is usually only truly novel if it calls existing theory into question or potentially alters understanding over a broad area of phenomena. With the above caveats, I would rank the relative importance of the intrinsic criteria in approximately the order in which they are listed. However, it would be illusory to think one could assign numerical weights and come up with a very meaningful result. With respect to the extrinsic criteria, I would rate them all about equal in importance.

When applying all criteria, however, I would tend to give preference to fields or programs which rate very high on a few criteria, or even on only one criterion, rather than to programs which rate only moderately high on several or all criteria. Actually, the high correlation between the criteria, especially the intrinsic ones, makes it difficult to give general statements. And, no criterion can be applied without regard to the question of cost and the problem of "critical size." Even a very worthwhile project is scarcely worth starting if the resources are not available to carry it through, and the various criteria must be balanced against cost. Some inexpensive projects may be worth undertaking even if the risk of failure is high.

    3. What changes, if any, appear warranted in the present allocation of federal funds among different fields of university research?

I believe this question cannot and should not be answered by any individual or small group of individuals. Universities—or at least the strongest universities—determine their priorities for academic research partly through the processes by which faculties determine who should be promoted or offered tenure positions. This is one of the principal reasons why I believe that universities themselves should take primary financial responsibility for the salaries of faculty with tenure and, to the extent they do not do so with their own resources, that these salaries should be paid from institutional rather than project grants. If these conditions are met, then it seems to me that university priorities should be respected in the allocation of funds, though they should not be absolutely determining, and that "proposal pressure" should become one valid index for assessing priorities among fields and should be given important weight in any overall allocation. Any personal opinions expressed below in response to the question must be construed in this light. They represent only one man's opinion.[2]

I would allocate relatively less to low energy nuclear physics, especially nuclear spectroscopy. I would allocate more, selectively, to ground-based astronomy relative to rocket and especially satellite work. I would allocate considerably more to chemistry, especially to physical chemistry and chemical kinetics. I would allocate more to applied mathematics, but I feel that pure mathematics is probably adequately supported. Within biology I would encourage allocation of resources to the more physical and quantitative aspects, both molecular and organismic. I would allocate increasing resources to interdisciplinary work in engineering and the social sciences relevant to (1) medical care and biomedical engineering, (2) educational systems, and (3) urban planning. In psy-

[2] The foregoing paragraph was added in June 1967.—Editor.

chology, I would try to encourage much more research into human learning, with particular reference to feedback and information concepts. There is need for greatly increased university support in the field of computer applications and information sciences. I would substantially decrease support for university research in agriculture oriented toward products and utilization of products and use the funds saved to support more basic research in the plant sciences and to investigate world food problems, as opposed to local productivity problems of farmers in the United States. I would encourage more theoretical research in the atmospheric sciences. I would slow the rate of growth in the fundamental biomedical sciences below its level of recent years.

4. Both Weinberg and Bode suggest a broadening in the composition of review panels as a practical administrative approach to evaluating the fruitfulness of basic research for neighboring disciplines. Such an approach is used by the AEC's Division of Research. Should it be adopted more widely in other government programs?

The same suggestion was also made earlier by the report of the Committee on Science and Public Policy of the National Academy of Sciences on federal support of research.[3] I would like to see greater representation from neighboring disciplines, more rapid rotation of panelists, and greater representation of younger scientists. One might consider the possibility of some more democratic way of selecting at least some of the panelists, for example, by nominations from grantees or even election by grantees, as is now done in France. I do not believe any of these suggestions would cause much change in the composition of panels, or in their decisions, but it would lead to greater public confidence in the system.

5. To what extent is it feasible and desirable to set the level of expenditures for various fields of university research without regard to the level of expenditures at industrial and governmental laboratories?

Clearly, they are not independent. I believe that all the work that is appropriate to universities should be supported in them. There are many kinds of research that are not appropriate for or cannot be done very effectively by universities—for example, standards work, work requiring a high degree of coordination and programming or continuity of effort by the same people over many years, work of a highly applied nature, work

---

[3] "The constitution of panels should represent perspective as well as specialty. Panels in given fields of science should include some members from allied fields" (National Academy of Sciences, Committee on Science and Public Policy, *Federal Support of Basic Research in Institutions of Higher Learning* [NAS, 1964], p. 83).

requiring extensive and sophisticated engineering support, work that has
to meet prescribed time schedules, classified or unpublishable work. It
should be national policy to support as much of the nation's research as
possible in conjunction with training and education. If this policy should
lead over a period of four or five years to a significant alteration in the
balance of effort between universities and nonacademic institutions, the
policy should be reviewed and possibly a reduction made in national
goals for higher education. Nonacademic research should not be supported on a "level of effort" basis but rather on the basis of the needs of
a specific agency's mission. Very careful justification and review at the
highest levels should be required before new government-supported
nonacademic research institutions are created—a convincing case should
be made why the objectives cannot be satisfied as well by existing establishments.

6. What should be done to balance the expenditures of mission-oriented
   agencies for basic research in fields related to their missions with support
   for other scientific fields by these and other agencies?

In general, mission-oriented agencies should not support basic research which is not related to their mission, unless a certain field of research is assigned to them as part of their mission because of a special
capability they have (for example, the AEC in elementary particle physics and the Navy in rocket astronomy or the logistics support of Antarctic
research). On the other hand, it is in the interest of the agency to inter-
pret mission-relatedness rather liberally.

Monopoly of a field of science by one agency should be avoided.
Every agency needs enough competition to keep scientifically and administratively honest. It would be desirable for the Executive Office explicitly
to assign responsibility for the health of certain fields of basic research to
mission-oriented agencies.

A discussion with
ALVIN WEINBERG

Government Allocations
to Basic Research

*In November 1965, an informal dinner-discussion with
Alvin Weinberg was arranged by Brookings at the
Cosmos Club. For the occasion, a small group was assembled, most of whom were not regular participants
in the seminar on science and public policy.*

IF THERE were anything at all new in his paper
"Criteria for Scientific Choice,"[1] Weinberg thought, it was the idea of
"imbeddedness" or the value that one area of science had for other areas
in which it is "imbedded." Mathematics offered an example: the "things
that you learn in topology are of relevance in illuminating areas in differential geometry or differential equations. . . ." Doubtless, it was not
merely the technical character of a field but also the character of its scientists that determined its broader significance at any given time. ". . .
[T]hose fields that happen to have people in them whose taste is broad
are just very much better off than the fields that don't. . . . [M]any of
the greatest scientists that I know just somehow have this instinct. They
have a breadth of vision, a breadth of taste. . . ."

Judgments about the merit of research were made readily enough
after the fact, a participant observed, but how well could they be made
before, which was when the Budget Bureau and the Congress had to

[1] Alvin M. Weinberg, "Criteria for Scientific Choice," *Minerva,* Winter 1963, pp.
159–71.

make them? The best scientific opinion was itself divided on the merit of the best scientific work, a professor noted, recalling the contradictory verdicts which two great contemporaries had pronounced on Georg Cantor's work on the theory of transfinite numbers, "which gave an enormous impetus to analysis for all sorts of practical applications. . . . Poincaré said, 'Set theory is a disease from which mathematics will recover.' And Hilbert said, 'No-one will drive us out of the paradise created by Georg Cantor.' "

On Public versus Private Allocations

The debate on scientific allocations should not be conducted by committees, behind closed doors, but by individuals in the open literature. Open publication and open discussion are as important in correcting errors in allocations as in science itself. A government administrator gave the example of the Whitford committee report on ground-based astronomy,[2] a serious effort which was hardly off the press before radio astronomers spoke up and said "you have forgotten all about us. . . ." And planetary astronomers "take great umbrage . . . that all the people interested in stars and galaxies are preempting all the telescopes and overlooking the fact that we need to look at planets. . . . So it is very important not to go off half cocked and accept one prestigious report as being *the* significant wisdom. . . ."

WEINBERG: In the arts, you do have a way of codifying artistic tastes. This is the role the artistic reviewer takes. . . . I would hope one could encourage . . . the emergence of a cadre of . . . scientific critics in the same sense. People who are willing to take these [planning and policy] reports and really subject them to a thoroughgoing and penetrating analysis—not one that just mouths the usual platitudes.

SOCIAL SCIENTIST A: [T]here just are entirely too few scientists . . . who are prepared to do that. . . . Nobody asks them for a final judgment and nobody expects it; but they express their opinions only in private. They have all their arguments in private, and the public be damned.

WEINBERG: It is not the mode. . . . [I]t is not quite polite, in some sense, to try to make judgments of this sort. . . .

[2] See *Ground-Based Astronomy: A Ten-Year Program,* A Report Prepared by the Panel on Astronomical Facilities for the Committee on Science and Public Policy of the National Academy of Sciences (National Academy of Sciences–National Research Council, 1964).

SCIENTIST A : This is an ethical issue in science—there is no question about it. . . .

SOCIAL SCIENTIST A : The mode for the scientific community was stated by . . . [Weisskopf] in *Science:* . . . "Now look, fellows, let us not criticize anybody else in public. Let us only speak for the strength of our own field, and that is all we should do in public."[3]

SCIENTIST B : I think a weakness in the position of the scientist since the Galilean trouble has been the agreement—tacit, perhaps—which arose at that time, that there would be a division of labor, that the scientist would make objective observations of the observable world and the humanist would make value judgments . . . , and if they kept out of each other's hair, neither would attempt to put the other in jail. That is what I call . . . "the truce of Galileo." This truce is breaking down and must. It would have made no sense to the pre-Renaissance scholar in science.

GOVERNMENT OFFICIAL : . . . [U]p until 1950-something-or-other, the battle was really between the scientists and those against science, and you had to protect science to let [it] . . . advance. But now that science has it made, you are back at the point where the scientists can begin to fight among themselves.

SOCIAL SCIENTIST B : . . . For a year and a half, now, we have been coming back to this question, directly or indirectly, intentionally or unintentionally, and always the consensus expressed by eminent scientists . . . is that it is not possible to make a scientific judgment as between fields in terms of what should or can be profitably allocated. They say, "For any field, we can tell you, within it, which lines are more profitable than others, more productive; but, as between fields, there is no way of making this judgment." Now, do they really mean that there is no way of making this judgment . . . or do they mean that "we do not choose to make any judgments about any other field, since we are in one of them ourselves?"

WEINBERG : I can't really say. I think there is a great deal of the latter. . . . For the first time, we are asking scientists to make value judgments in science that have the same quality as the value judgments that we make in other affairs of mankind. And these value judgments are the judgments of the merit of this way of allocating funds—large funds—for certain scientific activities as opposed to a different way of allocating funds. . . .

[3] This refers to a letter in *Science* by the physicist Victor Weisskopf, in the course of which he stated: "As long as we still live in a period of scientific expansion, the community of scientists should fight together for a larger support for science as a whole. This is better done if scientists restrict their public activities to the praise of their own fields and refrain from attacking the fields of their colleagues. There will be a time in the not-too-distant future, however, when much wisdom and insight will be required to establish a healthy and broad scientific frontier within the limitations of means which may be no longer small compared to the total national product" (*Science*, August 6, 1965, p. 586).

What Should Basic Research Budgets Be Related To?

Expenditures on basic research broadly relevant to the practical mission of either an agency or a laboratory, Weinberg argued, can reasonably be justified as overhead on the direct costs of that mission; and the residuum of research so pure that it cannot be allocated to any mission at all might, in turn, be considered overhead on the basic research which *can* be allocated. But the scale of each kind of overhead "should bear . . . some relation to the scale of the entire scientific and technical enterprise." How much is appropriate at any particular time is a matter of judgment; as the nation grows richer, "we can probably afford to be more and more relaxed [about] . . . the size of that overhead expense."

(Once when he was presenting this position to a group of high energy physicists, Weinberg related, J. Robert Oppenheimer, who was in the audience, jotted down the following comment on a match box that he handed to him after the discussion: "Jefferson would have considered you to be a monster.")

The overhead notion was convenient when total R&D expenditures were rising, a social scientist observed; but would scientists stick to it if these expenditures went down? "They like to ride the elevator up," an official answered. "They don't want to relate it when it starts down" [that is, to relate federal expenditures on basic research to those on applied research and development]. That was, presumably, the function of the recent efforts by the Office of Science and Technology to establish a separate federal budget for basic or academic science.

But why should expenditures on pure biology rise if the government decides to develop an antimissile missile (which could jump development expenditures one or more billion dollars a year)? one government official asked. It would be better, another proposed, to relate basic research expenditures to either of two other universes: "the social costs of unsolved problems" or "opportunities for the enrichment of society. . . ."

In the old days, academic research was an overhead on education. As the educational revenues, and the magnitude of the educational enterprise, mounted, why shouldn't we return to that system? a former professor wondered. If the principle were again accepted "that research is a tax or an overhead . . . or essential charge on the educational budget . . . , judgments would be very much sharper on how much is really necessary, how much is really profitable. . . ."

Alternatively, basic research might be regarded as a reward for the successful performance of a social mission. Thus, basic research would be supported at universities which were doing well at their mission of education and also at laboratories which had a consistent record of practical accomplishment. If universities were not discharging their educational mission satisfactorily because of excessive attention to research (as the Reuss committee claimed[4]), then expenditures on research at these universities should presumably be reduced. At the very least, one had to examine objectively the effects of research upon the quality of education; to argue that universities should receive more research funds because research was bound to improve the quality of education was to assert a matter of faith rather than to establish a matter of fact.

Is Pure Science Now Driving Out Applied?

Edward Teller has observed that basic science has become so successful at leading universities, Weinberg noted, that the best graduates no longer contemplate socially useful work. The observation was seconded by a participant who felt that recent developments had quite reversed the earlier doctrine of which Tocqueville and Vannevar Bush had spoken, that in America applied science drove out pure.[5] A scientist conceded that in the postwar years, there may have been some ground for this concern [that pure science was driving applied out of the universities]; but he denied that it was warranted today in the field he knew best,

[4] "The committee finds . . . that Federal research and development programs have harmed scientific higher education by excessively diverting scientific manpower from teaching, and by overemphasizing research to the detriment of teaching" (*Conflicts between the Federal Research Programs and the Nation's Goals for Higher Education,* Eighteenth Report by the House Committee on Government Operations, H. Rept. 1158, 89 Cong. 1 sess. [Oct. 13, 1965], p. 6).

[5] See Alexis de Tocqueville, *Democracy in America,* vol. 2, bk. 1, chap. 10, "Why the Americans Are More Addicted to Practical than to Theoretical Science"; and Vannevar Bush, *Science—the Endless Frontier* (Government Printing Office, 1945; reprinted 1960 by the National Science Foundation), p. 83. Actually, the passage referred to as Bush's was contained in the report of a committee chaired by Isaiah Bowman: "Under the pressure for immediate results, and unless deliberate policies are set up to guard against this, *applied research invariably drives out pure.*"

mathematics, where strenuous efforts were underway to dignify and unify both the applied and the pure aspects of the field:

The parent organization was the American Mathematical Society, founded about 1888. It established its own mission: to make mathematics in the United States equal in level to mathematics in any spot in the world. It had a long way to go. It was the fact that, when I was a student and you went to meetings of the society and you heard somebody raise the question, "We don't have very good undergraduate teaching," the guys would look over their shoulder and say, "Are you interested in research or not," and if the answer was yes, they would include you in the conversation, and if the answer was no, they would send you away. The result was the formation of the Mathematical Association of America, which was devoted to undergraduate mathematics. Then the mathematical statisticians found that they didn't have the requisite chemical purity. They formed the Institute of Mathematical Statistics. Even the symbolic logicians—and, Heaven knows, they are purer than anybody, until the invention of the computing machine—formed the Association for Symbolic Logic. Then, there has been the Association for Computing Machinery, and Heaven knows how many others.

Now, this represents the diversification in growth of mathematical interest. The parent organization, which is no longer parent, dominated the scene. . . . In the last years, they felt their position threatened. . . . Now, what is happening is an attempt to reintegrate this community to meet the crosscurrents that combine pure mathematics with applied mathematics, because the dogmas about the inapplicability of pure mathematics have been destroyed. The dogmas about the nonmathematical character of applied mathematics are being destroyed and there is now a process of reintegration.

Universities have one major institutional advantage over other laboratories, Weinberg observed: education is a continuing, vital social mission, whereas large laboratories established many years ago for particular purposes had difficulty in redefining their purposes and redeploying their budgets and their staffs to meet them effectively. Ultimately, he felt, it would be desirable "to have government laboratories as well as government agency laboratories"—that is, laboratories able flexibly to serve any important national purpose and not merely the limited purposes of a particular agency.

Was it realistic, a participant wondered, to take the thousands of people now engaged in full-time research on campus "and by squeezing their funds drive them either into teaching or out into honest, full-time research employment in other institutions than universities?" Even if it were possible, it would damage the universities, a professor replied. The university, a scientist suggested, had become such "a sacred cow" that "the withdrawal of support from the university in America in the latter half of the twentieth century . . . must be a pretty dreadful sort of thing to contemplate."

That, another scientist commented, was not being suggested—but rather how support should be extended. As the nation finds politically acceptable ways to support education directly and aboveboard, as the Office of Education has been doing increasingly, it will be less necessary to use the roundabout route of research grants. Institutions which have received relatively small sums for research might be satisfied with such new programs, a participant responded, but "the twenty top universities who are taking most of the [research] money and staffing most of the advisory committees" are unlikely to be.

As it did not now appear that the academic research programs of the "big three"—Defense, NASA, and the AEC—would expand, the future volume of government expenditures for university research would, in Weinberg's view, probably hinge on three factors:

1. Expenditures on biological research, which Congress had generously supported and should give greater support to. (Two biologists doubted that biology could be deemed any more important than physics or chemistry or archeology—if only, one said, because "You couldn't do biology without physics and chemistry." "The high energy physicists," the second pointed out, "did more for nucleic acid chemistry than the nucleic acid chemist did for nucleic chemistry. That is correct.")

2. The discovery of ways to attack certain social problems indirectly, by technological means,[6] and also, of course, the more strictly technical or socio-technical problems like pollution, transportation, and housing.

3. The role of the National Science Foundation. ". . .[M]ore and more of the problem of how much research is going to be done in the universities . . . is finally going to amount to [the] answer [to] the question of how big should the . . . foundation get."

When, after the war, major agencies supported research at universities, Weinberg declared, they did so "in the somewhat naive belief" that basic research in a field relevant to their mission "would actually get applied problems solved." As time has gone by, "the criterion of relevance has tended to be attenuated" and the basic research segments of mission-

[6] A point developed more fully by Weinberg in an address, "Can Technology Replace Social Engineering?" at the University of Chicago, June 11, 1966 (see *Bulletin of Atomic Scientists*, December 1966, pp. 4–8).

oriented agencies have become additional "National Science Foundations." Since universities are discipline- rather than problem-oriented, they are not the best institutions to help agencies solve their practical research problems. That function is better performed by government and industrial laboratories specially organized to perform it.

The Constituencies of Scientific Advisers

So long as the R&D budgets of DOD, NASA, and the AEC were rising, they could support research both on campus and at applied laboratories; now, however, rivalry and competition between university and nonuniversity laboratories has visibly increased. This competition was plainly exhibited in the Wooldridge report, which stated, in effect, that although the quality of research at the government's biomedical laboratories at Bethesda was very good, universities should nonetheless have first call on biomedical research funds.[7] Upon occasion, distinguished and influential university scientists have said, in effect, "Everybody knows that the brains are really in universities, and the money, as everybody knows, is in those stupid [government] laboratories, and, by God, I am going to do something about it."

This squabbling between academic and nonacademic scientists, Weinberg believed, "is getting sharper and sharper as the amount of money becomes scarcer." It has become a major problem that the government and the scientific community has to recognize, confront, and overcome.

Try as we may to be rational about allocations, a social scientist observed, such decisions are never completely rational, because they are made by men, and men are not completely rational. Decisions

. . . are made by men who are inherently limited by their experience—and

[7] Although NIH "salaries are likely to be lower than those available in universities and medical schools," the Wooldridge committee reported that its panels "were unanimous in their conclusion that the average quality of individual research conducted intramurally by NIH is in every way equal to that conducted extramurally." Nonetheless, the committee expressed "conviction that the government should not undertake the direct conduct of research activities that fit precisely into the pattern of scientific work that the universities or other non-government institutions are equipped to perform" and stated, ". . . we are inclined to the opinion that optimization of the NIH program for the period that lies ahead will require some decrease in the present proportion of intramural research" (*Biomedical Science and Its Administration: A Study of the National Institutes of Health* [Washington, D.C.: The White House, February 1965], pp. 36–37).

that is also where they derive their strength . . . ; and it is the choice of men and the background that they have, the blend of them in particular positions, that really disposes us to one or another course.

The main groups of men who make these [R&D] decisions . . . we are not going to change easily or quickly, and their composition has been roughly stable in the Congress. But we surely can change . . . our advisers and . . . the men running the major science agencies, or the men who are chosen as assistant secretaries, and so on—their disciplines and the people who advise them. This is very manipulable, within limits.

It seems to me, here is a very practical handle. If we are not satisfied with the general complexion of the allocations that have been made and the advice that is given, then these are the points at which changes are entirely feasible. For historical reasons, we have inherited a pattern of men—excellent [men]; I am not criticizing the quality of the men as individuals, but am commenting on their inevitable disposition. It is obvious that, if PSAC were composed of M.D.'s and microbiologists, they would lean in a rather different direction. If the director of the National Science Foundation were a political scientist, he would make a different set of choices than if he [were] a physicist, as the two directors have been.

Now, if we are satisfied with the judgments that have been made by these men, fine, and more power to them. . . . If we are not satisfied, this is the obvious course.

SCIENTIST: . . . [T]he whole advisory apparatus of the government is pretty much captured by people who represent . . . the university.

SOCIAL SCIENTIST: Even a narrow part of that——

SCIENTIST: . . . [T]hey say . . . that the brightest people in the country are the people who are full professors in the very best universities, and I think, in general, this is the case. . . .

SOCIAL SCIENTIST: I didn't know they gave IQ tests to candidates for appointment. . . . You know who comes out on top in the IQ tests—the psychologists, because they write them.

SCIENTIST: . . . [O]ther criteria have to be used. . . . [T]he insights would be less penetrating . . . , [but] the attitudes would be more judicious, perhaps, and represent the better balance. . . .

SOCIAL SCIENTIST: I think . . . the advisory apparatus is [emulating] . . . the French General Staff, in always planning to win the previous war against the Germans.

Science Is a "Good"

As the evening wore on, a social scientist finally gave vent to the following historical discourse:

One could argue that in American society there are, from time to time, groups or functions appearing which are *good* and recognized as *good,* to be supported and to have some access to the public treasury. You could go back into the nineteenth century. . . . We gave away land equal to five times the state of Pennsylvania; we supported the railroads; we supported the canals; and all through the nineteenth century, the protective tariff was a subsidy to every manufacturing organization.

In the latter part of the century, the Grand Army of the Republic was a "good," and we gave away the prairies in the Homestead Act to veterans; and so it went.

Coming down to 1930, suddenly the farmer became "good," and so we put so many of billions of dollars per annum into the support of the farmer, because the farmer was a "good." We have done the same thing for labor, first in [Section] 3(a) under the NRA [National Recovery Act of 1933], then [in] the Wagner Act. One group after another comes up and is recognized as "good" to be favored, to be supported, to be nourished.

Now, out of World War II has emerged Science and the scientists, and now the scientist is one of the "goods." He is, in fact, the best, the most recent, at least, of the "goods." And it is natural, and it is in accordance with historic tradition, that he is getting substantial public support.

When this interpretation was questioned by a government official, who suggested that it was not science but defense, space exploration, and so on, that were the publicly recognized "goods," the social scientist responded:

. . . [T]he Department of Defense, AEC, NASA, and so on, could be likened to streams of water: Some streams flowed faster and had more water than others. The scientists were given access. They could dip their buckets in and help themselves, or were invited to do so, and the configuration of support . . . would be simply that the scientists are not stupid, and they simply dipped their buckets into the biggest streams. . . .

SCIENTIST: The issue is, What happens when the buckets get too big for the streams—and the buckets are growing?

SOCIAL SCIENTIST: That was the case with the protective tariff. . . . [T]here was no satisfying the businessman. The tariffs went higher and higher.

OFFICIAL: . . . [I]f you are saying that science has come to the top as a social value in its own right, I would have to question it, because we are in defense-related science because we are afraid of something in the world. . . . We are in atomic energy because we did it to get ahead of the Germans . . . , and once we were in it, we couldn't stop. . . . We are in space . . . [because of] Sputnik.

SCIENTIST: That is not why we stay there, though.

OFFICIAL : I disagree. If the Russians were to abandon space, I think we would do something very different.

SOCIAL SCIENTIST : . . . I don't think I disagree. . . . I was referring to contemporary judgment. You are speaking about how we got there. I think you are right.

Science having risen to its present budgetary and political eminence "on the coattails of the military," what would happen, the government official mused, if peace broke out—"if the Russians and the Chinese . . . gave us such assurance that we could not reject it, that we were in for a period of stable world peace?" In answer, someone exclaimed: "The science foundation is the scientists' antipoverty . . . or antiwar program!"

The group has been talking in terms of major expenditures, a biologist now expostulated; apparently, they had in mind the exploitation of research rather than fundamental research itself, which could be very cheap. "As I have listened . . . I have just thought of dozens and dozens of fundamental discoveries which were very cheap. Avery, MacLeod, and McCarthy found the transforming factor of pneumococcus with very little expense, and they identified RNA and DNA.[8] Pasteur did work on tartaric acids for a few cents." In the thirties, Waksman started work that led to streptomycin with a $2,500 grant from the National Research Council. ". . . [F]undamental discoveries are cheap."

Toward the close, the discussion turned to some of the moral and social problems posed by modern science and technology. One scientist was concerned that the possibility of genetic control would raise ethical issues as severe as those raised by the atomic bomb. This did not disturb a biologist. "Knowledge doesn't frighten me. If I felt that one of my . . . graduate students could define the genetic code tomorrow, I would be perfectly happy about it." Of course, it would present difficult moral problems, "but I think we would get at the answer. . . . Alamogordo did something that the arrow did, or gunpowder." Another participant doubted that, try as they might, biologists could "create as many problems for us as the physicists. . . ."

"We have to develop a way of modifying our institutions with the same freedom . . . that we . . . modify our physical . . . or . . . mathematical postulates," said a scientist hopefully. ". . . [I]t is impossible," a social scientist responded, ". . . for the same reason that you cannot

[8] See O. T. Avery, C. M. MacLeod, and M. McCarthy, "Studies on Chemical Nature of Substance Inducing Transformation of Pneumococcal Types . . . ," in *Journal of Experimental Medicine* vol. 79 (1944), p. 137.

change a language. You don't go in and out of history. You are dealing with a different element."

OFFICIAL A: I think you can change it in some directions. We have changed the face of an awful lot of things in the last four or five years, in the space program, for instance. . . .

SOCIAL SCIENTIST A: We haven't changed much of the South in the last hundred years.

OFFICIAL B: We have changed our whole system of economics in the last ten or fifteen years.

SOCIAL SCIENTIST B: We have changed our whole attitude toward international relations.

Which made four optimists to one pessimist; and on that 80 percent degree of optimism, this summary may well close.

DAVID Z. ROBINSON

Resource Allocation
in High Energy Physics

RESOURCE ALLOCATION problems in the field of high energy physics have come upon us in various stages as the costs of the national research program have increased. It is the purpose of this paper to describe these stages and discuss some of the issues raised in the management of large government science programs. In part because of the program's high cost, and in part because of its great scientific interest, policy and decision-making in the program have become a concern of the President. The field of high energy physics (the study of the ultimate constituents of matter and the interactions and forces between them) is of tremendous scientific interest and has attracted to its study some of the best and most creative scientists in the country. International scientific prestige is to be gained by making important discoveries in the field (as illustrated by the numerous high energy physicists who have won Nobel prizes). In order to do experiments in a consistent and systematic fashion, it is necessary to have large accelerators with which particle creation, destruction, and interactions can be studied.

The Late 1940's: Agency-Level Coordination

Shortly after World War II, the high energy physics program was relatively cheap and confined largely to an understanding of nuclear structure and of the nucleons that make up the nucleus. The Office of Naval Research and the Atomic Energy Commission (AEC) instituted programs at many laboratories all over the country which were often jointly funded. A number of accelerators were built by universities, construction and operating costs being paid for under research contracts. The Navy and the AEC had large budgets of which the high energy physics program comprised only a very small part (although a significant fraction of the agencies' research budgets). Thus, although the overall level of support was set by collaboration between the Navy, the AEC, and the Bureau of the Budget, the program received little, if any, presidential attention.

The Early 1950's: AEC Dominance

Construction of accelerators producing energies greater than one billion electron volts required special organizations.[1] The technically most competent were the Brookhaven National Laboratory, an institution on Long Island, New York, run by Associated Universities, Inc. (a nonprofit corporation sponsored by nine eastern private universities), and the large Radiation Laboratory in Berkeley, California, directed by E. O. Lawrence, the inventor of the cyclotron. As the construction of two multi-Bev accelerators started in the early 1950's, the AEC, which supported both of these laboratories, began to take a dominant role in the United States government program, though the Navy remained involved with several extremely creative university groups.

This position of AEC dominance occurred despite some feeling that as accelerators produced higher and higher energies the scientific results were perhaps less and less applicable to the prime missions of the AEC —nuclear energy and nuclear weapons. However, the AEC's research budgets were still quite large, and the agency was willing to assign an increasing portion of them to the creation of new accelerators. Again, the level of resources was set in discussions between the Bureau of the Budget and the commission, which devoted considerably more attention to the program. The President was still little involved.

[1] Although other factors are significant, the most important factor in the cost and utility of an accelerator is the energy to which the particles are accelerated. The unit of energy is the charge on the electron times voltage, or electron volts (ev). Energies of a billion electron volts are labeled Bev in the United States and GeV in Europe.

1957–60: White House Coordination and Presidential Involvement

The proposal to build a two-mile-long, 20 billion electron volt linear accelerator at Stanford University brought further attention to the high energy physics program. The AEC saw clearly that this $100 million machine could not be justified solely in terms of its own mission but only on the basis of a broader government interest.

In order to obtain the best possible scientific advice, two panels were set up during this period jointly by the President's Science Advisory Committee and the General Advisory Committee of the AEC.[2] These "Piore" panels (named for their chairman, Emanuel Piore) were asked to examine the question of building the Stanford accelerator within the context of the *whole* field of high energy physics and to make recommendations. Obviously, the construction of such an accelerator had to be considered in the light of the total high energy physics program in the United States; and a determination of the scientific utility of a machine that would not be completed for six or eight years was very difficult and complex. The panels were specifically instructed not to consider the relation of the program to needs in other fields of science.

The panels made recommendations on six major policy issues:

a) The relative balance between funds for new construction and for accelerators already in operation. The panels recommended that special attention be paid to ongoing operations and at the same time endorsed construction of the Stanford accelerator.

b) The relative needs for university laboratories and national laboratories. The panels realized that a large facility such as the Stanford accelerator must be available to scientists across the nation, and so recommended, but also emphasized a possible future need for small university accelerators.

c) New accelerators and experimental concepts. The panels strongly endorsed the continued investigation and exploratory development of new accelerator concepts without prejudice to later determinations of the need to construct additional accelerators. In addition, they emphasized

---

[2] The panels were established in 1958 and 1960. A convenient source for the reports is Joint Committee on Atomic Energy, *High Energy Physics Program: Report on National Policy and Background Information,* 89 Cong. 1 sess. (February 1965), Appends. 2 and 3.

the need to improve techniques of particle detection, data reduction, and data analysis.

d) International cooperation. The panels also endorsed international cooperation and welcomed the exchange of scientists and close cooperation between laboratories such as CERN (the European Organization for Nuclear Research, at Geneva) and Brookhaven. It was emphasized that the desirability of joint construction and use of very large accelerators depended not only on their scientific usefulness and technical feasibility but also on their organizational and managerial arrangements.

e) Ten-year forecast. The second Piore panel was asked for a ten-year forecast of the needs of high energy physics. A quite detailed forecast —probably the first such forecast for a federal scientific program—was provided by an interagency committee of the Federal Council for Science and Technology in December 1960[3] and endorsed by the panels, which emphasized that the predicted high costs must be justified by the research results.

The pros and cons of long-range forecasts of this nature merit further discussion. Clearly, a number of benefits can be obtained. In this case, the forecast enabled the agencies to face up to the high cost of operating these accelerators and associated facilities. It showed for the first time the program's expected budgetary impact over a ten-year period and put the $100 million cost of construction in the context not of a one- but of a five-year building program. It also included highly useful manpower estimates. Finally, it enabled the executive branch and the Congress to make objective budgetary decisions in the light of the anticipated needs of the field as a whole.

But such a forecast also has some disadvantages. First of all, there is a tendency to look upon the numbers as "holy," and the government's ability to act flexibly may be lost because of the subconscious desire to adhere to a program outlined earlier. High energy physics is a rapidly changing field, however, and forecasts can really only be general approximations, since wholly new developments must be expected. For example, the first Piore panel recommended against building machines of higher energy, primarily because experience with lower energies had not yet

[3] See "A Ten-Year Preview of High Energy Physics in the United States," Prepared by Scientific Staff of AEC, ONR, and NSF, December 12, 1960, in *Background Information on the High Energy Physics Program and the Proposed Stanford Linear Electron Accelerator Project,* Report to the Joint Committee on Atomic Energy, 87 Cong. 1 sess. (1961), pp. 17–84.

shown the scientific promise of large, expensive machines that would justify their cost. Some five years later, a panel headed by Norman Ramsey strongly endorsed steps toward higher energy accelerators.

A forecast anticipating a natural rise in scientific activity, such as has occurred in the past, can also frighten or surprise many people. Furthermore, few other fields of science are treated in decennial terms, and so comparisons between fields cannot be made. The future state of the economy and the nation are extremely difficult to predict. We might have had a poorer program in high energy physics had a forecast of the type endorsed by the Piore panel been made fifteen years earlier.

Nonetheless, agency forecasts of total expenditures, if not of subsidiary budgetary detail, have turned out to be quite accurate. Clearly, they were useful in preparing the way for necessary increases of expenditure.

A detailed forecast points up a potential trade-off between operating and construction costs. In building the newer high energy facilities, predicted annual operating costs almost equal total construction costs. Increases in operating costs—a regular feature of budget discussions—can no longer be justified as necessary to exploit the original investment. It is possible, and in some instances may be preferable, to hold machine use and costs below the optimal level and to build additional needed facilities for the same total dollar expenditure. This relationship between capital and operating costs was not emphasized by the Piore panels, since the cost of operating large accelerators was not so very high at that time.

A ten-year forecast can also envisage the closing down of old facilities. Such predictions should be made cautiously, however, since new ideas can lead to productive use of these installations.

f) Manpower. One of the most difficult problems facing forecasters is to estimate manpower needs. One member of the second Piore panel predicted that there would be a great shortage of manpower to do the experiments called for in the panel report[4]—a view vigorously countered by the rest of the panel. The Ramsey panels, using more refined estimates, suggested instead that there would be a net outflow of high energy physicists into other fields of science. And indeed, this is the way things have turned out.

The decision to build the Stanford accelerator was personally made by President Eisenhower, after the advantages and disadvantages were pre-

---

[4] Eugene Wigner's separate "commentary" on the 1960 Piore report appears in *High Energy Physics Program . . .*, pp. 132–34.

sented to him, and announced at a banquet he addressed on the theme of basic research.[5] With this step, high energy physics became a matter to be dealt with at the highest level of government and a problem in political as well as natural science.

Further Attention and Congressional Interest

At present, decision-making and resource allocation in high energy physics involve a number of interrelated groups.

a) Advisory groups. In general, when a major decision has to be made, one or more outside advisory groups are called upon for opinions. For example, there may be panels of the President's Science Advisory Committee or the National Academy of Sciences and advisory opinions from individuals to the Atomic Energy Commission. The purpose of obtaining these outside opinions is to get as good a technical judgment as possible on the value of a particular program, so that decisions as to priorities can be made confidently. Because of the very long delay between design and first experiment, the users of the machine are not likely to be the leaders in the field today. Therefore, the President's Science Advisory Committee has consulted younger experimenters in addition to the most active present users.

b) Government agencies. The Federal Council for Science and Technology, composed of the chief science policy-makers in the principal agencies, has established an interagency panel (whose chairman is the associate director for research of the National Science Foundation) to define the annual high energy program and to make recommendations on specific issues that face the government. Obviously, the part of the program formulated by the Atomic Energy Commission is the most significant, since the AEC accounts for over 90 percent of government expenditure.

c) Executive Office of the President. The Office of Science and Technology and the Bureau of the Budget annually examine the nation's high energy physics program and, in conjunction with the agencies involved, make recommendations about the national program. In the case of pro-

---

[5] For the announcement by President Eisenhower in the course of a May 14, 1959, address at the Rockefeller Institute in New York, see Dael Wolfle (ed.), *Symposium on Basic Research* (American Association for the Advancement of Science, 1959), pp. 140–41.

posals for very large accelerators such as those at Stanford or at MURA (the Midwestern Universities Research Association), the President will personally be involved in the decision and will require detailed briefing.

d) Congress. The national budget for high energy physics is not presented to Congress as a single package, but since the Atomic Energy Commission is responsible for over 90 percent of the program, its part gets particular scrutiny. The Joint Committee on Atomic Energy has taken a great deal of interest in the program. It withheld approval of the Stanford accelerator until September 1961 because of political differences and a lack of confidence in the whole planning process. In addition, a number of individual congressmen have recently been mobilized by some members of the high energy physics community and their associated universities to support or oppose proposed large accelerators.

All the above groups have been heavily involved when decisions were made as to the construction of major accelerators. The operating budgets of existing accelerators, however, are usually much less controversial and are handled more routinely, with less involvement by the President and by individual congressmen.

The MURA Accelerator

In the mid-1950's, the Midwestern Universities Research Association, sponsored by fifteen major midwestern universities, set up a special center for the design and later construction of an accelerator. This center was staffed by extremely talented individuals who constituted one of the most imaginative accelerator design groups in the world. Although some of their early designs (for example, colliding beam accelerators) were judged impractical, they had invented a new concept (the fixed-field alternating-gradient synchrotron) which, at a fairly high cost, enabled the acceleration of a larger number of protons than the conventional synchrotron. This accelerator also had other advantages over the standard synchrotron.

In its 1958 report, the first Piore panel recommended construction of a very high intensity proton accelerator of at least 8 Bev energy. The 1960 Piore panel, however, cautioned that, while such a machine would be most useful in producing secondary particles, these particles might be produced more readily in a higher energy machine. Nonetheless, by 1962 the MURA group had prepared a detailed proposal which requested funds for the construction of a 10 Bev fixed-field alternating-gradient accelerator at a cost of $120 million. The proposal showed that this accelerator would yield a very much more intense beam of secondary particles than the 33 Bev accelerator then in operation at Brookhaven.[6]

It was obvious that such a vigorous design group could not be kept active without building an accelerator and that, if a decision were made not to construct the machine, the group would probably disband. In addition, the AEC, which processed the MURA proposal and obtained agreement on a cost estimate, felt that the accelerator would prove very useful. Accordingly, the President's Science Advisory Committee (PSAC) and the General Advisory Committee (GAC) of the AEC agreed to set up a new panel. This time the chairman was Dr. Norman Ramsey, a GAC member. It should be noted that the panel included not only high energy physicists but also some physicists indirectly concerned with the field and one geochemist. The group held seven two-day meetings over six months and in May 1963 submitted a report similar to the Piore panel report.[7]

At the time, two other proposals were in a much earlier state of preparation—one by the Berkeley group for a proton accelerator in the 100–300 Bev range, and the other, in a still earlier stage, by the Brookhaven National Laboratory for an accelerator in the 600–1,000 Bev range. The panel was asked to consider these additional, more tentative designs, to examine the entire field of high energy physics, and to present a program with some indication of priorities from a technical standpoint.

One of the panel's major recommendations was that the higher energy accelerators, which would only be available later, were of higher priority than the MURA accelerator but that the MURA accelerator was extremely valuable and should be undertaken if its construction would not significantly delay that of the higher energy machines.

Because the budgetary process requires yearly decisions, this type of recommendation is difficult to implement. No one could predict the precise budget situation in later years when there might be a different President and a different administration and when the economic health of the country might or might not permit the construction of another accelerator. The purpose of the recommendation was to issue a warning that a proposal was in the offing for a more expensive machine than the MURA

---

[6] When the beam of accelerated particles hits a target, a number of new particles are produced. Experiments can be made with these new, or secondary," particles.

[7] See *High Energy Physics Program . . . ,* Append. 1.

accelerator (the 200 Bev machine was estimated to cost $240 million by the Ramsey panel[8]), with a higher scientific priority. The Ramsey report was discussed by both the PSAC and the GAC, and although no formal recommendation emerged, the chairman of the AEC, Glenn Seaborg, and the President's science adviser, Jerome Wiesner, obtained a broader viewpoint than that merely of high energy physicists.

Given this advice, the AEC proposed to the Bureau of the Budget, in the fall of 1963, the construction of the MURA accelerator; the President had to act on this proposal in December. At the same time, a number of midwest congressmen wrote letters to the President supporting the accelerator, and articles appeared in the newspapers discussing it. One or two congressmen also wrote opposing the accelerator because they felt the program of the accelerator at Argonne Laboratory near Chicago might be harmed if the MURA accelerator were built.

For budgetary reasons, President Johnson decided not to construct the MURA accelerator. He considered the effect on the overall federal budget and how much of that budget he was willing to put into basic science. Given the priorities within science as a whole, he did not feel that he could propose to the Congress the construction of this new, expensive facility. Accordingly, the final step in the successful authorization of an accelerator, discussion and approval by the Congress, did not occur.

Some Policy Issues Involved in Resource Allocation

a) International considerations. High energy physics is a field of basic research particularly suitable for international collaboration: secrecy is not involved, wide international interest prevails, and experiments are best done at a few sites by many large groups.

The CERN laboratory is an example of a European collaboration which has been extremely successful scientifically. The high cost of the largest accelerators has led many to ask whether similar laboratories for new very high energy accelerators should not be built in the same fashion but on a worldwide rather than a regional basis.

[8] By 1965, the Atomic Energy Commission's estimate was $308.5 million. In June 1967, the Joint Committee on Atomic Energy stated that the 200 Bev "may cost up to $400 million" (*Authorizing Appropriations for the Atomic Energy Commission for Fiscal Year 1968*, Report by the Joint Committee on Atomic Energy, 90 Cong. 1 sess. [June 23, 1967], p. 36).

It is clear that international collaboration already exists, if by collaboration is meant free exchange of information, visits by scientists, and even experiments by visiting groups. But as yet, the United States has not been involved in a collaborative effort of the CERN type. The problems of joint construction and operation of a laboratory are not technical but political and organizational.

As the discussion in the Ramsey report shows, American scientists at that time felt the next step to higher energy could probably be met by domestic budgetary sources and that it was not necessary to set up an international organization for the purpose. They did suggest, however, that the subsequent step, that of a 600–1,000 Bev accelerator, which was some years off, might well be taken internationally.

The chief questions which would have to be faced in an international accelerator program include the following:

(1) Where will the accelerator be located? Americans would clearly not object if it were to be in the United States, but the other countries would also presumably want it located in their own regions. A solution would be to have more than one project; but in that case why not fund each separately and continue the present form of collaboration among the scientists?

(2) How will decisions be made? Who will determine budgets; how will purchases be allocated? More simply, how can physicists from all countries participate meaningfully in an effort that must be centrally directed? No one has yet really come to grips with problems of this sort in considering a joint United States-European-Soviet Union accelerator.

b) National management considerations. The faculties of many universities, spread out across the country, have the ability to conduct high quality experiments. But few large accelerators are available, and it is increasingly difficult for all high energy physicists to feel that they have an equal chance to use them.

It is now generally agreed that accelerator facilities should be available to all qualified users solely on the merits of the experiments they wish to do. The first accelerators in this country were, in fact, not run in this fashion. An occasional guest with a valuable idea could use the machine for some time, but control of the facility and the experimental program lay in the hands of the laboratory director.

The change in the type of operation for large accelerators has come about gradually. Usually, scheduling committees now examine the list of proposals and decide which to accept and in what order they should be scheduled. The committees now have representatives from other institutions, but their chairman comes from the laboratory and is fully aware of the capabilities of the equipment and staff.

Management arrangements for the accelerators vary. Brookhaven is managed by Associated Universities, Inc.; the Lawrence Radiation Laboratory, by the University of California; and the Argonne Laboratory was managed until recently by the University of Chicago.

Much attention is now being paid to the desire for national management of new large accelerators. Some of this pressure comes from users and some from university administrators who would like a connection with these important scientific facilities. The Atomic Energy Commission announced in 1964 that the Argonne Laboratory, while continuing to be operated by the University of Chicago, would have policy guidance from a new corporation sponsored by a group of midwest universities; this arrangement with the new Argonne Universities Association went into effect in November 1966.

Against a policy of diffuse "national" managements are the arguments for responsibility and efficiency. It is clear that the laboratory director must have adequate authority to run the laboratory on a day-to-day basis. There must be an effective resident group to keep the instrument and the associated research equipment operating well. This group will always have an advantage over outside users as far as competition for experimental time is concerned, because of its more intimate knowledge of the status of work on, and the capabilities of, the machine. To a degree, operation is more efficient when users from all over the country do not have to be accommodated.

However, high energy physics must not lose contact with the creative scientists in our universities, and to some extent national management can enlist their support more easily than local management. Working out an effective management which will not only be fair to all users but will *appear* to be fair is one of the difficult problems facing the government in developing operating arrangements for the new large accelerators.

c) Internal priorities. The proper balance of expenditures between high energy physics and other fields of science is a most difficult issue. Although one of the purposes of the establishment of the Office of Science and Technology was to aid in making such judgments, the mechanisms for doing so remain quite intricate.

In general, the decisions on building large accelerators determine the overall size of the program, for it is relatively easy to get operating funds once the initial commitment has been made. In any given budget year these decisions are made by the President in accordance with his opinion of the project's importance and his feelings about the status of both the AEC and the entire United States budget. Thus, the Stanford proposal was accepted and the MURA proposal turned down.

The annual budgets for high energy physics are determined in a context of annual comparisons. From 1961 to 1964 an increase of about 20 percent a year has been justified because of the field's scientific promise and because additional support was needed for research utilizing the new accelerators. Some of the increase has also gone for new construction.

In general, the discussion that occurs primarily between the AEC and the reviewing agencies in the Executive Office of the President concerns whether this increase is sufficient or too great in the light of the importance of the field and the other programs of the agency. To a great extent, the Executive Office relies on the AEC to determine growth rates, although upon occasion some effort will be made to adjust agency proposals because of unusual factors affecting the field as a whole. Agency decisions are made by scientific officers who have to decide between support for this field and other fields within their purview; in general, support is granted on the basis of the quality of the proposed work and the pressures from the machine's users.

A particular problem arises when an agency is either formally or informally designated as an executive agent. Here it is possible that the agency's narrow interest would be better served by a distribution of effort which differs from that necessary to carry out its responsibilities as executive agent. For example, the Joint Committee on Atomic Energy believed in 1964 that certain AEC programs which it backed, such as the "SNAP 10A" (system for nuclear auxiliary power), were suffering in part because the AEC had to expand high energy physics expenditures while operating under a budget ceiling imposed by the Executive Office of the President. The issue is discussed in a letter from the President's science adviser, Donald Hornig, referred to below. (See Appendix A, pp. 333–36, for the text of this letter.)

d) The desire for "national policy." Great pressure has been exerted for careful planning in this very expensive field. In 1964 the Joint Committee on Atomic Energy requested a letter from Donald Hornig setting forth the elements of national policy. The key points made in this letter were as follows:

1. The budget for high energy physics should be considered in relation to the government's science budget as a whole rather than only as part of the AEC budget.

2. A two-step program toward highest energies should be undertaken.

3. International cooperation should be sought where possible.

Subsequently, the Joint Committee asked the AEC to prepare a report on high energy physics policy to be presented to the President and to the Congress.[9] This report basically proceeds along the same lines as the Ramsey panel and Hornig's policy statement.

The sums spent on high energy physics are sufficiently large that all major decisions get detailed attention at the highest levels of the executive. Additional scrutiny is provided by the Congress, which can turn down or delay decisions but which, in this field, can very rarely initiate programs. Although early decisions were made solely in the context of agency budgets, more recently there have been some attempts to examine the field as a whole and, finally, to compare the needs in this field with those in other fields of science. The process is complex and tortuous, and while decisions on operating budgets remain decentralized, those on large accelerators are made by the President and the Congress, using the best technical and fiscal advice available.

DISCUSSION

The High Energy Politics
of High Energy Physics

WHAT CRITERIA should determine the volume of government expenditures in a particular field of pure science such as high energy physics? The discussion commenced on this question and then shifted to policy issues posed by the institutional characteristics of the field, whose sociology and politics seem as fascinating as its science.

Insofar as the value of pure research must be assessed by its scientific rather than its practical fruitfulness, two criteria appear relevant, several

[9] *High Energy Physics Program* . . . , pp. 9–61.

physicists suggested: the quality of the scientists drawn to a particular field, and the quality of their product—that is, of their output of new knowledge. On both grounds, they ranked high energy physics high. It has "caught the imagination of a high fraction of the most brilliant scientists of the country," despite the aggravating delays and red tape involved in arranging machine time.

> ... [O]ne of the things that indicates how really exciting a field it is is that so many good people want to participate knowing that it is probably the most unpleasant field of all . . . because there is such a shortage of machine time and they are going to have to spend a lot of time with scheduling committees and waiting for the one 24-hour burst of running time that they have and then go back home for a year. Despite all these difficulties . . . they are willing to face it.

And the output of important new scientific knowledge—"the number of really basic, even revolutionary principles that have been discovered in a recent period"—is unquestionable.

The "fundamentality" of the knowledge yielded by the field was also adduced as a criterion of its scientific merit. ". . . [A]lthough all basic research is fundamental, some research is more fundamental than others," and this, several physicists (not all in high energy work) asserted, was particularly true of high energy physics. ". . . [T]here is a degree of fundamentalness that this field . . . has which simply is not possessed by . . . many other fields, and you can make a very good point that it is not possessed by any other field." The physics panel of the National Academy of Sciences reportedly had taken an informal poll of its members asking what was the most fundamental field of physics, "and every single member of that panel said 'high energy physics.' "[1] But was high energy physics accorded the same status by scientists in other fields such as geology or psychology? One participant—a government official who was a physicist by training—believed that psychologists, for example, would accept the fact that high energy physics was fundamental to all branches of knowledge. Since "the ultimate structure of matter is really basic to all sciences," eventually it would bear on the problems of psychology as well as of other sciences.

This was disputed by both a social and a physical scientist. The former contended that "every scientist sets up a logical structure at the bottom of which lies his discipline." Insofar as the findings of high energy

---

[1] Apparently the panel referred to was that chaired by George Pake, which produced the 1966 report, *Physics: Survey and Outlook.*

physics were not demonstrably applicable to psychology, the field could be deemed "fundamental" to it only in a certain formal sense of occupying a particular place in one of many possible logical systems of ordering knowledge. The latter argued more pragmatically that the "basic interaction between the field of physics and other sciences" was based on the study of interactions at the electron volt level—that is, heat, light, electron transference, and so on. High energy physics, however, was now concerned with an energy level which "has no possible interaction with the rest of science." "That," rejoined another physicist, "is a statement of limited imagination."

Dissension within the Fold

In Britain as well as here, the scientific community had been rent with dissension over the high costs of high energy physics. "The British . . . Advisory Committee on Scientific Policy, ACSP, . . . wrote a report essentially saying, 'We don't spend any money on high energy physics unless you spend money on chemistry.' . . . This committee consists of seven chemists and two physicists. The physicists called it the Association of Chemists for the Suppression of Physicists. Now they have a new group that has seven physicists and two chemists."

A nonphysicist was not satisfied with this presentation by a government physicist. "You said there are only two physicists on [ACSP] . . . but after all . . . there is a fair representation of other scientists. . . . The [composition] of PSAC or any other group could be questioned. . . . The [British] AEC people were there . . . agriculture . . . some industry people. I think the key statement . . . was, 'There is a widespread feeling of discontent among academic scientists at this state of affairs, and an impression that nuclear physics is already getting a very large slice of a very small cake, despite the fact that the results to be obtained from it are likely to be of much less immediate practical importance than those from many other types of research.' "[2]

Scientists enjoyed fighting among themselves, the physicist replied, but fighting might make it easier for administrators to dismiss their requests. Physicists had fought over the MURA accelerator proposal "to a certain extent because the Argonne people felt this would hurt their pro-

[2] *Annual Report of the Advisory Council on Scientific Policy 1962–1963,* Cmnd. 2163 (Her Majesty's Stationery Office, October 1963), p. 5.

gram." To a much smaller extent, divisions had also arisen over the Stanford accelerator proposal; some scientists "were willing to say it wasn't worth the money, but none were willing to say so in public when the chips were down."

OFFICIAL : . . . [T]here was hardly one member of the Joint Committee . . . [who] at one time or another was not approached by a . . . representative from a high energy physics fraternity pointing out why this one project or that . . . was really not any good. The MURA project, for example. I could name you physicists . . . from different laboratories who individually came up and said, "This thing's not worth backing. Don't waste your time on it."

PHYSICIST : "Back mine."

OFFICIAL : Absolutely. That went into the Stanford one. The problem was, "Would it hurt my project?" You talk about selfishness? There has been a lot in this field. If you cannot get the scientific community to decide what they want, then why . . . be so critical of politicians and government administrators?

Formerly, large capital outlays for accelerators could be justified as necessary to sustain for a span of years research requiring relatively low annual operating budgets; and in turn, the relatively low operating budgets could be justified as necessary to exploit the usefulness of a major capital investment. Both arguments had, in fact, been employed; but they were no longer useful, since the annual operating budget of some accelerators now equaled their initial cost. The annual budget of every machine could easily exceed the cost of construction "if the people . . . operating it could do all the experiments they would like to do." Accordingly, the appropriate balance between capital and operating expenditures had become a very difficult problem—". . . [H]ow much do you spend for the future of the field and how much do you spend for the present?"

On Getting "There"

The point of departure for the high energy physics budget was "the problem of critical size," physicist A proposed. "It is a field in which you can't just go half way any more than [NASA] . . . can get half way to the moon. . . . [Y]ou have to get there or you might as well not start." Once the decision has been made to reach a certain energy level, the remaining possible budgetary economies are minor. "If you didn't want to have 25 percent of the physicists of this country involved in the program . . . , if you decided to restrict the people active in the field by not building computers and not giving them the equipment so they could even make proposals" for using existing accelerators, physicist B continued, there might be a net cost reduction of "5 or 10 percent." The variation in the cost of maximal and minimal machine usage is probably "not much more than . . . 15 or 20 percent of the total operating budget," thought physicist A. Physicist C characterized the structure of the field as a pyramid of accelerators rising from lower to higher energies. The newest highest energy machine,

> . . . you would want to run . . . fairly full time . . . [while] cutting back on [lower energy machines]. . . . I doubt that you would be . . . able to [reduce running time substantially on the highest energy machines]. . . . [T]his is one of the biggest sociological problems among the physicists. . . . [W]hen you have only one such machine for the nation or even for the world, this is not really very much running time.

Physicist A's remark about getting "there" was contested by a biologist, who, confessing his ignorance, nonetheless voiced his impression that high energy physicists did not really know where "there" was. "I understood there were on the drawing boards three generations of accelerators, each one of which would presumably get partly to the point. If we knew the exact dimensions of the one to get 'there' we would just build that one, wouldn't we?" However, physicist A stuck to his analogy, though allowing that "there" was "a moving target." Physicist C compared it to

> . . . opening a package which has a smaller package inside it, and you open another package and you have a smaller package, and so forth; and each time you open it, the question is, "Is the gift you are looking for inside the next package, or is it in another box?" and we really don't know. . . .
> The "there" would be defined, from my point of view, as really understanding what are the basic constituents of all matter and how they interact, and what are the principles underlying that interaction.

The issue of public policy, a Washington buff expostulated, ". . . is not whether getting 'there' in high energy physics is an absolute good. I think we could all agree that it is an absolute good. The question is whether getting 'there' in high energy physics is worth more in proportion to what it is costing . . . than to get to several other 'theres'. . . ." To this challenge one physicist responded, ". . . [O]ne of the reasons we are pushing high energy physics so hard is [that] we know what to do. We have a plan. We can see where we are going."

NONSCIENTIST A : No.

NONSCIENTIST B : No. I think that is true of everybody. Everybody.

BIOLOGIST : Oh no, oh no. . . . [T]here are times when science is at a dead end. There just isn't any idea. . . . If a scientist really feels that he can spend some money in a sensible way on something, I think this is a very important datum to take into account, perhaps the most important.

NONSCIENTIST C : Is there any scientist who can't think of a way of spending money on something?

Repeatedly, the physicists expressed their belief that the findings of high energy physics would ultimately prove of great social value, although it might take ten "or even a hundred years" to judge the dollar value of a discovery. ". . . [T]he answer you give now as to what was the value per dollar spent on looking for phenomena of electricity would be completely different from the dollar value that Faraday would put on it at the time he did it, and . . . the same is true here."

This position was strongly challenged by a scientist, who firmly declared, "Never in the history of science have so many bright people worked so long and spent so much money and given rise to so little in the way of practical accomplishment." The long period in which Faraday's discoveries awaited practical application would not recur today:

We are in an era where there are thousands of companies just looking around ready to jump on to any slightest glimmer of a possible practical application. . . . [T]here wasn't any fifty-year period after the transistor was invented, for instance, and there wasn't any fifty-year period after we made the laser beam, and there hasn't been any appreciable time lag in any major field that you can name today.

"The transistor was an application," retorted the physicist. "In general, the interval is necessarily much bigger between a really basic field and a problem that is still not being understood than it is when you are essentially doing the applications."

"When you are dealing with resources of this magnitude," mused one of the most respected scientists in the government, "I think you are not going to get them unless they are related to some specific need."

When high energy physics was in its earlier stages, it was very essential to the very big job that the AEC had to do, and there was no problem about getting support . . . under those conditions. Now that it has advanced to a stage . . . beyond the need which can be justified by the activities of the Atomic Energy Commission, it has to stand on other considerations, and up to the present time in the history of government anyway, the objective of science for itself has not rated the same support.

You can go back through history. Only because of airplane development . . . could [you] get $100 million wind tunnels. You couldn't get them to advance the science of aerodynamics. It was only because the government had a big investment in very high speed airplanes, and you could prove that you were going to save money if you advanced the science of aerodynamics with these big tubes.

. . . NACA [the National Advisory Committee for Aeronautics, the predecessor to NASA] tried to present to the Bureau of the Budget and the Congress a need for research on aircraft structures. . . . [It] got a hearing but . . . [no] money. It was only when . . . [NACA] could focus on a research airplane which . . . [would] pave the way for supersonic military aircraft [that money was forthcoming]. . . . The same thing is happening in the supersonic [civilian] aircraft.

In the atomic energy field, a government official countered, aversion to pure research did not prevail. On the contrary, "There has been a feeling that . . . the executive branch was more tender with basic research than it was with development projects." He continued,

. . . [A]t the same time . . . when the Joint Committee [on Atomic Energy] was pushing AEC to go ahead with atomic power development, and they weren't . . . they were coming in for a big accelerator. . . . [T]he Office of Science and Technology . . . is primarily dominated by basic research scientists . . . [with] a built-in bias . . . for basic research and basic research gadgets, as against development projects. I think there has been a very definite feeling in Congress and in the Joint Committee that this is going on in the executive branch.

An OST staff member acknowledged that this feeling existed but not that it was warranted. ". . . [W]e all would feel that we have to push technology, as we have to push science, because we are in an increasingly technological society." It was, however, easier to identify and to evaluate the goals of technological than of basic research programs. Differences between the Executive Office of the President and the AEC and the Joint Committee had arisen only over the question, ". . . [A]t what point do you stop pushing technology and start using it?" (He did not elaborate the point, but evidently he felt that the committee sought to push the development of certain nuclear technology, such as the "SNAP 10A" system for nuclear auxiliary power, for which no national need had been demonstrated; whereas, for its part, the committee had argued that sometimes new technology had to be developed and demonstrated before its usefulness was recognized.)

The problem of where these great instruments should be located was mentioned only briefly. "There is obviously an advantage to having an accelerator within walking distance, . . . and next, it is a short automobile ride, and then it becomes a plane trip, and then it goes across the ocean." The man on the site has a great advantage, "because he knows what the machine is doing; he can look and see . . . where there is space where he can put equipment, he can make . . . the right proposal for the right time. Even if you . . . picked proposals just on scientific merit, the guy close to the site would have an advantage." To a certain extent, the interests of these resident scientists at the accelerator center and visitors or "users" from other institutions conflicted. Essentially, the residents inherited whatever privileges accrued to those who conceived and designed the machine and supervised its construction; and naturally, they wanted it built in their backyard. Contrariwise, the users wanted it near them. A good resident staff was necessary to operate the machine effectively; but if it was so good and so large as to preempt the machine, the users would lose out. Though bitter, these conflicts had, at any rate, remained largely private, and "knives . . . [had been] thrust in the backs of scientists and university administrators instead of bureaucrats."

Which Agency Should Manage the Program?

Which agency should manage the high energy program? "The AEC has been a magnificent source of support for the high energy physics program of the country." However, during tight budgetary periods—and the total AEC budget has been declining somewhat in recent years—the AEC's designation as executive agent for rising high energy physics budgets may, AEC staff feel, hurt certain other civilian nuclear programs. The AEC "sometimes feels it is pushed [by the Bureau of the Budget and the Office of Science and Technology] into a position of supporting high energy physics when it would rather spend more money in reactors. . . ." One possible solution might be to assign a line item in the AEC budget to the high energy program and permit no trade-offs between it and other AEC programs. However, this "would be strenuously resisted by the AEC"; in any event, it would prove unworkable should Congress reduce the total AEC budget without indicating where the cuts should be made.

An alternative, to transfer the high energy program to the National Science Foundation, "would be a bad solution," a physicist stated, because NSF, unlike the AEC, does not have staff familiar with the management of such massive construction projects. ". . . [I]t is just a matter of practicality and history . . . that the AEC has the competency, the ability, the history of management of these large programs; they have been dealing with the laboratories that are most capable in this field. It just doesn't make sense to change over."

All of this was conceded by a seminar member who did not, however, conclude that it presented such an insuperable obstacle to transferring the accelerators to NSF if that were in the public interest, which he believed it was. "You wouldn't say Haworth is inexperienced in running these big machines, though the staff might be. They could transfer personnel." [NSF Director Leland Haworth had formerly been director of the Brookhaven National Laboratory and AEC commissioner.] As an agency authorized to support all fields of pure science, NSF was better able than the AEC to determine how much should be allocated to any one field such as high energy physics. The real reason high energy physicists opposed such a transfer, he asserted, was because it might endanger their funds, which would bulk much larger in the $500 million NSF budget than in the $2 billion-plus AEC budget.

This explanation several physicists immediately denied. ". . .[I]f you actually made a formal transfer . . . and said, 'O.K., here is $100 million to NSF, and here we are transferring these people over who can run this kind of program,' " one declared, ". . . this would just be an add-on in the NSF budget the first year and would then be used as a justification for increases in later years." Another observed that "this was done with NASA in the beginning. They transferred a lot of Defense Department programs into NASA . . . [without] difficulty." Nonetheless, the critic remained critical. High energy physicists, he intimated, believed they might be more harshly treated at NSF by scientists in fields not so generously funded. As an indication of the defensiveness of physicists in the larger scientific community, he cited *The Nature of Matter*, which should, he suggested, have been subtitled "The Nature of Politics," having been issued so fortuitously just before hearings on high energy physics by the Joint Committee on Atomic Energy.[3] "This document is addressed very much to fellow scientists, trying to persuade them that they should

[3] In *The Nature of Matter: Purposes of High Energy Physics*, ed. Luke C. L. Yuan (Brookhaven National Laboratory, 1965), thirty leading physicists discuss the purposes and problems of high energy physics. The volume was issued in January 1965 (and this seminar session took place on January 26); the Subcommittee on Research, Development, and Radiation of the Joint Committee on Atomic Energy held hearings on high energy physics research on March 2–5, 1965.

give all that money to high energy physics, as much as it is addressed to the public and the Congress."

Responding, the physicists were equally unpersuaded. The initial pressure to consolidate the high energy program at the AEC had not come from high energy physicists, one physicist observed. "There was a period a few years ago when the experience [with the AEC] wasn't always so good. . . ." High energy physicists were then urging that federal support be diversified, with NSF and the Office of Naval Research picking up more of the tab; but the Budget Bureau had objected, "preferring to see one dominant agency. . . ." Others confirmed this. The AEC had not wanted primary responsibility for high energy physics "very badly," recalled an AEC participant; however, the Joint Committee on Atomic Energy had "argued [that] it ought to be there from the point of view of the best performance of the mission. . . ."

In any event, a Capitol Hill participant asked, was the particular executive agent all that important in the shaping of a government-wide scientific program? ". . . I thought when the executive branch reviewed this [high energy program] they didn't, in the inception, review it from [the standpoint of] an agency mission at all but across the board, from the scientific point of view," he continued in an even tone of voice that could eliminate any suggestion of irony for some listeners, while accentuating it for others. During that scientific review, "presumably NSF cranks in their comments"; so does it make any difference what agency finally administers the program?

A National Budget for Science?

What was being done, one seminarian wanted to know, "to develop a general budget for science and to weigh the needs of high energy physics against the rest of science?" The Piore and Ramsey panels, which drafted ambitious proposals for high energy physics, had been specifically instructed *not* to consider the needs of other scientific fields. However, the President's science adviser, Donald Hornig, had advised the Joint Committee that the needs of high energy physics should be considered in the context of "the overall national science program" rather than in competition with expenditures for the development of nuclear technology. Just what, then, *was* this "national science program?"

Although the character and meaningfulness of the R&D review procedures by the highest budgetary and scientific agencies in the Executive Office of the President were thereupon discussed at length, it may be that some participants departed knowing little more about them than when they came. ". . . [I]t is done in many ways," one official replied.

> Obviously, the Bureau of the Budget and the President and the Office of Science and Technology, in the budget review in the spring and in the fall, get a feeling of the kind of pressures and the kind of things that are being asked for in all agency budgets. Dr. Hornig sits in the budget review as a member of the Executive Office of the President and gives his advice to the Bureau of the Budget, which the bureau . . . is free to take or not to take, as it sees fit.
>
> By looking at the kind of pressures on the National Science Foundation budget, the kind of pressures on the Defense [science] budget, the kind of pressures on the AEC [science] budget . . . it is possible to get a feel for . . . [such a question as]: "Given the fact we can't spend money in NSF this year on this basic research program, does it make sense to push for the MURA accelerator?" That kind of question and discussion goes on in the Executive Office, and by the President, all the time.
>
> This year . . . [OST] did look at basic research in universities on a government-wide basis . . . and on that basis made various budgetary decisions. . . . There is a special analysis in the . . . budget . . . which discusses overall R&D programs, and there is a time . . . [in the year] when the bureau . . . considers science programs as a whole . . . in conjunction with [OST]. . . .
>
> There are adjustments made [in agency budgets] on the basis of the total science look.

The process, a sympathetic private observer commented, was difficult because it was "multidimensional," involving all kinds of "cross sections." "You are looking at . . . an agency cross section . . . , [at] certain fields of science like oceanography, high energy physics, and so on, across the whole government; and, most recently, [at] . . . university research. . . ." The final decision about the budget for a particular agency science program was, someone from the Executive Office Building conceded, not easy:

> There are many factors that go into it. Your judgment of the capability of an agency to perform. Somebody used the word "history" here [". . . budgets are made mostly by history," a private observer had earlier remarked]—what the record demonstrates by way of performance. The ability to get money. There are many considerations. But this judgment is no more difficult here than in many other areas [of federal budgeting]. I would say it is more difficult than in some areas . . . with more physical, tangible kinds of bench marks where you can judge production and so forth. . . .

The discussion drifted off in a fresh direction, but subsequently, an effort was made to pick up the thread again. Budgeting in Washington for different scientific fields did not, apparently, take place in an academic environment. ". . . [S]cientists are no longer so naïve [about] . . . how to develop a political process to generate pressure. . . . [The government responds to] the pressures that are being applied, and these come through several channels, such as special studies by the Academy of Sciences and so on. . . . None of this is either good or bad. . . ." But how were the final allocations in the putative "national science program" made?

OFFICIAL X: What facts [does OST] . . . use for this assessment?

OFFICIAL Y: Well, . . . the facts of the stake in the various fields and the [agencies'] opinions . . . of the various programs.

OFFICIAL X: [Does OST] collect this information together for this assessment?

CITIZEN: Is it available to the public in any document?

OFFICIAL Y: The budget is available to the public.

And so the discussion went round in circles, dashes, spirals, and curlicues, the scientists perhaps expressing greater faith than the nonscientists in the rationality of scientific allocations (if only because of the proven excellence of the scientists' allocating, and spending, the money). One nonscientist said that, in his long experience in government science programs, technical considerations entered little into the final budgetary decisions. "It is a question of goals, values . . ."; and with that formulation a physicist agreed, "It is an estimate of values." As the evening drew to a close, one man familiar with government water power projects commented, "This may be sacrilegious, but, so far, I haven't heard anything about this problem . . . that puts it in any different category than the decision we face in this country as to whether we build a dam on the Ohio or the Columbia. . . ."

WOLFGANG K. H. PANOFSKY

Big Science
and Graduate Education

THE DIVISION of basic research into "big science" and "little science" has become popular nomenclature. I confess that I dislike the terms greatly, because they imply a discontinuity whereas, in fact, a continuum exists and because, though they do point to a difference in the method of doing science, no difference in scientific motivation is entailed.

What one usually means by little science is research carried out in the traditional academic pattern; that is, research supervised by a professor, assisted by graduate students and a very small number of technicians, and supported by some central shop facilities, access to a computing center, etc.

Big science is research where investigators generally operate in a group and where, in effect, some segment of industry is mobilized to support the work. This may occur either by large purchases or subcontracts or by establishing facilities large enough for this type of work and partially industrial in character.

There is, however, much so-called little science which has, in fact, now adopted many of the features associated with big science due to the increasing realization in some university departments that a certain "critical size" of staff is required in order to compete in a given field. The interdisciplinary laboratories for materials science, a substantial part of which is devoted to solid state physics, are a manifestation of this tendency. Even theoretical physicists generally object to being "isolated" and prefer to work in the company of an active and productive group of fellow theorists. In short, some of the often repeated, so-called evils of big science as related to scholarly work, such as multiple authorship of papers and increased specialization, apply also to much recent small science. University research budgets of investigators in little science are not too dissimilar from those of university scientists participating in the work of national centers with large research tools.

However different one judges big science and little science to be, the fact remains that these terms describe extremes in the range of methods suited to particular areas of basic research. In my discussion, I will restrict myself to basic *academic* science—that is, to work which, in general, is initiated by academic investigators who have a joint interest in education and in the advance of knowledge.

In recent times, elementary particle physics has been the main example of big science. However, other fields of academic interest (such as astronomy, radio astronomy, nuclear structure physics, and even solid state physics) are, in many cases, undergoing a transition toward the methods of big science. My dislike of the big science–little science dichotomy stems from this gradual transition. Much of the science still described as little is not really as little as all that. If one looks in detail at the laboratories of individual investigators, one finds that instrumentation is much more extensive than it used to be, that the services available on a university campus are much more lavish than in the past, and that budgets for travel, consultants, or guest lecturers, leaves of absence, and the like, have also generally grown much larger. Therefore, to identify little science nostalgically with the good old days is misleading. Even more misleading is the implication, discernible in many public statements on the subject, that little science is identified with "virtue" and big science with "vice" so far as the relationship of research to education is concerned.

A Range, Not a Dichotomy, of Method

The main theme of this paper is that little and big science do not exist as such; the terms, as I use them, represent only extremes of a continuous range in the methods of experimental science.

It has become apparent of late that, in many areas of research, certain activities which have been conducted in the little science mode would be substantially more effective if conducted more in the manner of big science. However, many investigators resist such a change because adoption of the big science format may involve personal inconvenience and may be regarded by professional colleagues as a sacrifice of academic values. Let me illustrate this problem by the crisis which nuclear structure physics now faces.

Until relatively recently, nuclear structure physics was carried out with instruments generally used only by resident investigators at universities or research institutions. All research during what one might call the golden age of nuclear structure physics, before World War II, was carried out in this manner. Nuclear physics was then concerned both with what is now classified as "nuclear structure physics" and as "elementary particle physics." The only elementary particles accessible to laboratory methods at that time were neutrons, protons, and electrons; since the maximum energy attainable at the time was in the nuclear binding energy range, the methods of both fields were largely identical.

Since the war, elementary particle physics has moved into a higher energy region where the tools of research have become so large and costly that access to them must be shared. Nuclear structure physics, on the other hand, has remained in its original energy range, and its instruments have generally remained as single institution devices. Even this, however, is changing as a result of new technology; nuclear structure physicists now use electrostatic generators and variable energy cyclotrons which cost several million dollars. (Moreover, the operating costs associated with electrostatic generators have so surprised supporting agencies that administrators have grown reluctant to authorize too many of these "big" pieces of equipment for this field, which still likes to be considered a "little" science.) In addition, during the last few years there has been a revolution in particle detection which permits a combination of high energy resolution and high data rates. This, in turn, has led to the adoption of powerful means of on-line computation to handle the vast volume of information generated. High energy linear electron accelerators have also been recognized as productive instruments for nuclear structure physics at low energy excitations but at high transfer of momentum to the targets under investigation. The Atomic Energy Commission has invented the term "intermediate energy physics" to describe research programs utilizing high energy accelerators in the 50 Mev to 1,000 Bev range; nonetheless, work in this range does not actually have a separate scientific purpose but is largely nuclear structure physics conducted with a certain class of tools. In short, we have here a concrete, but by no means unique, example in which, for scientific and technical reasons, the methods of big science may offer commanding advantages over traditional methods.

In spite of these developments, most nuclear physicists, when convened into committees and asked to forecast the future of their science, tend to project a world in which each university has an almost identical machine in its basement operated by the professor and his graduate students, all doing fairly similar kinds of physics although at an expanded rate and using the new techniques when possible. When one asks the committee members separately why this was their forecast, they are quick to acknowledge the power of the new methods (which can, in fact, be practiced more productively in the big science mode), but they are apt to say that they are not willing to follow the path of iniquity trod by the high energy physicist. To put it more bluntly, the concern to avoid the methods identified with big science has led many a nuclear structure physicist to limit the scope, if not the effectiveness, of his research. This attitude has led to grave problems for government administrators who are faced with many relatively similar proposals for multimillion-dollar installations at a large number of universities. Each proposal contains somewhere a sentence like, "The proposed installation is an ideal establishment for the training of graduate students." My remarks are not intended as a reflection on the quality or the educational value of much of the individual nuclear structure physics work in this country; they do, however, identify an overall dilemma.

The roots of this dilemma are clear. The prevalent opinion appears to be that big science is "bad" for the training of graduate students while small science is "good"; therefore, in the interest of education, investigators are willing to limit their research interests to small science methods, and the government is expected to make similar sacrifices in its management of research funds. It is therefore of considerable importance to examine critically the validity of the premise that graduate students' training is indeed poor if the student is being directed in his dissertation at a big science laboratory.

Five Reasons for Graduate Student Research

The fact that advanced research and graduate education are inseparable is axiomatic to almost all writers on the subject and might even be taken as the definition of education leading to a Ph.D. However, the reasons for this fact are rarely examined critically. Let me offer five general reasons why a graduate student should receive primary research experience as part of his Ph.D. program: (1) His acquaintance with, and direct participation in, an exciting and significant piece of original research will motivate him further toward original research work. (2) He will learn techniques that exist only in research involving genuinely new questions and to make judgments in the choice of research problems, tools, and methods. (3) He will work with his professor and others, who, it is hoped, will teach him creative approaches to research and increase his education beyond classroom learning. (4) Close association with graduate students maintains the vitality of the research faculty by exposing them to searching, unbiased questioning. (5) In original research, the student can be assigned individual responsibility for a given piece of work and as a result develop resourcefulness in dealing with difficult research situations and learn to take personal responsibility for the solution of a scholarly problem.

In the light of these criteria, let us examine the extent to which these objectives are met in the spectrum of methods between little and big science. During the last decade, the primary example of so-called big academic science has been elementary particle physics. In this examination I will, therefore, restrict myself almost entirely to elementary particle physics as an example of big science.

Clearly, the first four reasons given above for involvement in research by a Ph.D. candidate apply to valid research conducted in any mode or method. The first criterion cited, of student participation in an exciting piece of primary research, brings immediately into focus the paradox which I noted in nuclear structure physics. If, in order to remain in little science, a professor chooses to limit the range, and even the fundamental significance, of the problems he can attack, does he not at the same time deny to at least some students the opportunity to participate in truly exciting and significant research? In this instance, then, the tables are turned, and emphasis on the virtues of little science may actually hurt graduate education.

The Problem of Individual Responsibility

Conversely, the strongest argument against big science as a proper adjunct to graduate education lies in the fifth criterion—that is, the value of individual research responsibility. In a big science such as high energy physics, it is increasingly difficult to select topics for Ph.D. theses that will permit a graduate student complete responsibility for an important piece of research. If the requirement for the Ph.D. included the condition that the candidate's thesis be publishable in a reputable journal as an article of which he is the sole author, then few degrees in high energy physics would be given. The reason is that, purely physically, it is often impossible for a single scientist—even a professor, let alone a graduate student—to take full responsibility for a major high energy experiment; moreover, pressure for running time at major facilities is so great that it is hard to justify devoting the facilities to student practice.

Of course, most of these problems are neither new nor restricted to big science. There have been many cases in which, over a period of years, a professor has developed an elaborate piece of equipment, such as an X-ray spectrometer, molecular beam apparatus, or similar instrument, and would not dream of permitting a student to use it without extensive supervision. However, this situation obviously becomes more frequent, and thus more serious, as we move toward big science. As a result, a larger proportion of post-Ph.D. than of pre-Ph.D. contributors are apt to participate in high energy physics experiments. A few years ago, I noted the ratio of pre-Ph.D. to post-Ph.D. physicists working on the 184-inch cyclotron operating near 600 Mev and on the 6 Bev Bevatron at the University of California Radiation Laboratory. The ratio was twice as large on the lower energy machine. This is not surprising. Since big science requires collaboration among many workers, the fraction of responsibility devolving on a single student will necessarily be smaller. This partial responsibility, however, is often quite as educational as full responsibility for an experiment involving less total effort; and the senior investigator will generally attempt to delegate to the student as complete responsibility for a "subexperiment" as is compatible with the success of the entire undertaking.

The question remains whether this kind of research gives the student a worse or a better education. Clearly, it is a *different* education, one in which he learns both the purely scientific aspects of very important work and how to collaborate efficiently with others. On the other hand, he suffers from being unable to work solely along his own lines, although he is able to contribute extensively through original ideas.

We would therefore conclude that, from the standpoint of the fifth criterion listed above, graduate education in big science may, by and large, be inferior to education in little science but that, from the standpoint of the other four criteria, it may in many cases be superior, particularly if the student is permitted to participate in a piece of truly exciting and important work.

Sharing Facilities and Risks

By its very nature, big science usually involves the sharing of unique facilities by several investigators. This, in turn, leads to the need for an acceptable decision-making process governing access to the common equipment. So long as the supply of shared facilities adequately satisfies the demand (as has been the case in astronomy until relatively recently), few problems arise; but if the demand by qualified scientists overloads the facilities, "social problems" can become severe.

It is evident that the necessary process by which an investigator has to justify a proposed experiment repeatedly to a committee or an administrator represents a departure from academic tradition. Traditionally, after the appointment of a professor following a careful examination of his qualifications and of the facilities available to him, his work (at least in principle) is justified only to posterity, not to any review committees. But experimental science, big or little, has for many years now departed from this academic tradition. Support of any experimental work is extended only for a limited interval, and so even the little scientist has to justify his work repeatedly, usually to a committee of his peers. Again we encounter a continuum rather than a dichotomy between little and big science.

There is a corollary to this departure from academic tradition which may also interfere, to some extent, with the involvement of graduate students in big science research: the professor, in effect, has to ask the student to share with him the risk of being denied access to the accelerator, telescope, oceanographic ship, rocket, or other shared facility. The more adventuresome and strongly motivated student will gladly share this risk; after all, any original research is risky to a graduate student in terms of the time that may be required to complete his thesis. From local experience, I see little evidence that a creative student is affected in his thesis choice by the problem of shared facilities; nor, as will be shown below, does the time from B.S. to Ph.D. differ significantly between elementary particle physics and other fields of physics.

Increasing Specialization—the "Data-Reducer"

Increased specialization both of subject and of method has been the unavoidable result of the growth in the content of science, the variety of tools, and the magnitude of specific experimental enterprises. During the first part of the century, we have seen the increasing division of physicists into experimentalists and theorists. With the death of Enrico Fermi, we lost one of the few remaining men who might validly be considered a leading contributor to both experimental and theoretical physics.

We are now generating a third kind of physicist, who, for lack of a better phrase, I will call a "data-reducer." Usually, he has received a better education in theory than most experimentalists but is neither a creative theoretician nor an experienced designer of complete experiments. Such physicists start their research, for example, by taking pictures in a bubble chamber exposed to a high energy particle beam; they are not involved in the design or operation of the bubble chamber or accelerator. They subject these pictures to analysis, generally with extensive use of computers, and then draw physical conclusions. As a result, in addition to becoming conversant with current problems in modern physical thought, they learn a great deal about modern data-processing techniques. However, if, after receiving their Ph.D.'s, they move to smaller institutions or engage in research where they must design experimental apparatus "from scratch," they generally encounter difficulties, since their experience has been severely limited.

The fraction of graduate students who receive their Ph.D.'s in high energy physics as data-reducers is increasing. We should not regard their education as better or worse than that of experimentalists or theorists; it is just education in a different branch of the science. Many with Ph.D. experience in each of the three areas have become excellent, creative physicists. The ever increasing amount of knowledge and variety of techniques, accompanied by the limited capacity of the human brain, produce serious problems for education, particularly graduate education, which are certainly not uniquely connected with the relation of big science to graduate education. The increasing number of degrees given to data-reducers is a consequence of increasing specialization rather than the degeneration of scientific education.

The phenomenon of the data-reducer is not new. In astronomy, the student has been operating in this mode for decades; he certainly does not design or build telescopes or, in general, devise original methods of observation. Even in little physics, students in "experimental science" have often received their education without designing any apparatus. At the turn of the century, the mark of a reputable physics department was to have a 21-foot-radius diffraction grating in the basement for spectroscopic research. A graduate student would frequently prepare his Ph.D. thesis by mounting a specific element in an arc source, exposing photographic plates on the focal circle of the grating, and then spending the bulk of his time measuring and analyzing the spectral lines on the plates. Many other examples of this kind of thing could be cited. Although this type of research was probably not very valuable to education, that was how many highly prominent physicists received their graduate training. The only new feature of current graduate education in, for example, high energy physics, is that a larger fraction of students are completing thesis work as data-reducers.

Employment of "Big" and "Little" Science Ph.D.'s

We have thus identified numerous ways in which education in big science differs from that in little science, but we cannot conclude which is "better" or "worse" until we know what weight to put on each of the criteria given above. In principle, one would like to be able to determine this by observing the careers of students educated in either the little or big science mode and ascertaining which were better prepared for productive scientific work. To do this objectively is at best a large task and at worst a hopeless one, since defining what is meant by "successful" or "productive" work is difficult. I have made a somewhat sketchy attempt to examine how the career of a physicist may be affected by receiving his Ph.D. research experience in big or little physics. For this purpose, Omar Snyder of the Stanford Linear Accelerator Center analyzed the employment in December 1965 of those who had received Ph.D.'s from the Stanford and Berkeley physics departments from 1956 to 1965. Although this is clearly an oversimplification, we equated elementary particle physics with big science and all other fields of physics with little science (Table 1).[1]

[1] I should like to express my appreciation to Omar Snyder of the Stanford Linear Accelerator Center, for collecting and tabulating the data on physics Ph.D.'s presented in Tables 1 and 2, and to the academic authorities at Stanford and the University of California at Berkeley for permitting him access to the material.

TABLE 1. *Employment of 1956–65 Stanford and Berkeley Physics Ph.D.'s as of Fall 1965*

Occupation	Ph.D. received in			
	Big science[a]	Little science[b]	Big science[a]	Little science[b]
	Number		Percent	
Teaching	110	133	52	46
Major university	(83)	(84)	(39)	(29)
Minor university or college	(27)	(49)	(13)	(17)
Basic research at national laboratory	41	14	19	5
Applied technical work	62	145	29	50
Industry	(26)	(94)	(12)	(32)
Applied government laboratory	(36)	(51)	(17)	(17)
Total	213	292	100	100

a. Elementary particle physics.
b. All other physics fields.

Roughly the same fraction of big and little science Ph.D.'s were involved in teaching, though the former were more likely to be found in major university departments. Relatively more big science Ph.D.'s were engaged in basic research at national (mainly Atomic Energy Commission) laboratories, whereas small science Ph.D's (many of whom were trained in solid state, atomic, and molecular physics) were decidedly more likely to be doing applied work for industry.

The most striking conclusion to emerge from a more detailed examination of the data is the relation between the choice of a thesis supervisor and subsequent occupation. It appears that, in both big and little science, the research professor had a great deal more influence on the student's career than did the style in which the thesis research was conducted.

No significant variation was noted in the average time that elapsed between receipt of the bachelor and Ph.D. degrees in the major subfields of physics (Table 2).

We have identified certain differences in the nature of the graduate education and subsequent employment of students in little and big science but are not able to conclude which form of education is better. As either form can be highly valuable to the student and should be considered an essential asset to the country, *criteria for the support of research in the various fields of physics should be based primarily on their scientific rather than educational value.*

TABLE 2. *Years between B.S. and Ph.D. Degrees for 540 Students in Eight Fields of Physics*[a]

Field	Mean years[b]	Number of students					Percent of students				
		Total	4 years or less	5–6 years	7–8 years	9 years or more	Total	4 years or less	5–6 years	7–8 years	9 years or more
Astrophysics, space	6.24	16	3	4	6	3	100	19	25	37	19
Atomic, molecular	6.18	99	14	34	29	22	100	14	34	29	22
Elementary particle	6.01	222	30	93	51	48	100	14	42	23	22
Nuclear structure	6.64	95	9	35	21	30	100	9	36	22	32
Plasma	6.40	14	1	4	7	2	100	7	29	50	14
Solid state	5.82	46	8	19	10	9	100	17	41	22	20
Classical	6.76	27	2	9	7	9	100	7	33	26	33
Applied	6.68	21	1	9	5	6	100	5	43	24	29
All fields	6.25	540	68	207	136	129	100	13	38	25	24

a. Physics Ph.D. degrees awarded 1956–65 at Stanford and Berkeley.
b. Harmonic mean.

TABLE 3. *Number of Physicists, Ph.D. Physicists, and Volume of Research Expenditures in Various Fields of Physics, 1963*[a]

Item	Total	Field[b]					
		Plasma	Particle	Astro-physics	Nuclear	Solid state	Atomic
Number of physicists	15,150	800	1,630	1,180	3,200	7,080	1,260
With Ph.D.'s	7,360	400	950	590	1,540	3,260	620
New 1963 Ph.D.'s	693	35	110	50	154	226	118
Research expenditures from all sources (in millions of dollars)[c]	$493	$50	$125	$59	$69	$173	$17
Federal government	400	43	125	49	69	95	15
At universities	216	8	100	25	36	36	11
Research expenditures per new 1963 Ph.D. from all sources (in millions of dollars)	$0.7	$1.4	$1.2	$1.2	$.4	$.7	$.1
Federal government	.6	1.2	1.2	1.0	.4	.4	.1

a. Fiscal year 1963. Source: National Academy of Sciences–National Research Council, *Physics Survey and Outlook* (NAS-NRC, 1966), pp. 92, 104, 111.
b. Scope of the fields listed as follows: plasma; elementary particles; astrophysics, solar system physics, cosmic rays; nuclear; solid state and condensed matter; atomic and molecular.
c. Includes expenditures for plant as well as operating costs.

The question is often asked whether education via big science is not "too expensive" and whether the government should not, therefore, favor little science. This is not, of course, a fair question, since it assumes that the entire cost of the research should be charged against education. If such calculations were made, we would find, for example, that the cost per graduate student in space research, which has a very small academic base and little participation by graduate students, is vastly higher than in theoretical physics. There is no reason for such incommensurate cost ratios to be uniform. Nevertheless, even if computed by this overly simple method, the variation in cost per student educated is much less than is commonly thought, particularly if total federal expenditures for *basic* research are related to the number of Ph.D.'s in a given field. Table 3 indicates federal expenditures in 1963 of about $1 million per Ph.D. trained in elementary particle physics, astrophysics, solid state physics, and plasma physics; about half that amount in nuclear structure physics (not including that employing higher energy machines); and about $100,000 per Ph.D. in atomic and molecular physics.[2]

[2] After a period of relative stagnation, atomic and molecular physics has become, in

The reasons for this relatively small variation are complex. Although the cost of a given experiment that might result in a Ph.D. thesis is much smaller in solid state physics than in high energy physics, the federal government supports much basic research in solid state physics in which students do not participate. On the other hand, in elementary particle physics, the involvement of students is generally encouraged in all aspects of the field. To put it differently, in some fields of big science (such as elementary particle physics), all aspects of the field ranging from instrument development to theoretical work are linked with academic life and, hence, with students, whereas in other fields (the most notable example being plasma physics), much work is conducted at non-academic laboratories. Whether this is, or is not, a desirable situation is a matter we will not discuss here. Clearly, however, those fields of basic research which are not strongly represented in academic departments must obtain scientists from other fields and thus become consumers, rather than producers, of talent. Contrariwise, fields (of either big or little science) that are strongly represented in university departments, such as high energy physics, nuclear structure physics, and atomic and molecular physics, are net producers rather than consumers of scientific talent.

Maintaining the academic status of all fields of basic science, whether conducted in the big or little science mode, is clearly of overriding importance both for the vitality of the field and for the continued production of its practitioners. As the tools and methods of science change, we cannot afford to cast all graduate education in the nineteenth-century mold. To do so would detach important segments of science from the educational process, with a consequent loss both to science and to education.

---

recent years, the most rapidly growing subfield of physics, both because of new techniques and because of the need for its data for applied purposes. As a result, the methods in this field are evolving rapidly and there will probably soon be an increase in cost per student.

DISCUSSION

Scientific Truths
and Educational Consequences

PANOFSKY OPENED the discussion by stressing again the main point he sought to bring out in his paper: research and education should be judged by the quality of their products, not by their institutional or technical machinery. If some scientific fields are more expensive than others, and require more research dollars per Ph.D. produced, it does not follow that they are therefore any worse educationally or that they do not belong on campus.

The most expensive thing of all would be to remove such a field from its academic base. ". . . [I]f you train no Ph.D.'s in a given field, . . . the cost of Ph.D.'s becomes infinite." The field then becomes "a net consumer of talent, and not a producer"; it becomes a drain on other fields and may also suffer qualitatively because of the lack of intellectual stimulation provided by unbiased young graduate students. Something of this sort happened in plasma physics, which, as a highly classified field, developed, in large part, independently of universities. Science has always had varied ways of approaching the truth; in astronomy, for instance, students have for long years been as dependent for their data upon large and expensive machines manufactured and operated by specialists as are students today in high energy physics. No fruitful approach to the truth should be foreclosed.

What about the Students?

Well and good in theory, one participant remarked, and good also, perhaps, for the professor who reigns over a contingent of graduate students; but what about the students? Do they really like this corporate system of high energy physics, in which they have so little opportunity to work independently? It depends on the student's interests, a scientist responded; and "the scientific question comes first" in determining this.

There is no evidence that present-day graduate students are deterred by the complications of teamwork or accelerator time scheduling. Some graduate students *are* concerned about these matters and some are not, another scientist declared. It depends on their makeup and motivation.

Should the reduced professorial-student contact characteristic of big science lead to the special selection of graduate students who can best tolerate and benefit from this kind of relationship? The question was raised but not clearly answered. Patently, "decreased . . . student-faculty contact" was a widespread problem in higher education; and professors were increasingly involved in other activities than teaching. "I remember when I came to ———, we used to have a faculty meeting as to . . . which two people, [of the twelve in the department, were] . . . to go East to a meeting during that year. There were two trips permitted. When there is a meeting now in New York, there is nobody home."

". . . [I]t is very rare in experimental science that a student originally conceives of the question" on which he does his dissertation, it was observed. "The literature is too big. And it is also very rare that he independently develops his entire apparatus from raw material to final product and does not follow a logical chain of investigations that his professor has supplied." At Stanford, for example, graduate students are involved in perhaps 90 percent of high energy experiments; they control most of these for a period of time and are responsible for subexperiments. But "no laboratory director would permit a student to submit an independent proposal for an experiment which takes hundreds of hours of running time where a senior professor or investigator does not take major responsibility."

SOCIAL SCIENTIST A: What you have really said is that the time is allocated to professors who suballocate it to students or involve them to some extent.

PHYSICIST: It is allocated to a senior investigator. . . .

SOCIAL SCIENTIST B: You are saying that the graduate students build the pyramid; but they didn't design it.

PHYSICIST: The graduate students work on things that they can get through in a reasonable amount of time.

Nevertheless, several protagonists of big science insisted, this experience could be as exacting, as absorbing, and as rewarding as the classical modes of research. The example was cited of a brilliant graduate student at an eastern university who participated in an experiment that yielded one of the most important discoveries in contemporary physics. "He participated in the excitement of seeing these data show up, he was engaged in all the controversy—[about] whether [the data were] . . . meaningful or not. . . ." Such a student had a more stimulating educational experience than a student working independently at a routine task of, for example, measuring a new energy level in a complex nucleus.

To be sure, the more complicated a high energy physics experiment, the larger the ratio of postdoctoral to predoctoral persons generally engaged on it. A laboratory director will feel that more experience is required than that signified by a new Ph.D. before a man can be entrusted with extensive and expensive staff and equipment. "In big science a man has a hard time to blossom from a new Ph.D. to a principal investigator."

Can Modern Physicists Become Engineers?

"I participated in big science in the ———— laboratory, '35 to '39," said one participant, who went on to open up a new vein of criticism.

> At that time the young graduate students all had to manufacture their own equipment . . . and to be very much on their own. Of course, they had to participate in the team in running the . . . [machine], too, but the net result of their actually getting in there and working with equipment and knowing how to design it . . . was . . . that when World War II came along, these people were the leaders in much of our radar development. . . .
>
> Recently, I have been at one of the universities that is operating on a so-called user basis where they have these data-reducers . . . and the films and so on come into the university—shipped down from Berkeley . . . —and so there are some screens where the girls sit and decide on one kind of event or another kind of event. . . . [F]inally this physicist gets these numbers that these girls have obtained by following . . . orders, and so then he does something with it.
>
> What is there in the nature of that experience that prepares that guy for the next emergency?

Such a scientist "cannot design circuits," a physicist conceded. "He cannot think too intelligently about signal and noise problems. . . ." But he has had a different training that is no less rich or valuable than that of physics students a generation ago. He will have actually designed the energy beam at the accelerator and analyzed the beam purity so that he knows exactly what went into the Bev chamber; he will have worked out the procedures that the girls will have to follow in order to reduce the experimental observations to numbers (though, once outlined, the procedures themselves are mechanical enough for the work to be delegated to girls). All told, the student will have learned a great deal more than he would have twenty years ago about complex programming and data processing. When the data processing is concluded, "you are in the same place you have always been in science . . .—trying to fit . . . [the observed data] to . . . alternate theoretical models.

> . . . [I]t is only a change in means, and in the process, the graduate student has learned something which is extremely valuable in being prepared for the next emergency. . . . I am not sure [if] for the next emergency we are more in need of scientific people who know how to fix vacuum systems and design electronic circuits or whether we are more in need of people who can handle vast amounts of information and are trying to make sense out of it along specific scientific lines.

To be more certain of this answer, a lay participant repeated the question about the larger utility and transferability of the skills acquired by present-day students in "big physics." During World War II, he recalled, the physicists working on radar and the atomic bomb had become engineers, and it was because they had become such good engineers that these projects succeeded. Could the modern high energy physicist become a good engineer or had he grown so highly specialized that he had lost his former adaptability?

These modern physicists could indeed become engineers again but they would become *different* engineers than in World War II—and "the country may very well need more of the kind of engineer they are apt to become now . . . ," a physicist replied. ". . . [T]he physicist who has designed logic systems for discriminating events in the background of a lot of less desirable events [that is, in isolating the significant phenomenon from a cloud of extraneous events, such as detecting a faint signal amidst high background noise] . . . is a very good engineer for that type of thing. . . . There are many military problems of just that nature."

Does Big Science Exist or Not?

At about this point, a disgruntled participant interrupted with two basic questions which, he felt, had been avoided in the discussion. Was there, or was there not, a difference (1) between big and little science and (2) between the quality (or if that term was too elusive to measure, the objective character) of the education each afforded?

The answer given by a physicist to the first question was yes, there is a difference, although its significance has often been exaggerated, and there is, in reality, more of a continuum than a difference between the two. Science can be defined as "big" if it "mobilizes segments of industry in industrial-like organizations. . . ."

> In effect, when Luis Alvarez started his activity in Berkeley, he . . . mobilized a certain fraction of Eastman Kodak to support him because there is $500,000 worth of film a year involved. Or IBM is in fact partially mobilized to reduce data, and so forth. So there is a tremendous difference, which goes all the way from a space experiment, on the one extreme, where a given scientific question can mobilize a very large segment of industry, to the other extreme, where you make a very personal investigation of a specimen.

And beyond present differences in the scale of scientific inquiries, this physicist believed, a broader historical trend is discernible. ". . . [T]here are dynamics in which, as simpler problems are being solved in all fields of science, there is a general drift toward needing more and more elaborate methods for answering questions. . . ."

SOCIAL SCIENTIST: You think Rutherford was wrong when he said, "We have no money, so we have to think"?

PHYSICIST A: That statement, I think, really is incorrect, now. People do not do things the hard way because they enjoy doing things the hard way, because they think it is so easy to get money . . . it isn't worth trying to think of a better solution. . . . [T]hat kind of statement is often made, and I don't . . . see any . . . evidence . . . [that it is] true. . . .

PHYSICIST B: You couldn't have discovered the Van Allen belts in space without sending something up there.

Following this interruption, the second question was answered as follows: The negative aspect of education in big science is that the graduate student is denied the privilege of making, and learning from, his own mistakes, and he is also denied the degree of responsibility he can have when working with less elaborate and expensive equipment.

> . . . [Y]ou can't teach graduate students how a radiation detector works and how to adjust it in an experimental run at the . . . synchrotron in Brookhaven. He has to learn it somewhere else because there is so much competition for the resource. He doesn't have the opportunity to learn from his own mistakes as much as he does when he works independently [that is, at small science].
>
> That is . . . the largest negative thing . . . [about big science] training. He has to learn by other people telling him, "This is the way you run it, and you cannot have personal experience." That is on the negative side

of the ledger. On the positive side of the ledger is that he participates in the discovery of natural phenomena in a very personal way which otherwise he wouldn't have the opportunity to do.

On the question of whether science should be considered as "big" and "little" or rather as a continuum, physicist B was reminded of "the comparison of small and big business, where it has been proposed that a much more appropriate system of classification would be to adopt the size grading system for olives: the smallest [grade] . . . is medium, and it goes, medium, large, giant, mammoth, and colossal. Would this be a better system?"

To what extent is big science generated not by the inherent requirements of discovery—the outposts of nature being taken more cheaply than her heartland—but by a national penchant for spectaculars that may be as applicable to science as to the cinema? "There is an open invitation, the way the system of [government] funding works," an economist suggested, "for people in various subfields to think up more and more expensive equipment." People sometimes think up "gigantic projects" because it may actually be easier to get them funded.

To which one physicist replied, it was still easier to get less money. ". . . [I]f you can think up a cheap way of making a high energy physics experiment, they will come running to you." And a second added, "The cheaper experiments are also done first."

Effects on the Sociology of Science

What effects have important and unique scientific facilities had on the social system of research at university departments scattered across the nation? Major efforts have been made to perpetuate the latter system, a scientist observed, at the price of some inefficiency in the utilization of national accelerator centers. "The most *efficient* thing would be to have the best possible staff at . . . [the center] and tell everybody else to go away." By supporting university user groups and reserving large blocks of accelerator time for them, the government has sought to accommodate the traditional system of small science to the operating requirements of big machines. Nonetheless controversy has arisen about managing and arranging access to the machines.

It will always be controversial because more and more people are interested scientifically in what is going on in fewer and fewer places. . . .

> This . . . concentration in one place . . . clearly causes tremendous problems. It also goes counter to the academic tradition. The academic tradition is . . . [to select a professor] very carefully and once he has been appointed you don't review what he does in research. . . . In shared facilities, every single time a professor wants to propose an experiment, there are seven committees reviewing whether what he is doing is really worthwhile.
>
> This concentration of shared facilities . . . is . . . very distasteful to many members of the community, and it is very much at variance with the traditions of academic independence. . . .

On the other hand, the comparative cheapness of supporting user groups freed from the leviathan costs of building and operating an accelerator has enabled high energy physics research to spread more widely across the country. Even a place as remote as the University of Hawaii can now function in the field. "They have two young experimentalists and two theorists, and they are collaborating as a sort of satellite group from Berkeley and [are] doing very nice work."

Another consequence of big, government-financed machines for the sociology of university science is the presence on campus of innumerable secretaries, technicians, and professional personnel. The emergence of this army of the academically uninitiated and perhaps uninitiatable is not simply due to big science. The "tremendous influx of nonacademic people" listed in the phone books of most big universities is due "mainly . . . [to] the . . . increased standard of living, everywhere. . . . Professors now have secretaries. There is a computer center, and there are a few more men in the shop, and the comptroller has his accounting department, and so forth." Of course, the phenomenon is accentuated by a giant facility. On (as well as off) campus, such a facility presents as many temptations as drawbacks. "If you put it near a given university, that university gets the negative impact but also the advantage. . . . If you isolate it from teaching, then you lose an academic base. If you interweave it completely with the teaching activity, then you completely unbalance the academic structure of that university. . . ."

Was not the best solution to these problems, a government scientist asked, the establishment of national facilities, such as Brookhaven, which would be associated with no single university?

Such an arrangement would prevent both adverse and beneficial effects on campus, a physicist replied. But the laboratory's isolation from university life would also make it difficult to attract an able staff. That, it was said, was the experience at Brookhaven until a university was established nearby at Stony Brook, "and now you can suddenly get some absolutely first-class physicists who work at Brookhaven because the university is there." Brookhaven has, however, been unusually successful in building up affiliated university user groups, who have done excellent work. How well user groups will function with the new generation of large accelerators remains to be determined. They have been successful thus far largely through the fortunate invention of the bubble chamber, which enabled dispersed groups to function with relatively modest local facilities. The viability of such groups depends not only on administrative, social, or political principle but on technical developments. "Some techniques simply don't lend themselves very well to user design and operation, and some techniques do." And regardless of how many outside users there are, a first-class professional staff is needed to operate the installation.

Summing up, Panofsky said, ". . . [M]y main thesis is that it is worthwhile to put up with many of the negative features of big science to keep it involved in education. . . . [E]ven if there is an apparent inefficiency or controversies on the decision-making process . . . , it is worth a great deal of sacrifice . . . , institutional invention, and tolerance on the part of government and academic people to maintain this involvement."

PART III

On Budgets
and the Congress

ELMER B. STAATS

Making the Science Budget for 1967

EACH YEAR'S budget-making for research and development or any other field constitutes an inimitable blend of the routine and the special. No brief presentation can do justice to either, but I shall try to indicate some of the major decisions which we at the Bureau of the Budget had to make in preparing the R&D budget for fiscal year 1967.[1] The outcome of these decisions is summarized in "Special Analysis I,"[2] which is a good point of departure for the present discussion.

"Special Analysis I" indicates that there are some eleven agencies with major expenditures for R&D, ranging all the way from the Defense Department down to the Smithsonian Institution and covering virtually

[1] This paper was originally presented orally on February 2, 1966, shortly after the release, on January 24, 1966, of the United States budget for fiscal year 1967. The budget, which is normally transmitted to the Congress in mid-January, contains the President's proposals for government obligations for the coming fiscal year commencing July 1. A fiscal year (FY) is designated by the terminal year: thus, when Staats refers to "1967," he means FY July 1, 1966–June 30, 1967; "1962" means "FY 1962" or July 1, 1961–June 30, 1962; and so on. Most of the decisions in the FY 1967 budget would, of course, have been taken during the latter months of calendar year 1965.—EDITOR.

[2] "Special Analysis I: Federal Research, Development, and Related Programs," reprint of pages 113 to 132 from the *Special Analyses: Budget of the United States, Fiscal Year 1967* (Bureau of the Budget, January 1966).

every area of scientific inquiry known to man. This analysis provides at least a bird's-eye view of the vast range of these government activities. Judged in either absolute or relative terms, the major decisions in this and recent years' R&D budgets—that is, the major *changes* in the level of proposed R&D expenditures—fall heavily in nondefense areas. Thus, since 1962, the level of military R&D (including in that category both Defense Department and AEC programs) has risen only 4 percent, compared with some 330 percent in other areas (including, of course, space, but also transportation, pollution control, pesticides, health, water, agriculture, and pure science such as that sponsored by the National Science Foundation).

Department of Defense

To start with the Defense Department, the major issue we faced this year—when, incidentally, the research and development budget is almost the same as last year—was the adaptation of R&D programs to the situation in Vietnam. As it turned out, most of the ongoing work was such that it left very little flexibility, and in fact, the thing that is surprising to us is that the final product yielded so little that is directly related to Vietnam or conventional warfare.

There was an increase in the smaller aircraft field, in helicopters. The C-5A (a cargo aircraft), which was started the previous year, is a major step-up of about $100 million—from $157 million to $258 million.

There was a further postponement of the Nike-X decision; that is, whether to deploy this antimissile missile. I can remember a meeting at Cape Cod with President Kennedy during the 1963 budget preparation, when this issue was postponed for a year. It has been postponed for a year each year since. A major, tough decision remains to be made with respect to the Nike-X.[3]

---

[3] On September 18, 1967, Secretary of Defense Robert McNamara announced that a "light" defensive network of Nike-X antimissile missiles would be deployed during the next five years at a cost of $5 billion (see *New York Times*, September 19, 1967, p. 1).

National Aeronautics and Space Administration

The principal effect on NASA of the overall budget level was the postponement of the Voyager program (for the unmanned orbiting of and landing on Mars) for two years, from 1971 to 1973, and the cancellation of the Advanced (earth) Orbiting Solar Observatory program. All of the implications of this budgetary figure for the Apollo (manned lunar landing) system are not yet clear, but it will certainly have some effect.

The Gemini (two-man earth orbital) program, I believe, was not affected, but the budget does reflect some reduction as a result of the prospective completion of the Gemini program.

Atomic Energy Commission

We faced several tough issues in the AEC budget for 1967. Three projects were canceled or terminated, each for somewhat different reasons:

1. We agreed with the AEC to terminate the Experimental Gas-Cooled Reactor at Oak Ridge, where we have spent some $57 million. This was a very tough decision. It might have been made the year before but was not so clear at that time, because we did not have all of the data that we had before us this year. It is hard to attribute this cancellation simply to a tight budget. A tight budget helped to precipitate it, but here was a situation where $30 million or $40 million more would have been required to complete the project. Both the AEC and the Tennessee Valley Authority, which had earlier been interested, retained very little interest in the project, and so it was canceled.

2. The Medium Power Reactor Experiment at Oak Ridge, which was one of the advanced small nuclear power projects, was also terminated, because it lost out in a cost-benefit analysis to the advanced liquid-metal-cooled reactor at Livermore.

3. We had to make a decision with regard to the large seed and blanket reactor that had been in the budget heretofore. Because of the unique situation in California, they were much interested in it. The AEC, supported by Admiral Rickover, had stated formerly that this was one of a

kind, a special situation in which the state was sufficiently interested to put up a large part of the financing. We remained interested in this type of technology and will continue to explore it. Nonetheless, the project was terminated this year because Rickover, in effect, changed his mind about its feasibility; and in any event, if we had decided to go ahead with it, a cost escalation of about 100 percent was indicated.

We had tough decisions to make on the meson factory at Los Alamos, a $55 million facility with $10 million annual operating costs, which was in competition with the Alternating Gradient Synchrotron project at Brookhaven. We ended up by putting both of them in. What will happen in the Congress remains to be seen.[4] They are closely related projects, and both have heavy scientific as well as political implications.

The Fast Flux Test Reactor was put in this budget; it is a project of some $75 million, starting out with $7.5 million in 1967, with a virtual commitment to move ahead the following year.

One of the old problems we had in the AEC area was the merchant ship reactor. Like some of the others, this was an old customer in the budget. We decided to close it out, but $500,000 remained for further studies—which is less than we put in for further studies during the previous two years. The Maritime Administration was much interested and hoped to get the Defense Department's endorsement; Defense has been interested but has never quite been willing to put its name on the line. The AEC has been involved purely from the research standpoint. The real question, then, was, Who takes the responsibility for determining that a merchant ship reactor is feasible and economic and has a high enough priority to compete with all of the other items in the budget?

Other Agencies

In the Department of Health, Education, and Welfare, the principal problems we faced in the 1967 budget were the usual ones about the budget level of the National Institutes of Health (NIH). Again, how much should there be for extramural research? A strong interest was expressed in stepping up the health research facilities program. We started out with around $100 million for this, if I recall correctly, and ended up

[4] For FY 1967, Congress appropriated funds to complete work on the synchrotron and to initiate work on the meson factory (that is, for site preparation and architecture-engineering design).

with some $15 million, as the successive waves of budget cutting took place.

Grants in the NIH area were increased from about $453 million to $486 million. This is a more modest increase than we had in the previous several years—perhaps more modest than will come out of the Congress.[5] But the increase was largely for broadened institutional support, raising indirect costs, and the usual noncompeting research grants, which average about three years.

It will be interesting to see the effects of new legislation on these programs. We really haven't seen the full impact on R&D budgets of such recent acts as those dealing with professional assistants, medical libraries, clean air, water pollution control, and regional medical centers. Although the R&D budget of HEW increased $162 million over 1966, the full financial impact of this legislation will begin to show up next year and the years following.

The principal question at the National Science Foundation was the rate of growth, as it has been almost every year. We placed particular emphasis upon the Science Development Program [see pp. 101–13]. There was somewhat less emphasis upon facilities. Provision was made for completion of a 150-inch telescope and some expansion of weather modification research.

In the Department of Agriculture, the emphasis was, again, upon trying to rationalize the research program, which had been victimized, in some ways, by too much proliferation and too great insistence upon putting money into about fifty agricultural experiment stations. We have had something of a crusade on this in recent years, at the Bureau, in an attempt to rationalize the program.

Last year, we agreed with Secretary of Agriculture Orville Freeman that we should try to close out a number of these installations. When then Budget Director Kermit Gordon went down to Texas to see President Johnson, we agreed that he should take along a bookful of installation closings which he was going to announce as a package, McNamara style. Well, we ended up with some success. We got about $2.5 million of savings out of it after all of the bloodshed. We have some $5 million of proposed experiment station reductions in the 1968 budget but are approaching it on a somewhat different basis—through the regular budget process.

[5] The eventual figure for NIH grants was $519 million in fiscal year 1967, according to the verbal report of Hugh Loweth of the Budget Bureau in January 1968.

There were also some reductions in university agricultural research, which ran counter to increases in the university research budgets of other agencies.

I will just mention briefly a few of the highlights in other agency budgets.

At the Department of the Interior, there were increases for the Office of Saline Water, for the Bureau of Mines' oil shale work, and for research in the recovery of waste material and scrap metal (which is part of the National Beautification Program).

Practically all of the increase in the Department of Commerce research budget was in the transportation area, but there was some in the weather field, particularly in weather modification.

At the Federal Aviation Agency, we deliberately did not propose a particular amount of money for the supersonic transport. Although we have a good idea what the amount is, we felt that, in dealing with industry and for other reasons, it was not a good idea to commit ourselves at this point.

Interagency Scientific Activities

"Special Analysis I" contains a section on across-the-board reviews ("Selected Government-wide Scientific Activities . . ."). This is a matter in which Representative Henry Reuss has had a particular interest.[6]

We have been concerned about how to get an across-the-board perspective in budgetary review. There have been a number of areas—such as oceanography, meteorology, water research—where a large number of agencies have been active in carrying on research. At one time or another, with the cooperation and help of the Office of Science and Technology, we have undertaken across-the-board reviews of such programs in seven or eight agencies.

The "Special Analysis" summarizes budget totals in six areas—atmospheric sciences, medical research, oceanography, space programs, water research, and science information. But, to be frank about it, these programs tend to be summaries prepared after the fact rather than to result

[6] See the discussion by Congressman Henry Reuss, Donald Hornig, Elmer Staats, and others, in *The Federal Research and Development Programs: The Decisionmaking Process*, Hearings before a Subcommittee of the House Committee on Government Operations, 89 Cong. 2 sess. (January 7, 10, and 11, 1966), particularly pp. 47–65.

from any kind of prior planning. We hope that we can improve this process as time goes on and so far have done more in the fields of oceanography and meteorology than any place else.

There are very practical limits to this process, however, because what we are really trying to do is review a program in advance of the budgetary decisions that take place in the agencies or in the Budget Bureau. The fact that an agency or bureau science adviser may feel that his program should have a certain budgetary level doesn't necessarily mean that the secretary of his department or the agency head is going to agree. There are limitations to what can be done in programming oceanography or weather or water or medical research or research in any other area that involves a large number of governmental units.

I would like to say just a brief word about the role of the Office of Science and Technology (OST) and the Federal Council for Science and Technology. OST has been extremely helpful. Donald Hornig and his staff have worked closely with the Budget Bureau, and we have all worked together as part of the President's staff. There have been no secrets between us. There has been a full sharing of the considerations that go into these decisions. They are a part of the budget process and have been extremely helpful to us.

Basic R&D Policies

In spite of our efforts to quantify benefits and costs, budgeting remains a highly judgmental process. There is very little in the area of research and development that you can prove or demonstrate by a cost-benefit analysis, as you can, for example, in the public works field. Nonetheless, we have sought, in one way or another, to apply a number of policies.

Particularly during the last two or three years, we have made a conscious effort to try to develop centers of excellence in universities. The idea is to take institutions that have at least some promise of excellence and to build on their present capability. They need federal support, encouragement, and money.

We are also trying to distribute research more broadly. A new policy approved by President Johnson in September 1965 stated that, while we will continue the centers-of-excellence concept, we will also seek to spread our research and development assistance more broadly.[7] Some

---

[7] The policy was enunciated in two statements issued by the President on Sept. 13 and

700 institutions award the bachelor's degree in science. We probably cannot help all of them, but the idea is to extend support to a larger number than at present. The President has asked Hornig to report to him, I believe quarterly, for a while at least, on the progress that is being made in this area. The director of the National Science Foundation, Leland Haworth, is the chairman of the interagency committee attempting to implement this policy.

Thus, we have had a policy of trying to emphasize institutional, rather than project, support. By that we mean more and more unrestricted money, which the institutions can use without the restraints of narrow project limitations.

We have sought to relate manpower and dollars. Now this is probably the area in which we have had the greatest difficulty. We have to be honest and confess that we do not now have adequate projections of manpower needs or a full understanding of either the manpower requirements of R&D or the effect of R&D on new manpower supply.

With respect to the growth of university research grants, we have tried to keep ahead of the game. In the 1966 budget, we agreed with Leland Haworth and Donald Hornig to aim for a 15 percent growth in basic research funds going to the universities. We came out of Congress with some 17 percent in toto (not always allocated as we had requested, but nevertheless, overall, about a 17 percent growth). This year, because of the budget stringency, we are not doing as well. We will emerge, I believe, with something close to 10 percent.[8]

On large R&D projects, we feel that a great deal more can be done through cost-benefit analyses, although, as I have already indicated, there are limits to the usefulness of this method.

We must always remain alert to targets of opportunity afforded by a unique capability—a combination of good people and a good environment. Such opportunities will always arise, and we want to be able to take advantage of them even though they may not fit into a preconceived program and budget.

14, 1965: "Memorandum from the President to the Heads of Departments and Agencies," and "Statement of the President to the Cabinet on Strengthening the Academic Capability for Science throughout the Nation."

[8] In January 1968, Hugh Loweth of the Bureau of the Budget estimated the rise in federal expenditures for academic research at 6 percent in FY 1967 and 2 percent in FY 1968. A 13 percent increase (from an estimated $1.45 billion to $1.64 billion) was proposed in the FY 1969 budget; see Barbara Field, "Research Outlook," in *The Chronicle of Higher Education,* Feb. 12, 1968, p. 1.

One of our chronic, and very difficult, problems has been to maintain some balance between inhouse and extramural research. The people who are doing research in government laboratories feel that we favor extramural programs, and from criticisms we have received from some outside organizations I am sure that they feel that more money should be spent outside rather than within the government.

Some new inhouse facilities are being developed, such as the environmental health center at the Research Triangle in North Carolina; some ten water pollution laboratories, most of which were authorized several years ago; a major strengthening of the Bureau of Standards; and the Electronics Research Center of NASA in Boston, which is partly for inhouse research and partly to strengthen NASA's own capability to supervise contracts. But we still don't have a clear picture of when it is best to undertake research in-house and when it is best to undertake it by grants or contracts.

Nor do we have a very clear idea of when it is best for the National Science Foundation to finance basic research and when it is best for the program agencies to do so. Efforts have been made to define the relation of the NSF basic research budget to those of Defense, NASA, HEW, and other agencies, but this is very difficult to do. All that we can say is that we have tried to ensure that the program agencies had an adequate level of support for basic research and that they, rather than NSF, assumed responsibility for any research closely related to their mission. You can find exceptions to this rule, but, in general, that is our basic policy.

We have encouraged cost-sharing, which is part of what I had in mind by "targets of opportunity." After five or six years of effort, we have issued a policy in which indirect costs are no longer the only area where cost-sharing between the federal agencies and the sponsoring institutions can occur.[9]

Fiscal policy will always play a part in R&D decision-making. Political considerations will always play a part. We will always have, to some degree, to balance our basic research programs against our research and development effort. Vannevar Bush used to say that we should spend at least 8 to 10 percent of our total R&D budget on basic research. I am sure he did not regard this as a formula, but he was concerned that our basic research not be allowed to lag—as it had been during World War

[9] See Circular No. A-74, "Participation in the costs of research supported by Federal grants," issued by the Bureau of the Budget, December 13, 1965.

II—because when budgets are stringent it is easier to cut basic research than other R&D.

Finally—and this, in some ways, is the $64 question—how do you decide what the balance should be in the support of basic research in different fields? NSF faces this problem internally, and the Budget Bureau faces it on a government-wide basis. How do you decide that it is more important to build a 200-Bev accelerator, which costs $350 million, than it is to put that same amount of money into medical research or water research or some other field of basic research? There are no real tests that you can apply that will provide a formula or an automatic answer. And this brings me back to the point that I started with, that budgeting in this field, as in many others, is always going to be a highly judgmental process.

DISCUSSION

Is the Whole Budget Any More Than the Sum of Its Parts?

W A S   T H E availability of scientists and engineers considered in making up the federal R&D budget? one participant asked. "Availability" was not easy to calculate, it was observed, particularly in development programs, since technically trained personnel were not blocks of uniform composition and utility but highly versatile and flexible men. During NASA's great expansion, a government official recalled, it was charged that the space program would absorb all of the nation's technical manpower and rob other programs—particularly programs of civilian technology—of needed personnel; but this, in fact, did not happen.

The Relation of Budgets and Manpower Resources

Has any major R&D proposal ever been curtailed because of manpower considerations? another participant asked. James Killian was not, he noted, naïve or inexperienced. "He was an able and reasonable, disinterested man." Why, if manpower limitations had never proven an obstacle to the success of the nation's R&D programs, had Killian concluded that the availability of trained manpower had not been sufficiently considered before the government decided to launch upon one or another major program such as landing on the moon?[1]

"I don't know," one government official replied directly enough, proceeding to indicate how wrong he thought that conclusion was so far as the moon was concerned. NASA had done its job without hurting any other national program; it had instituted educational programs to "replace as many scientists and engineers as . . . [it] took out of the national pool," and it had progressed so far toward its 1970 goal that the national space effort was already [in February 1966] laying off some twenty thousand people.

". . . [N]obody knows much about the subject" of technical manpower, this official believed, and many anticipated shortages were projected by academic men who knew nothing about the aerospace industry:

They took the academic amount of $20,000 per researcher and applied it to . . . [the NASA] budget and found there couldn't be that many

[1] This is a reference to the following conclusion in a 1964 report by a committee of the National Academy of Sciences chaired by James R. Killian: "Before the government reaches a decision to undertake a great technological program (e.g., the lunar landing or the supersonic transport projects), it should make a careful assessment of the impact of the decision on the deployment and utilization of scientists and engineers.

"In view of the way in which certain government decisions have radically altered the pattern of deployment of scientists and engineers in recent years, it might be supposed that major decisions had been preceded by careful studies of their probable impact on the market for scientific and engineering manpower, and, more broadly, of their effect on the general direction of scientific and technological effort in the United States. Yet, so far as we can learn, no adequate studies of the impact of these decisions were in fact made before the decisions were taken. Indeed, meaningful studies probably could not have been made, partly because the information on which to base them was not available" (*Toward Better Utilization of Scientific and Engineering Talent, A Program for Action*, Report of the Committee on Utilization of Scientific and Engineering Manpower, National Academy of Sciences [1964], p. 13).

According to a reader of the discussion transcript, this conclusion "seemingly is taken out of context and the discussion somehow does not seem wholly relevant to the conclusions of the panel." As the title of its report suggests, the panel was mainly concerned with improving the utilization of scientists and engineers, regardless of whether they would prove to be in long or in short supply; indeed, the employment situation at the time was mixed, with both surpluses and shortages of specialized talent. Nonetheless, the report generally appeared to assume that long-term demand either would or *should* exceed the supply. The seminar discussion constituted a free-flowing (not, of course, a meticulous or scholarly) commentary on that assumption.

people. It turned out, in the subcontractor's plant, the item is not $20,000 but maybe $150,000 or $180,000 per scientist or engineer.

In other words, they . . . took the criterion that they knew about and tried to apply it and raised a lot of fears. There absolutely was no time in this program when . . . expansion was curtailed by [lack of] people— as a matter of fact, when some of the loudest noises were being made, there was unemployment among engineers in the [aerospace] centers. . . .

The men and companies involved in NASA's work were familiar with large expansion programs, this offical continued. Sperry, for instance, had gone from eight hundred to thirty-three thousand people in a very short period. NASA kept in close touch with the top people in the aerospace industry, and any company receiving a contract had to demonstrate where and how it would get the personnel to do the work.

DOD's experience resembled NASA's, according to an industrial participant. Just before Korea, Deputy Secretary Donald Quarles declared that manpower limitations would prevent the expansion of Defense activities. But they were not encountered during the sharp expansion that shortly followed. Today, the problem of technical manpower resources could be "almost totally" disregarded. "Perhaps if we go up another 50 percent . . . in some given area, yes, but overall, the manpower resources are splendid."

NASA's experience confirmed this outlook. After-the-fact studies showed that during the year of greatest expansion, major contractors "absorbed 28 percent of the personnel requirements . . . without hiring a soul. In other words, either they were hoarding or they upgraded people who had capacity to be upgraded." (Were people, also, shifted from commercial to government work? someone interjected.) And the studies showed that, as of the start of a given year, the firms hired ten thousand more persons than they had previously thought possible. "When you underestimate the versatility and the ingenuity of American industry to get on with the job, you make a mistake in this country."

But, another official wondered, wasn't that making light of a complicated problem? Was it so easy to determine, for example, if, because of the NASA program, universities have greater difficulty in hiring engineering faculty or if "the Department of Defense has programs crawl up a little and are less efficient and less productive than before?"

The question was not answered directly, but its purport was disparaged indirectly. Industry's great flexibility rested, to a degree Killian, for example, had not appreciated, upon its ability to upgrade people rapidly, so that technicians could do what an engineer had previously done and engineers could do far more than was expected. This ability (and, it was added, the possibility of moving qualified personnel from other activities back into R&D) gave the national pool of technical manpower a degree of flexibility far greater than that contributed each year by the additional number of scientists and engineers graduated from academic institutions.

Dr. Killian's main error, as an official saw it, was assuming that the 20–25 percent annual rate of expansion of federal R&D expenditures that prevailed from the late 1950's to the early 1960's would continue. "He did not foresee the stabilization of total R&D spending that has occurred the last fiscal year and this fiscal year, which has . . . taken some of the compression off the demand. . . ." Federal science agencies made the same mistake a couple of years ago when, asked for a five-year projection of their budgets, they estimated federal R&D expenditures of $22–23 billion by 1970. "This just simply isn't in the cards, as far as we can see. . . ."

"As soon as you put a good, hardheaded incentive contractor in a contract," said a good, hardheaded R&D administrator, "he looks to the scarcest commodity there is, which is that upper 5 percent. . . . [T]he greatest critical shortage . . . is in that top group. It isn't in warm bodies which call themselves engineers. . . . There is a real shortage of highly qualified, imaginative people. . . . That is the only shortage that I have encountered. . . ." In the late 1940's and early 1950's, a professor recollected, the same situation occurred in medical research, when it was argued first that the Veterans Administration and then that the National Institutes of Health could not expand their research greatly because of a shortage of medical researchers—a shortage, however, that "has never shown up." And, an economist thought, the point about medical research

> . . . could be extended . . . to the labor force as a whole. Three years ago it was widely contended that as the economy expanded the demand for labor would consist largely of the demand for highly skilled workers, whereas the pool of unemployed consisted of unskilled workers. In fact, demand has expanded and unemployment has shrunk. The unemployed have been taken into employment. There has been an upgrading among the ranks of the employed and the shortages have not occurred.

However, two participants pointed out, it was not sufficient to consider only the supply of research manpower, without considering where it came from. The government might be able to buy all the medical and physical science research personnel it needed, but did that not contribute to the national shortage of physicians and of college science teachers? And, though the necessary numbers of researchers might be sustained, was not their average quality going down?

Three Kinds of Political Influence

During the last decade, a good many participants believed, political factors had grown more important in R&D budgetary decisions. They took at least three main forms.

One form was geographic—a pressure to put money in a particular place. In part, an official indicated, such pressure was founded on the "false premise . . . that this is a bright, shiny new nickel and all you need to do is to have an R&D installation in your state or your district and you are in, because everything will group itself around it and you will have full employment." "Aren't you getting too sophisticated . . . ?" rejoined a participant who suggested that the gross sums now involved in the construction and operation of R&D facilities were quite enough to make them attractive political plums. That would only be a "one-time effect," the official replied, like building a bridge, "plus the operating benefits, the number of employees it brings to the area"; but ". . . the notion is abroad . . . that an R&D installation now will bring you a lot of [additional] economic development benefits. . . ." That notion was at least questionable. Thus, although the large NACA (now NASA) Lewis Laboratory had been working on propulsion engines at Cleveland since 1939, "there is not a single engine manufacturer anywhere near Cleveland. . . ."

Even if the theoretical point were questionable, remarked a congressman, "what difference does it make?" The political pressure remained. "Has anyone rejected an installation," a participant asked rhetorically, "because the [theoretical] point . . . has not been established . . . ?"

A second form of political influence was, of course, programmatic. "Agriculture has a terrific clientele. . . . It is hard to cut anything out of agricultural research. This has gone up and up and up." The medical research budget "defies all explanation. . . . It is all out of proportion . . . in terms of a balanced budget presentation on research for the government as a whole. But it is not out of proportion in terms of the political significance that medical research holds for this country." Research on problems of pollution might well be the next area to receive a big financial boost.

Finally, a third kind of political influence was that resulting from such congressional inquiries into the broad national goals of research and development as those conducted by Representatives Elliott, Daddario, and Reuss. This type of critical examination and elucidation, it was observed, had no taint of sectarian motive and was an entirely legitimate and constructive political activity.

The influence on budgetary allocations of special reports by the President's Science Advisory Committee, the National Academy of Sciences, and other bodies was briefly considered and the conclusion reached that, particularly when the report has its origin in a public problem identified by a government agency, it is likely to have a measurable impact. Examples were the report on *Restoring the Quality of Our Environment*; the Gilliland report, which "had a decided effect on policy decisions"; and, some years earlier, the DeWitt report on Soviet professional manpower.[2]

Reports by committees of Congress and by the General Accounting Office also had a decided effect, and there were indications that President Johnson, in particular, took them very seriously. ". . . [W]henever . . . some member of Congress or a committee . . . feels it has a good issue that needs to be brought out and put before the public," said an old Washington hand, it is likely to have some effect on the budgetary process.

Does an "R&D Budget" Exist before, or Only after, the Fact?

One professor noted certain similarities between the budgetary process in government and in industry.

> After the fact, it is easy to go down a list of projects and say, "This is in" and "That is out," for all these good reasons, and it makes it look as though that was the process by which the budget was arrived at. That

[2] *Restoring the Quality of Our Environment*, A Report of the Environmental Pollution Panel of the President's Science Advisory Committee chaired by John Tukey, was issued by the White House in November 1965; *Meeting Manpower Needs in Science and Technology*, known as the "Gilliland" report after Edwin R. Gilliland, chairman of the PSAC Panel on Scientific and Technical Manpower, was released in December 1962; and the study of *Soviet Professional Manpower*, by Nicholas DeWitt, was published by the National Science Foundation in 1955.

is, we apply these difficult judgments to the specific projects, and when we get finished, we add up the total and that is the budget. But if I look at a figure here on page 115 . . . I find a curiously linear relationship over the years from '58 to '67, which suggests there may be some aggregate effect at work here. My question is: Is the total figure decided first and then the breakdowns made within it, or [is it done] . . . by adding up all those good things that should be done?[3]

"Neither," was the answer he got; the Budget Bureau seldom thought of budgets in terms of R&D per se but rather in terms of the programs or functions of which R&D was a component. Some people think otherwise, because of the special analysis of R&D obligations which is included as an annex to the budget. But that annex is an after-the-fact aggregate; agency allocations to R&D are not considered in the context of a national R&D budget but rather in the context of each agency's budget and mission. Most of the so-called R&D budget results, after all, from decisions in only three budgets—those of Defense, NASA, and NIH—and these are made "on mission grounds."

The professor was dubious:

This is quite different from every budgeting process that I have ever looked at. It is usually quite hierarchical. That is, the funds are broken down by major categories and there is a stability in these categories, and then the breakdowns continue from that point.

This suggests that everybody in the government competes for every dollar. The only constraint is the total—that there is no sublevel consideration. That everybody is after whatever it is under a billion dollars, and it is free competition. I find that hard to imagine.

That isn't exactly right, four present or former Budget Bureau hands agreed. The budget ". . . isn't open season to get your hunk of $112 billion." From the earliest planning stages to the days of final decision, there is a constant "iterative process" of back and forth discussion between agency and Budget Bureau officials. At the outset, the agency indicates in broad terms "what it is thinking about and . . . what trade-offs it expects to be able to make," while the bureau, in turn, gives the agency "a guideline as to what the ball game . . . can stand in that sector of public policy"—and "when the President has given . . . his third roll-

---

[3] The reference here was to a graph of obligations for research by six major federal agencies and by the total federal government, fiscal years 1959–67, in "Special Analysis I: Federal Research, Development, and Related Programs" (*Special Analyses: Budget of the United States, Fiscal Year 1967* [Bureau of the Budget, January 1966], p. 115).

back order," the guidelines "begin to have some meaning." "There are all kinds of interactions back and forth, and the notion of a very clean model of decision-making—someone sets a ceiling and you allocate within it . . .—just doesn't help [to] describe what happens at all."

A second professor seemed as unpersuaded as the first:

> . . . [C]ompare this [process] with industrial budget-making, where every laboratory director in a large industrial company does commercial research and not government-supported research. He makes up his budget by approving projects and believes thoroughly that he has aggregated a number of projects; he has examined each of them and evaluated it and included it. And then if you look at the end result, the R&D budget for next year, in any company, in any industry, that has been studied, can be predicted by a simple three-variable equation: the R&D budget last year; the anticipated sales or cash flow next year; and another factor, which is, whether you are tending to increase or decrease your R&D budget and how do you relate to others in the industry.
>
> This simple three-variable equation will give you a prediction within a quarter squared of 99.4 for the next year's budget—and no laboratory director believes it.

"It wouldn't work on the federal budget," rejoined a close observer of that budget. "Without having looked at the numbers, I would guess that something close to 60 or 70 percent of the increase in the R&D budget in the last four years is accounted for by NASA. And it is not continuing to increase, and . . . this is the principal reason for the rough stabilization of the total R&D budget.

The professor persisted, "You say you face these difficult trade-offs. Well, there are no trade-offs unless there is a budget constraint." And a participant from the Hill rallied to his support: "The RDT&E [research, development, testing, and evaluation] budget in Defense is $6 billion or $7 billion . . . , but they know what the total is, and the restraints work before they come up [to the Budget Bureau or the Hill] and they have to be within the bounds of acceptability."

PROFESSOR: I had a student do a thesis for me in a large industrial firm, and he was trying to find the criteria by which items get into the budget and do not. He spent a summer in a large electronics company, and you expected to find projects approved and rejected. He was looking for a criterion and never found one rejected because of this informal communication. Nobody proposed something that they didn't already know would be approved.

GOVERNMENT OFFICIAL: That is not true in the federal budget.

The difference in outlook was at least partially resolved by one participant who indicated that opponents had really been arguing about two
different points. "Are we arguing about whether there are predetermined accrued ceilings applicable to various sectors of the budget, or
[whether] . . . there [is] a predetermined accrued ceiling for R&D expenditures? I think the answer to the former question is yes, and the
answer to the latter question is no."

Two Final Points

The justification for the government, and particularly "mission-oriented
agencies," to sponsor basic research was the penultimate matter taken up
by the group.

A NASA representative reported the rationale advanced by Hugh
Dryden in 1949 for supporting the basic research of good men. Periodically, their work should be reviewed and the "state of the art" summarized; and from such a summary, a designer or an engineer could say,
". . . [O]n the basis of that review, that body of information, I can do
something, I can produce a machine or a tool or try something new with
respect to material."

The productive, creative research ideas, an industry representative declared, "come from about 5 percent of the people and they seem to repeat . . . , [while] 20 percent of the people . . . have worked . . . all
their lives and they never seem to produce a . . . thing except another
paper which no one reads. . . ." Though a government official agreed, he
did not believe it was desirable for the government to support only "the
repeaters." Many problems have to be worked on, he observed, even
though one cannot know who will come through with the key ideas. ". . .
Edward Teller was working on the H-Bomb idea for many years and
didn't get anywhere. . . . I am not sure one can predict who will get the
idea and when." To make progress, one needs a ripeness both of ideas
and of the technology necessary to implement them. "The Air Force
wasted a lot of money on space ideas when the technology wasn't ready
for it."

A different matter was of concern to one participant: the government's inattention, in his opinion, to the vital phase of *engineering* new
civilian technology.

[NASA] . . . doesn't do just development; [it] . . . engineers the thing to where it is a completed product; it is put into use; it works and you get something out of it.

The DOD—they don't just do research and development; they engineer it all the way to the end.

We seem to have a feeling in this country that if the government does research and development and it worries about the engineering of the things that go into NASA, DOD, and the AEC, that . . . all other elements are picked up by the private sector. The point that worries me is, there are so many things in the private sector that industry will not pick up, cannot pick up, because there is no profit motive. . . . Now, we keep saying something about transportation, air pollution, water retrieval, and so on. These are all major problems in this country, and . . . we don't need any research on these, we don't need very much development. We need somebody to engineer it, build it, and if it works, say, "Boys, that is the way we do it from now on." If it fails, somebody has to pick up the tab. . . .

One thing that sticks in my craw is this business of sewage disposal. A plain, ordinary mundane thing. We still dispose of sewage the way we have for centuries, almost. Yet, if a man comes along and invents a new way of digesting sewage, and he does it in his laboratory—and he does it in five-gallon crocks, eventually—and it works, now, the next step is to build a pilot plant and see if it will work with a million gallons a day. Now, just try to find somebody who will build that.

You go to any city and say, "I want to have you build this new sewage disposal plant. It may work. There is a four out of five chance that it will work." What will the city fathers say? "Oh no, we are not going to waste the taxpayers' money. We have got to build a plant that is sure of working, because if we build one that doesn't work and tear it out we will never get re-elected." And the state board of health will say, "We have no history of the performance of this thing. We won't let you build it."

Somebody's got . . . to step in and do this sort of thing. This is all through our economy. Sewage disposal, transportation, water retrieval, rain making, and so on. It is not taken care of by NASA, DOD, AEC, and it is not being taken care of by private industry.

My plea is that we find some way of supporting these sorts of things, not just through research and development, but engineer them and get them working so the people can use them.

If there was such a demand for improved sewage disposal, why, it was asked, did not private industry use its own money to develop improved sewage plants? The answer came in the form of a question: "Who would make a profit on it?"

The new budget, two officials reminded the highly skeptical partici-pant, had two or three hundred million dollars precisely for the con-struction of such sewer and water plants.[4] And there, as the group ad-journed, a most interesting issue was left suspended in the air.

[4] "New obligational authority of $100 million is requested in 1967 for grants to communities and metropolitan areas for water and sewer facilities. The grants are available only to those communities which (1) plan, jointly with other communities where necessary, for the comprehensive development of the entire urban area involved and (2) develop an adequate program for meeting the water and sewer needs of that area" (*The Budget of the United States Government, Fiscal Year Ending June 30, 1967,* p. 114). This program of the Department of Housing and Urban Development appears, however, to emphasize area planning rather than the development of new kinds of water and sewer works.

HERBERT ROBACK

Presenting Scientific
and Technical Programs
to the Congress

W H A T D O E S the Congress need to know about
scientific and technical programs for intelligent legislative action? How
can the executive best respond? What are the strong and weak points in
the process of policy and program development as a joint endeavor of
the legislative and executive branches of the government?

The observations set forth herein are those of one Capitol Hill staff
member. Perspectives of the legislative and executive branches differ. It
is well to remember, also, that the Congress itself is not a monolithic
institution. It speaks with many voices. It has two houses and many committees, each with its distinctive style of work, legislative responsibilities, and institutional practices.

Background Information

The Congress needs information on many subjects to properly discharge its duties in authorizing and funding federal programs. Beyond
data on the specific program requirements, the Congress seeks basic information to gain perspective, to collate related government activities, to
identify developing problem areas, to educate new members, and to inform the public. Scholars and students, government administrators and

233

news reporters—all interested citizens—look to the Congress for sources of basic information not readily attainable elsewhere. The Congress, through its committees and hearing process is a convenient forum for the assembly of expert witnesses, presentation of technical and policy papers, and public discussion of important national issues.

Standing committees of the Congress initiate broad basic studies from time to time, preparatory to considering new legislation or in connection with annual authorizing or funding bills. When a matter cuts across many departments or agencies, or is of contemporary interest to a broad public, a select or special committee of inquiry may be formed, as in the case of the Select Committee on Government Research, the Elliott committee.[1]

The standing Committee on Government Operations in each house, with across-the-board jurisdiction over the executive branch from the standpoint of economy and efficiency, also is in a good position to examine problems with a broad reach and multiagency involvement. In fact, the Committee on Government Operations in the House has created a subcommittee for research and technical operations, following a recommendation by the Elliott committee.[2]

Free from the annual grind of authorizing and funding legislation, the select committee with limited tenure, or the standing committee with broad, flexible jurisdiction, performs important functions of information-gathering and education. To a large extent, though by no means exclusively, the committees depend on executive departments and agencies for the gathering of information that underlies the formation of national policy in scientific and technical areas. Committee staffs may define the areas of inquiry and prepare detailed questionnaires. The National Academy of Sciences or university groups or other nonprofit organiza-

[1] H. Res. 504, approved by unanimous vote on Sept. 11, 1963, established a select committee of nine members "to make a complete, full, and thorough investigation of the numerous research programs being conducted by sundry departments and agencies of the Federal Government. . . ." Representative Carl Elliott, sponsor of the resolution, was named chairman. The resolution directed the committee to make its reports to the House of Representatives by December 1, 1964. The committee expired with the Eighty-eighth Congress on January 3, 1965.

[2] By the summer of 1966, the Research and Technical Programs Subcommittee, chaired by Representative Henry S. Reuss, had held hearings and issued reports under the titles *Conflicts between the Federal Research Programs and the Nation's Goals for Higher Education* (H. Rept. 1158, 89 Cong. 1 sess. [Oct. 13, 1965]); *Plugging the Dollar Drain: Cutting Federal Expenditures for Research and Related Activities Abroad* (H. Rept. 1453, 89 Cong. 2 sess. [April 27, 1966]); and *Federal Research and Development Programs: The Decisionmaking Process* (H. Rept. 1664, 89 Cong. 2 sess. [June 27, 1966]).

tions may be called upon for special studies. But for the most part, the executive branch, through its large action agencies, its coordinating councils, and its grant or contract leverage on research and development, commands superior resources for these information-gathering tasks. Many needed inquiries are sparked by congressional requests. The administrator who would serve the Congress well responds promptly. He also anticipates the needs for basic studies and conducts them on his own initiative.

One of the difficulties in this informing and educating process is that the basic information for rational policy determination is often lacking, or can be gathered only at great expense in time and money, or even when gathered, is too tentative or inconclusive for intelligent policy formulation. Thus the fault may lie not in a dilatory executive response but in the elusive nature of the material.

A perusal of the reports of the Elliott and Daddario[3] committees on research and development reveals numerous questions of national scope and import which the executive as well as the Congress ought to be better informed about. These include questions about the adequacy of government organization for the full use of scientific resources, shortages and misuse of scientific manpower, neglected areas of scientific research, the relationship of science and technology to economic growth, lack of uniformity in grant and contract procedures, dependence of the universities on federal financial support, and techniques for judging the quality of scientific output.

In one sense, these are perennial questions. They will be asked again and again, and whatever answers are forthcoming will, in the nature of the case, be tentative, related to contemporary issues and subject to revision with the passage of time. Nevertheless, we can depend on the Congress to continue the never ending quest for broad knowledge as a foundation for intelligent public policy.

The Program Picture

Congress' interest in a myriad of details often baffles and irritates administrators, but Congress also wants to see whole the picture of each spe-

[3] On August 23, 1963, shortly before the Elliott committee was established, a Subcommittee on Science, Research, and Development was established by Chairman George P. Miller of the House Committee on Science and Astronautics. Representative Emilio Q. Daddario was named chairman of the subcommittee.

cific program. When programs are presented by agency officers, there will be close questioning about their extent and duration, their cumulative costs, the costs of accessory or supporting systems, and the relationships among programs of similar types, which may have avoidable duplication.

In posture hearings and budget reviews, the broad picture is painted by the department or agency head; the details are filled in by the technical and administrative experts who accompany him. Secretary of Defense Robert S. McNamara went further than other department or agency heads in taking upon himself the responsibility for presenting comprehensive statements of department policies and programs in the context of world-wide developments. In 1965, for example, his posture statement to the House Armed Services Committee ran to 207 mimeographed pages in the unclassified version. It tried to set out the whys and wherefores of the department programs rather than simply to tick off line items.

Perhaps other administrators ought to take a page from Secretary McNamara's book and attempt a lengthier explanation of policy, saying where the agency is now and where it is going. The programming concept, which has been developed to a high degree by the Defense Department, fits in well with this approach.

The Congress is wary of the zealous or ambitious administrator who wants a modest appropriation as a "foot in the door" to commit the Congress and ensure larger appropriations in the following years. Of course, it may be good politics and policy to start with modest proposals in order to gain time for educating the Congress to the larger dimensions and wider implications of the program. If so, wisdom dictates that the administrator act in concert with the sponsoring committee. To put something over by misrepresentation or concealment of the future plan of action is not rewarding in the long run.

While the Congress wants to see the picture whole—to see where a given course of action is heading—the complex committee structure does not lend itself to unified treatment of comprehensive programs involving multiple agencies. There is no neat way to divide up the legislative workload, no easy way to change committee jurisdictions to accommodate broad national programs. Many committees have an interest, just as many departments and agencies have an interest, in given programs or policies.

The situation is not hopeless. Committee jurisdictions are flexible enough so that total program information can be collated and reviewed even if authorization and funding are parceled out among several committees. The Congress depends mainly on the coordinative mechanisms of the executive branch such as the Office of Science and Technology, the Federal Council on Science and Technology, and the Bureau of the Budget to perform these integrating tasks. Indeed, congressional committees have provided the spur for much of this integrative study and analysis. For example, in a 1963 appropriation act, the Congress directed the Bureau of the Budget to provide for each succeeding year "a horizontal budget showing (*a*) the totality of the programs for meteorology, (*b*) the specific aspects of the program and funding assigned to each agency, and (*c*) the estimated goals and financial requirements."[4] Weather services and research (the programs which prompted this directive) involve at least seventeen government agencies.[5]

In oceanography, another area of research involving many agencies and scientific disciplines, considerable progress has also been made in recent years toward identifying component activities and presenting a coordinated program to the Congress.[6]

Automatic data processing, which is of interest to most government agencies and vital to research and development because of the latter's large costs and difficult management problems, was the subject of a comprehensive Budget Bureau study at the behest of a congressional committee.[7] Specific legislation was pending, but more facts had to be known, problems more clearly identified, and management alternatives more carefully examined.

---

[4] P.L. 87-843, 76 Stat. 1097, approved Oct. 18, 1962.

[5] See *Government Weather Programs (Military and Civilian Operations and Research),* A Report by the House Committee on Government Operations, H. Rept. 177, 89 Cong. 1 sess. (March 17, 1965). The report was prepared by the Military Operations Subcommittee under the chairmanship of Representative Chet Holifield. The basic data were assembled by the Science Policy Research Division of the Legislative Reference Service. This was the first major assignment of the newly formed division.

[6] P.L. 89-454, 80 Stat. 203, approved June 17, 1966, created the National Council on Marine Resources and Engineering Development and the fifteen-member Commission on Marine Science, Engineering, and Resources to make comprehensive studies and development plans in this field. These bodies have an eighteen-month tenure under the act.

[7] U.S. Bureau of the Budget, *Inventory of Automatic Data Processing (ADP) Equipment in the Federal Government,* Prepared for the Subcommittee on Census and Government Statistics of the House Committee on Post Office and Civil Service, 88 Cong. 1 sess. (Oct. 25, 1963); and *1964 Inventory of Automatic Data Processing (ADP) Equipment in the Federal Government,* 88 Cong. 2 sess. (July 1964).

Repeat Performances

Congress prefers a dual legislative process of authorization and appropriation by separate committees. In a bicameral legislature this means
that an ordinary policy or program requires four-way consideration—
separate action by two committees in each house—not to mention the
joint action of conference committees when there is disagreement between the houses.

The practice, in recent years, is for all major programs to receive
yearly authorizations. Thus, the foreign aid program, the antipoverty
program, the atomic energy program, the space program, the defense
program—using the term "program" for the total agency budget—are
reviewed each year before their respective committees of jurisdiction.
These reviews take the form of posture hearings, program justifications,
line item reviews, or some combination of these forms. After action by
each committee in each house and agreement between the two houses of
Congress, an authorization bill is signed by the President and becomes a
law. Then the process is repeated (often concurrently) before the appropriations committee of each house, and an appropriation act is the final
result.

One can argue which is more important—the authorization process or
the appropriation process. The authorizing committees consider themselves the policy-making committees since they set the program boundaries and the budget ceilings. By parliamentary rule (or statute) funds
ordinarily cannot be appropriated before a program is separately authorized by law. On the other hand, dollars are what make the world go
around; dollars have a way of making their own policy. While the appropriations committees cannot appropriate more than is authorized,
often they appropriate less or nothing at all. An authorization statute can
remain a dead letter for decades for want of an appropriation, but this is
the rare case. Usually, appropriations come within shouting distance of
the authorizations, and in the defense and space and atomic energy business, they are frequently quite close.

The National Science Foundation, which sponsors and supports a
large part of the basic research in universities through grants of federal
funds, gets no yearly authorization. Its program authority stems from the
1950 enabling legislation, and its yearly course of action and general

destiny are shaped by the decisions of the appropriations committees. Even though the Congress places a high value on basic research, and the appropriations committees have done rather well by the National Science Foundation, there are those who believe that congressional evaluation of scientific policies and basic research trends would be more effective if a yearly authorization requirement were superimposed on the foundation funding process.[8]

By custom and precedent, the House of Representatives is the initiator of appropriations. Although in theory the Senate contests this funding primacy, it has not seriously challenged the practice. The House Committee on Appropriations is the single most powerful committee in the whole Congress. It holds the key to the door of the public treasury. It usually takes a tough-minded attitude in anticipation of padded agency budgets.

The agencies, for their part, may pad their budgets in anticipation of cuts. It is a vicious cycle, but there is no malevolence in it. By the time the appropriation bill is through the committee, both claimant and dispenser of funds should understand each other fairly well. If the agency head suffers a deep budget cut, there is always the Senate Appropriations Committee ready to hear appeals or reclamas.[9] Frequently, the Senate is the restorer (at least partially) of funds cut by the House.

House-Senate compromises on the budget tend to be a somewhat arbitrary splitting of differences rather than a careful reevaluation of each line item. Still, the administrator must be prepared to make a convincing case in the money court of appeals. The bulges of budget fat are not too difficult to see. The lean hard budget stands up better against punching.

From the executive agency viewpoint, how the Congress handles its yearly budget is a matter of great concern. The budget is the key to agency operations. It is the yearly plan of action and the claim on funds and resources. In the budget document are crystallized the agency's plans for the coming fiscal year, its hopes, its expectations, its tentative com-

[8] See the debate on the bill (H.R. 5404) amending the National Science Foundation Act, which passed the House of Representatives on April 12, 1967 (*Congressional Record,* daily ed., April 12, 1967, p. H3978). Representative James G. Fulton, ranking Republican on the Science and Astronautics Committee, declared himself in favor of an annual authorization for the National Science Foundation, but the final bill contained no such provision.

[9] "Reclama" has come into general usage in the federal budget process, having the same general meaning as "appeal." *Navy Contract Law* (2d ed., 1959) identifies "reclama" as "a colloquialism originating in the Philippine Islands."

mitments. The dentiny of the yearly budget affects the larger destiny of
the program or of the agency itself.

Preoccupation with the budget often makes the administrator impatient and irritated with the repetitive process of authorization and appropriation. He sees the required attendance of top-level officers at lengthy
committee hearings as a waste of time and talent. The Department of
Defense, which in a previous administration strongly resisted the yearly
authorization statute, now prepares a single-package presentation for
both authorizing and funding purposes. Even the administrator who is
reconciled to this dual process may be resentful that still other committees, though they lack authorization and funding leverage, may want to
know all about his agency and its program because of implications for
small business, for example, or because of a desire to review the economy and efficiency of operation.

The administrator will do well to give the highest priority to all
congressional requests, whether for routine information or for personal
appearances. The Congress, although it depends heavily on its standing
committees for legislative expertise, does not favor a monopoly or overcentralization of committee power and influence. Committees with
overlapping or even concurrent jurisdiction are means for broader dis-
semination of knowledge about agency policies and programs within
Congress. Intercommittee rivalry, in other words, has beneficial aspects.
Several committees looking at the same problem, oftentimes from different points of view or for different purposes, serve to broaden perspectives, bring out hidden or neglected facets, and get more people interested.
The committee structure is part of the internal checks and balances
system within the Congress. Repeat performances are to be expected;
they should be planned for and accommodated.

Minute Detail

What Congress demands of the executive in the way of information may
not always coincide with what many believe it ought to have. For example, efforts toward budget reform frequently run up against the hard
wall of congressional insistence on types of information which are more
meaningful to politicians than to policy-makers. The result in recent
years has been to retain certain conventional categories of information

while recasting the budget in program terms so that the Congress as well as the executive will see the picture whole.

Those who peruse the voluminous printed hearings on program authorizations and appropriations often despair at what appears to be aimless questioning, the preoccupation with minute details, and lack of follow-up inquiry in important program areas. One must remember that the legislator is a politician as well as a statesman. Questions of interest to his constituents may seem irrelevant to those who wield the broad brush and see the big picture. But these questions, nevertheless, will continue to be asked, and the conscientious administrator will make adequate response.

The legislator as well as the administrator is a very busy person. He has many demands on his time and attention. His constituents besiege him constantly with innumerable requests, and his legislative concerns run the whole gamut of domestic and world affairs. Therefore, he depends heavily on his committee chairman and on the professional staff for continuity and competence in committee work. Of course, the legislator who wants to be reasonably well, if not fully, informed has an obligation to do his homework. He must be willing to give sufficient time to study, hearings, conferences, and the technical work of drafting bills and reports.

This obligation is matched on the executive side by the government representative who must be sufficiently briefed or backed up by his subordinates to supply the information requested, to be responsive and candid, and to give honest answers to relevant (or even irrelevant) questions. The witness who is uninformed or disingenuous is wasting a legislator's valuable time and jeopardizing his own program.

The government witness who is reasonably well acquainted with congressional practice and precedents and the content of the previous year's hearings will be apt to make a better appearance and impression. He will know that the Congress wants hard information, not soft soap. Perhaps because the nature of the political trade develops such attributes, the congressman is impatient of wordiness, vagueness, equivocation, inconsistency, and irrelevance in others. He wants information that is concise in detail on the points at issue.

Executive Lobbying

Executive lobbying of the legislative branch is a fact of political life. It is the contemporary style that the President have a program for peace and prosperity and social progress and that it be presented to the Congress in terms of specific legislative and funding measures. The President's program then becomes the measuring rod for congressional performance. Whether the Congress is good or bad, fast or slow, efficient or unwieldy, is rated by the extent to which it adopts in legislative form the administration's program.

The President, in the modern manner, does not sit by passively during this period of congressional consideration and concern. He lobbies the legislators by personal telephone calls, breakfast conferences, outings in the presidential yacht or at the ranch. His lieutenants beat a daily path to Capitol Hill, buttonholing recalcitrant legislators and conferring with legislative leaders on strategy. Through press conferences and televised broadcasts, the President also appeals to the public over the heads of the Congress. As chief dispenser of patronage and party favors, and as chief spokesman for party principles and positions, the President has added leverage in gaining legislative acceptance of his program.

The agency head or bureau chief who has suffered budget cuts or program excisions on the executive side may be inspired to lobby the Congress through the back door. This is risky business and often a painful personal dilemma because it divides loyalties. Many officials have squirmed uncomfortably on the witness stand while making a pitch for a desired agency program that has not been included in the administration's program. The usual justification is that they are giving their own opinion when they fail to hew to the line. If the particular committee favors the agency position, clandestine lobbying is tolerated. It offers a source of inside information and arms the committee for critical commentary on the administration cutbacks, with the Bureau of the Budget frequently taking the onus rather than the chief executive himself.

Officially the Congress frowns on excessive self-advertising or promotional work by executive agencies. There is even a criminal statute (18 U.S.C. 1913) barring federal officers or employees from using appropriated funds to lobby for legislation. The administrator-lobbyist will insist, if cornered, that he is merely responding to congressional requests for information. And of course, it is understandable that the agency wants to put its best foot forward with the Congress as well as the public. If dull prosaic testimony and technical jargon before congressional committees can be lightened by exhibits, displays, and other graphic renditions, so much the better. A picture is worth many words, and it makes a good prop for news photographs the congressman can hang on his wall or send to a constituent.

NASA is one agency that spices up its testimony with numerous visual aids—movies, scale models, slides, brochures. Techniques of these kinds are helpful, but they should not be allowed to become too razzle-dazzle. The Congress is willing to be shown and to be convinced; it doesn't want to be oversold.

Field Visits

An important part of the educational and informing process for members and committees of Congress is the visit to the field—at home or abroad. Inspections, briefings, conferences, and discussions at the field site, activity, base, or installation are useful in many ways. Field personnel usually are pleased by congressional visits and honored that their work is noticed or their responsibilities appreciated. They are eager to demonstrate technical operations, to cite achievements in performance and management, and to talk directly with elected officials who may be in a position to influence their individual programs or activities. The congressmen, for their part, are proud to see visible evidence of great facilities built, weapons and spacecraft tested, forces deployed or maneuvered—the varied manifestations of their country's might and main.

There are subtle as well as obvious advantages to seeing and touching things and talking with people at the operating level, far away from the stuffy hearing rooms or the arid disquisitions of professional briefers. It is not exactly a gimmick, for example, that the Joint Committee on Atomic Energy calls a meeting in a nuclear submarine submerged and under way. Members of Congress who have been places and seen things have more graphic images of programs in action, a better understanding of men and machines at work, a greater interest and incentive to ask penetrating questions of top-level administrators. More often than not, people in the field are more frank and outspoken than wary, case-hardened bureaucrats in Washington. Their angle of vision may be narrower, but they are doers rather than talkers, and members of Congress, with their practical bent, always like to know how things work out. Thus firsthand observations give opportunities to counter glib assertions and glossed-over difficulties and problems in the committee room.

External Factors

Congress lives and works in a political environment which is and must be sensitive to changing tides of public opinion, world crises, and urgent demands of the domestic economy and society. The effective administrator cannot take a stiff-necked attitude toward the political necessities. His long-range planning is important and necessary, but he must realize that the Congress is moved less by the intrinsic merit of these plans than by compelling external pressures toward one type of program or another.

New missile or space systems will be pushed if Soviet military technology is active in the same area. The fate of the supersonic transport will be shaped as much by the decisions of European manufacturers as by our own government agencies. The Apollo program, with its ten-year draft on the nation's scientific, technical, and other resources, its $20 billion-plus cost, and its heavy impact on the destinies of whole communities, regions, and occupations, was based not on the planners' judgment about the optimum use of the nation's resources during the decade of the 1960's but on the simple political judgment that we ought to beat the Russians to the moon and on the accompanying scientific judgment that the enterprise was feasible in a ten-year span. This was an executive determination, but it was supported strongly in the Congress when the post-Sputnik excitement was still strong. And if there were afterthoughts and soul-searching in some sectors of the Congress and elsewhere, this merely reflects the fact that other problems intrude and other urgent needs invite attention.

As a comparatively long-range and very costly program, Apollo had these advantages when initially presented: its goal or mission was finite (landing on the moon); it was a response to a basic community impulse (reaction to the Soviet threat); it was a big, bold, new enterprise in the American tradition; it was manageable in its dimensions (resources were available or could be mobilized); it was predictable (even if tentatively) in its timing and costs; and it was largely within the purview of a single committee in each house of Congress to promote and protect it.

In other types of programs, in which many executive agencies and committees of Congress have an interest, where the values are high but their realization is not so immediately compelling and the immediate goals are less clear (for example, oceanography), or where differences prevail in philosophy and outlook between sharply contending interests, the particular subject matter is likely to be more exposed to recurring congressional debate than to immediate congressional action.

Boldness and Innovation

In the contemporary governmental scene, the Congress is not ordinarily the innovator of policy. The Congress is the reviewer and appraiser and ratifier. The President initiates and proposes; the Congress disposes by review, evaluation, modification, and sometimes by delay or outright rejection. The policy that finally prevails is a partnership effort, wherein the President identifies and gives form to the national need, and the Congress reconciles and accommodates the conflicting economic, regional, and local interests which bear on the national need. In this sense, the Congress ensures that policies will be more widely accepted and supported, and hence more stable and enduring, even though some costs resulting from compromises may be entailed.

These relationships are not invariable. When the executive is strong, the legislative influence seems weaker by contrast. When the executive is weak, Congress is disposed to fill the vacuum. There are times when the Congress initiates a program because it commends itself to common sense and public acceptance but has encountered a blind spot in the executive eye. Often the role of the Congress is to goad reluctant agencies into useful programs or to give bold support where executive action is reluctant or timid. The nuclear navy, as one example, owes its timely existence to the forceful position of the Joint Committee on Atomic Energy.

There are also bold executive proposals or programs which the Congress delays or rejects for reasons of politics or economy or, occasionally, perversity. It is often remarked that the President makes too many legislative recommendations to the Hill and that the Congress could not possibly act on all of them in a given legislative session, or even dare to approve all the federal expenditures such programs would entail.

There are programs that the Congress cannot reject, either because they deal directly with the nation's defense, or because we are deeply committed, as in the lunar landing program, or because the wheels of government cannot be allowed to grind to a halt, as in the case of the yearly supply bills, or because the programs are politically appealing, especially in an election year, as in the cases of pay raises for postmen or funds for heart research. The Congress does, however, increase or decrease appropriation requests; it does modify legislative drafts that come down from the executive; it does pioneer new developments or chart new courses. In short, the Congress does legislate—as the Constitution intended.

Common Sense

Those who are concerned about the seeming vagaries of the political process and the piecemeal approach of congressional committees to programs which are national in scope and import must reconcile themselves to this aspect of congressional life. The Congress, as I said before, is not a monolithic body. It does not represent homogeneous interests. It is not a long-range planning body. It wants to leave open the options for common sense, for political maneuver, for compromise of conflicting interests, and for rapid adjustment to changing public demand.

I once remarked in another context that common sense is a valuable legislative commodity not always found in administrative hierarchies or technical groups—a kind of freewheeling judgment based on long experience, healthy cynicism, exposure to conflicting claims and varied sources of information, and close touch with the people.[10] Congress ofttimes can see more clearly than the technical experts what is wrong, or what is needed, or what is excess.

Common sense judgments rather than refined studies of cost effectiveness or complex theoretical justifications impel the Congress to take the initiative in pushing programs in promising technical areas which may seem too costly to the budget-conscious administrator. The Congress is economy-minded but not at the expense of technical progress and scientific advance. The Congress looks askance at ambitious proposals which have not been carefully thought out or which seem to reach too far be-

[10] See "Congressional Interest in Weapons Acquisition," a paper read at the Army Logistics Management Center, July 12, 1962, reprinted in part in *Armed Forces Management* (February 1963).

yond useful applications. But the Congress is not conservative about innovation. It is action-minded and hardware-oriented. It wants to see programs take shape and facilities be built. It refuses to be distracted by theoretical arguments or caught in the progress-retarding "requirements merry-go-round." It provides a needed corrective to excessive administrative caution in planning and budget-making.

The common sense approach should not be understood as a license for ignoring relevant information or for playing hunches and guesses in place of making reasoned decisions. I merely want to emphasize the fact that technical experts are not always right, not always in agreement, not always aware of the broader implications of this program or that proposal. The role of Congress is not to out-expert the experts through hordes of technical advisors and large scientific or engineering staffs. It must give a large measure of faith and credit to the integrity and veracity of the agency representatives who come before it. It must depend on the executive largely for basic data and program formulation. But the Congress reserves the right to probe and criticize and take issue, to hear others, to make up its own collective mind, to do what the situation calls for.

Advance Consultation

Policy positions that are sprung on the Congress by leaks to newspapers or by surprise announcements in speeches or testimony at public hearings are not always well received. Congressmen individually and as committee members do not like to be caught by surprise. They are supposed to be well informed. Their interested constituents expect it, and the committees on which they serve are charged with continuous oversight of the agencies within their areas of jurisdictional interest.

The Atomic Energy Commission has a statutory mandate to keep the Joint Committee on Atomic Energy "fully and currently informed" on all of its diverse activities. This is an ambitious and demanding requirement, more explicitly emphasized than that of other standing committees, which assert the same privilege with lesser degrees of intensity.[11]

[11] Following the investigation of the Apollo fire, the House Committee on Science and Astronautics wrote into the authorization bill for the National Aeronautics and Space Administration for fiscal year 1968 a requirement, modeled on that of the Atomic Energy Act, that the agency keep the House and Senate space committees

The meaning of the statutory phrase is subject to interpretation and varies with the politics and personalities on both sides. Generally, commission-committee relationships have been good and the informing obligation mutually beneficial.

Advance consultation between agency heads and congressional committees is no sure guarantee of policy or program acceptance and approval, but it increases the chances considerably. And more often than not, advance consultation results in useful suggestions for changes in wording of policy statements or draft bills or reorganization plans which enhance the likelihood of ultimate acceptance by the Congress as a whole and by the public.

The informing process should be continuous. It cannot be limited to the annual appearances for program authorization or budget appropriations. Intimate congressional acquaintance with the course of agency affairs develops better understanding, greater acceptance, and more effective appraisal of annual presentations.

This requires balance and judgment on both sides. Committee intrusion in the administrative process is to be avoided. But committee exclusion altogether or for long intervals jeopardizes programs. The administrator too independent or indifferent to the congressional interest is as bad as the administrator too weak and timid to move without full congressional approval and endorsement. Achieving the balance requires mutual confidence and candor and consummate skill.

Free Flow of Information

From time to time the congressional channels of information are blocked off. The so-called doctrine of executive privilege, for example, may come into play as a tactical weapon against certain kinds of congressional investigations when political controversies are engendered between the two branches. In Congress, historically, this is not a popular doctrine, and in fact, some members refuse to accord it the dignity of a doctrine, regarding it as a naked assertion of executive privilege protected by no constitutional mandate.

"fully and currently informed" of its activities. The bill passed the House with this provision, but it was struck out after the Senate voted down an identical amendment on the ground that the requirement is implicit in section 303 of the National Aeronautics and Space Act of 1958.

The contemporary practice of having close presidential advisers in scientific and technical areas poses one form of the problem. For example, the Joint Committee on Atomic Energy's statutory right to be kept fully informed was seriously encroached upon by the anomalous two-hat role enjoyed by the chairman of the Atomic Energy Commission in a previous administration, when he was adviser to the President on atomic energy affairs as well as chairman of the commission.[12] When in matters of importance in the atomic energy field he put on his hat of presidential adviser, he thereby claimed a privileged position beyond the reach of the Joint Committee or even of his colleagues on the commission.[13]

This potential of presidential advisers for withholding information was one of the reasons for creating the Office of Science and Technology. By giving the office statutory status and organizational identity separate from that of science adviser to the President, even though the same person might also be director of OST, the informational benefits of that strategically placed office were, in some measure at least, placed at the disposal of the Congress. It was only after the Office of Science and Technology was created that the President's science adviser became a major source of scientific information to the Congress. His appearance was and is requested before many congressional committees interested in scientific and technical programs.[14]

In other, less formal, ways than the assertion of executive privilege information is often withheld from the Congress. The excuse may be that the documents or communications requested are unofficial or preliminary or concerned solely with internal management. Or restraints may be placed by agency heads on subordinates who might be inclined to talk too freely or to voice opinions distinct from the official agency "line."

Where strong centralizing tendencies are at work, as in the Depart-

[12] Admiral Lewis Strauss served both as chairman of the AEC and atomic energy adviser to President Eisenhower.

[13] See the separate views of Representatives Chet Holifield and Melvin Price in the report of the Joint Committee on Atomic Energy to amend the Atomic Energy Act of 1946 (H. Rept. 2181, 83 Cong. 2 sess.), pp. 112–114.

[14] See *The Office of Science and Technology,* A Report prepared for the Military Operations Subcommittee of the House Committee on Government Operations by the Science Policy Research Division of the Legislative Reference Service, 90 Cong. 1 sess. (March 1967), particularly pp. 35–40. Dr. Jerome B. Wiesner made his first appearance before Congress as director of the Office of Science and Technology. He testified before the Military Operations Subcommittee about systems development and management on July 31, 1962.

ment of Defense, the insistence on an official position can become troublesome. The separate military departments are discouraged from voicing independent views, and military officers are discouraged from differing with their civilian administrators. The Congress has attempted to safeguard some of these channels of information by statute; thus, the secretaries of the military departments and the members of the Joint Chiefs of Staff are assured direct access to the Congress.

Pinning Down Responsibility

The trend to executive conformity in policy positions and the discouragement of lateral communications by subordinates to Congress without clearance through proper agency channels deprive the Congress of a wealth of information—differences in fact, opinion, and judgment which are the yeast of creative policy formation and the raw material for intelligent policy evaluation. But it must be recognized that, while the Congress seeks to overcome rigid conformity by statutory prescriptions and extensive hearings and investigations, the Congress itself encourages centralization by its insistence on pinning down responsibility.

If errors of judgment are made or acts of misfeasance committed, the head of the agency is called to account even while efforts are made to identify the individual offender. The identification process is not easy. Offending officials, having completed tours of duty, may be long gone from the scene. Decisions have many sources and contributors. The successful decision always has more claimants to paternity than the wrong or unsuccessful decision.

By calling the agency head to account, the Congress may encounter an assertion of administrative responsibility that will in effect be prejudicial to the free flow of information. On the premise that the head of a department or agency is responsible for the actions of his subordinates and accepts that responsibility, he may refuse to disclose information that might pin responsibility to particular individuals for agency actions under fire. Secretary McNamara asserted this doctrine in refusing to identify Defense Department employees who censored speeches of military officers.

Secretary McNamara's role as a strong executive has created mixed feelings, ambivalent attitudes, not only in the military departments, but on Capitol Hill. On the one hand, Congress wants the Department of Defense to be strongly controlled, civilian run, well managed. On the other hand, it wants professional military men to have a decisive voice in national policy matters which lean heavily on military issues. It fears overcentralization and possibly overcivilianization, as exemplified by the semiderogatory references to the "whiz kids."

Assertion of responsibility by a strong executive may lead to a self-defeating attempt to do too much and to delegate too little or to manage so tightly from the top that initiative dries up down below. The Congress itself, by statutory reorganizations, has contributed to a high degree of centralization in the Defense Department.

Organization and Management

Committees of Congress are critics as well as protectors of programs. Congress not only authorizes programs and appropriates funds; it also checks on performance. This is frequently termed the legislative oversight or surveillance function.

All committees exercise surveillance in one degree or another to ensure that legislative policy is being effectively carried out or that funds appropriated are being spent in an efficient or economic manner. The Committee on Government Operations, on whose staff I have served for some years, examines economy and efficiency in the federal government at all levels. In this sense, our committee has across-the-board jurisdiction.

The Committee on Government Operations also handles presidential reorganization plans and thereby exercises correlative jurisdiction with other committees, since sooner or later most government agencies are involved in presidential reorganizations.

As an example, the Office of Science and Technology was created by a presidential reorganization plan, and this plan came to our committee early in 1962. Hearings were held and a favorable report was submitted to the Congress. This is a kind of reverse legislative process in which the President drafts the law, so to speak, and the Congress has the veto power. A plan has the force and effect of law after a sixty-day waiting period if the Congress does not pass a disapproving resolution.[15]

[15] Departments of government, as distinguished from agencies, can no longer be created by reorganization plan because of a statutory prohibition. New departments come into being through the regular legislative route. Thus the Department of Transportation was created by a bill reported by the House and Senate Committees on Government Operations in 1966 and enacted into law.

Organization is relevant to policy formation since reorganizations frequently signal or accompany changes in policy. In fact, controversies over organization more often than not are disguised policy arguments. Where technical programs are costly and complex, often involving several agencies, the Congress demands continuing assurance that proper attention is being paid to organization and to management. Efforts to achieve coordination and to avoid or minimize duplication are well received. The agency head who can demonstrate his zeal in pursuing economy and good management practices improves the chances for program acceptance.

Multiple-agency involvement is a complicating factor in research and development management and technical program organization. For example, where the Defense Department, the National Aeronautics and Space Administration, and the Atomic Energy Commission all have an interest in a program, such as the SNAP (Systems for Nuclear Auxiliary Power) program, difficult problems of funding and continuity of development arise. The program may be promising, but if the user agency has no formal requirement for it, the developing agency is hard put to justify its continuation. Even more complicated problems arise in satellite communications, which involve a host of government potential users and several development agencies as well as a private corporation with government representation on the board of directors. As technology advances and the federal government becomes increasingly committed to supporting the major part of the national effort in research and development, these complexities will multiply, posing new challenges to the executive and legislative branches alike in devising effective means of organization and management.

What conclusions can be drawn from this quick roundup of congressional attitudes and practices? The government executive or administrator charged with presenting scientific or technical programs to the Congress can do many things to improve his presentation, to develop good working relationships with the Congress, and to advance the cause of sound national policy in these fields.

He should take the initiative in, or respond promptly to requests for, developing broad background information that underlies the formation of national policy and that places his own agency mission or program into the proper context of national needs and government-wide endeavors to fulfill those needs.

Regarding specific program justification, he should be prepared to discuss in an intelligent and informing manner program goals, time-scales of effort, and total system requirements and costs. The program package of the Department of Defense offers a useful model.

The administrator should organize his material for efficient presentation to various congressional committees that are interested and be prepared to respond to many sources of congressional inquiry. The Defense Department again offers a useful example in its consolidated posture statement.

Budget padding is a device to be avoided. A candid discussion of agency and program needs and a demonstration that the budget request has been carefully considered before being presented are more likely to induce congressional cooperation.

Familiarity, particularly on the part of a new administrator, with the presentations of his predecessors and with the past history of the agency or program is helpful in responding to many kinds of congressional inquiries. Committee chairmen usually are seasoned by long tenure and experience. If the administrator is not careful, he will find himself being told about his own agency.

Care should be taken in preparing materials for presentation to the Congress. Excessive technical jargon and long-winded statements are to be avoided. Graphic materials, hardware samples, and the like are useful in presentations. Private conferences are valuable supplements to public hearings. But a certain dignity and restraint are preferred to excessive zeal.

Sincere invitations to committee members to visit field installations, view test exercises, and the like, are well received. The administrator should arrange for congressional visits so that they are informative and interesting but informal, permitting the congressmen to set the pace and talk to whomever they wish.

Threats and competitive performances of adversary nations weigh heavily in congressional decisions relating to research and development programs. Idle suppositions or unverified speculations about what the adversary is doing are not persuasive. If there is substantiated intelligence or indicated evidence, it will be attentively received.

An administrator who is timid or hesitant about formulating bold new programs when needs are urgent or crises acute loses out in the shuffle. Even if the agency head or the Bureau of the Budget clamps down, there are ways and means of putting these programs before the Congress.

Important decisions or new policies should be, as much as possible, a matter of prior consultation with the Congress. The informing process must be a continuing one, calling for good working relationships and mutual confidence.

Blunt or devious resistance to congressional demands for information is to be avoided. Policy formation is a cooperative and not a competitive process between the executive and legislative branches of government.

Evidence of efficiency and economy in program execution and agency performance, including necessary reorganizations, is looked upon with favor. The need to demonstrate good management methods, particularly as technical programs become increasingly complex and costly and involve several agencies, is a continuing one.

DISCUSSION

The Functions and Foibles of Congress

CONGRESSIONAL HEARINGS, it would appear, have more functions than a Cheshire cat has lives: to learn, of course; to educate the public as well as the Congress; to make a record; to advertise; to dramatize.

The Multiple Functions of Hearings

. . . [W]hen there is an important program that is going on, committees like to have those important heads of agencies and high-ranking admirals and generals. They lend a little color, and they have a little news value, and they dramatize the issues. It is important, in some ways, to kind of tune up a hearing. These hearings can get awful dull, and fellows can drone on and on—just like at some of these meetings. . . .

. . . [S]ome administrators are careless on the record. They say whatever comes to mind, and they are not worried about the record, and sometimes it doesn't make too much difference, because, when the record is voluminous, a busy member can't really go over the ground. . . .

But "really important decisions aren't necessarily made on the record; they are made in chambers. They are made *in camera,* by understanding administrators and committee members."

"Wouldn't those records be a little more convincing if a little greater effort were made to have the opposition represented—to have the critics fully heard?" it was asked. "For instance, the [National] Coal Association is now heard . . . before the Joint Committee [on Atomic Energy], and . . . that is all to the good; but that is not the standard thing in the average agency presentation. The real hard critics are not . . . heard." It would be useful to have more critical testimony, a congressman agreed; most witnesses do represent the agency viewpoint. "I would just love to have an opportunity to hear some people who are not from ———— [an agency] but who are sincerely concerned about the whole program, and with a critical view of it." One difficulty, another participant from the Hill rejoined, is that critics simply don't know enough about the program; ". . . if you are not on the inside looking out, but on the outside looking in, it makes a difference." And if it is merely a matter of philosophical differences, congressmen really do not need that kind of advice, because they already have a position on space, defense, health, and so on, and know how they would vote on it.

Still, the congressman persisted. Even if qualified critics are not readily available, "our committee needs help from people who can ask better questions than we ourselves." "Basically, that job has got to be done by the staff," he was told. But the group shortly reviewed other ways of getting advice.

The personality of a committee chairman has great influence on the fortunes of a committee and the nature of its hearings, it was observed. "If a chairman . . . is not interested or doesn't have the time, there isn't very much you can do, even if the other members are raring to go; after a while, they kind of fall off. . . ." And a chairman's character and interests also determine the character of the staff he hires.

Loyalty comes before performance on the Hill. . . . You want a staff to serve all the members, but it has to be chosen by a chairman who wants to see a good job done. Therefore, the committees vary in their performance and in their receptivity to technical and scientific information. This is something which you really can't cure by any organizational means. . . . [M]embers like Mr. ———— will say "We need more staff," and I will say "You are overstaffed now. . . ." In terms of staff abilities, [Congress] . . . is about 50 percent effective. Half of the people ride on the backs of the other half.

Any committee staff member who tries to affect, rather than to reflect, the policies of his chairman, is unlikely to last very long.

There are a lot of people who come and besiege the Hill . . . and want to be staff, because they have ideas that they want congressmen to perpetuate or further for them. Sometimes the congressman is either generous or benign about the issue, and he lets them work out of his orbit of interest, and if he doesn't watch himself, he will find that in his name a lot of people are being asked to do a lot of things. . . . The staff man who goes too far out on his own, he not only isn't worth very much, but he isn't going to last very long.

A basic function of congressional hearings is to keep the executive on its toes by subjecting its proposals to rigorous, independent scrutiny. ". . . [T]he quality of the questioning is a real contribution to keeping the administration quality up." Nonetheless, few major agency proposals catch the cognizant committee by surprise; most have been developed over a period of time, and the committee has usually been consulted in private.

Often, the mere announcement of a hearing sets a "timetable . . . for decisions." In former years, "the Joint Committee [on Atomic Energy] would set a hearing, and then AEC would make a decision." In general, a congressman said, a hearing "will force the administrative agency to set their own house in order and clarify their own position so that they can express it logically and justifiably. . . ."

Complaints were frequently voiced at the overlapping jurisdictions of competing committees, someone commented, and it was not unknown for an agency to give short shrift to an intruding committee or to ask its authorizing committee what another committee wanted with certain information. This attitude was unwise, however, because the more committees and the more congressmen who knew about a program, the better off that agency would be. "If it is a good program," a congressman inserted, and the point was conceded.

The ambivalent attitude of the executive toward the congressional review function was illustrated by the National Science Foundation's uncertainty about whether the Science and Astronautics Committee should or should not hold annual authorization hearings on its budget.

On the one hand, they like to be noticed, recognized, and supported. On the other hand, they are afraid they are going to get their funds cut. So, generally speaking, the executive agency tends to resist a repeat performance for authorization as well as appropriation; but any committee that is worth its salt . . . wants to be in on the policy process, and the way it does it is by requiring yearly authorizations.

Other Avenues of Advice

Of course, hearings are not the only way by which committees obtained scientific and technical information and advice. Three other common mechanisms for getting advice were discussed by the seminar: the Legislative Reference Service, panels of specialists, and the National Academy of Sciences.

The new Science Policy Research Division of the Legislative Reference Service, it was noted, could provide useful help. However, its staff would always remain small, because the Congress would never give the service enough money to "build a bureaucracy." Therefore, the division faced the danger of "being swallowed up by one little subcommittee," so that it would be of no use to the rest of the Congress. The best use of LRS was probably "to help the Congress ask the right questions. . . ." This LRS sought to accomplish by conducting background studies before hearings were convened and by suggesting questions to committee members and staff during the hearings. At the time of this discussion, the Science Policy Research Division had been in existence about six months, during which period it had undertaken studies for six committees of the House and five committees of the Senate. As, in the domain of science and technology, the decisions which Congress has to make were not solely technical but technical "mixed with something else—economics, geopolitics, local politics, institutional interests, and so on"—the division has had to speak the language both of the legislator and of the scientist-technologist and to serve as translator between the two.

In a succeeding session, it was noted that the LRS performs a valuable service simply by collecting readily available facts and arraying them so as to bring out the underlying policy issues. "The facts speak for themselves, and very loudly, sometimes."

The second mechanism for getting advice, the panel of specialists, could help a committee to explore unresolved issues, such as what we should do after landing on the moon; but several participants pointed out the dangers of having advisers trying to "second guess" the responsible executive agencies on detailed and complicated technical problems.

Another danger of the technical advisory panel was that of institution-alizing, and hence restricting, the sources to which the Congress could go for advice.

> . . . [T]he Congress, individually as a member or collectively as a com-mittee, never will rest content with regularized sources of information. They reserve the right to talk to anybody and everybody, and preferably an informed constituent. But in any case, the whole universe of the coun-try, and sometime of the world, is their source of information. . . . [For-mal scientific advisers] will find they are sitting around while . . . [the Congressmen] are talking to somebody else, and they are going to be awful mad about it, because they are not consulted.

An advisory panel such as that appointed by the House Committee on Science and Astronautics can be useful, one seminar member felt, if it "brings up issues six months or a year in advance of an executive posi-tion. . . . [T]he committee can inform itself before the executive posi-tion gets frozen. . . ." Another concurred that a panel might be useful "if it is willing to really work. . . ." On the other hand, its meetings "can become a kind of ritual." What often happens, he continued, is that a few committee members who "are a little closer to the intellectual or the scientific community . . . will spend more time with them, and that community will find a receptive member; but [the advisory panel] will not be touching the heart strings or the brains of the Congress. It only has one or two members in tow who are willing to travel along with it." Panel members can get into "rather rarefied argumentation, and you kind of lose the committee; and in the worst aspect, it is a way of publishing papers that will not be accepted by reputable magazines."

A third mechanism for getting advice was the National Academy of Sciences. Originally, during the Civil War, it had served as "an arm of the Union cause . . . to see why Army saddles got mold on them, and why boilers in the Navy blew up, and it was a very practical outfit. . . ." Subsequently, however,

> . . . it became a kind of elder statesman or, in some people's opinion, [a] stuffed-shirt outfit. It went very remote from the political concerns of the day. So, when you ask the National Academy to do something for the Congress, there are a lot of butterflies floating around in a lot of bellies; and, then, if they agree to do it, after consultation, they have a big problem of who is going to take credit for it. Shall we sign our own names to it? I don't want to sign my name to something I don't believe; so they have to spend half of the research effort identifying protocol. This

is a real problem: How can the National Academy speak in a single voice to the Congress?

"Surely," declared a private participant, "it is no secret there was some feeling on the Hill that the academy is in league with PSAC [the President's Science Advisory Committee] and the executive and does not offer the Congress truly independent advice?" "There is a conspiracy in the scientific community, and there is no question about it," replied a participant from the Hill, "and that is to prevail upon the Congress to be understanding and to grant them all the funds that they ask for."

The Value of OST to the Congress

Has the scientific machinery in the Executive Office of the President helped the Congress to discharge its functions in the area of science and technology? it was asked. This machinery was initially set up mainly to help the President, not the Congress, a congressman pointed out. Subsequently, the Office of Science and Technology was established, in part to provide a high level policy agency that would be accountable to the Congress.

> One of the reasons why I backed the bill to make it statutory was because we found ourselves running up, in Congress, against decisions that were being made in the executive branch and without congressional hearings or without any congressional participation. So far, it hasn't been of any help to the Congress, because it hasn't functioned for the benefit of the Congress. It is like the Bureau of the Budget. It functions for the President.

Another problem that Congress has encountered, the congressman continued, was getting the administration to state a policy. Thus, the Joint Committee on Atomic Energy had difficulty getting a policy statement from the Office of Science and Technology on national energy resources as well as on high energy physics research. (However, the President had enunciated a policy on space exploration.) Without a clear statement of administration policy, a committee chairman was in a weak position when he had to go on the floor of the House and ask for funds for a program.

Could the Office of Science and Technology be used by a congressman, formally or informally, to check on agency submissions, a congressman wanted to know. "Here I am an individual congressman . . . and I have some doubts about testimony that [for example] NASA is giving me. Would it make sense for me to call OST and say, 'Is NASA telling me the truth?' "

NASA OFFICIAL: I don't think that is the kind of question you want to ask them. [*Laughter.*] . . . If you just say, "Are they honest or dishonest?" they won't answer you; but if you say, "I want to get the merits of this issue," you will get help from them. . . .

ANOTHER CONGRESSMAN: I don't think the ordinary member of Congress has to go to OST for this kind of information. There are other people to whom he is closer and whom he trusts, where he can get this information. . . .

The President's science advisers have been anxious to help the Congress in any way that they can, said a government official. Their testimony has been "straighforward" and "succinct." The science advisers have come from private life into government service only for brief periods of time and so approach these issues unbureaucratically, with "a sincere desire to be as frank and candid as they can in discussing them." Granted, there are certain restraints on their ability to be completely candid. When a problem falls wholly within the province of a given agency, it is only right for OST to consult that agency to see how the question should be answered; "but I am sure there would be an honest attempt to give the very best answer that it is possible to give, without covering up." If the Congress has found some difficulty in determining the administration's policy in certain areas, that may have been due to the intrinsic difficulty of formulating a policy. For example, "most people would agree that you can't set a 1970 target date for high energy physics in the same way you can set a date for getting to the moon. . . . There are many complexities . . . that make it very difficult to pound out a concrete plan for any field of science. . . ."

At first one congressman had said that OST had not been of much help to his committee, and then he seemed to take a more positive view of its service, a participant remarked. Could he clarify his view?

CONGRESSMAN: It has just been set up. We haven't been able to obtain much in the way of help from OST. It has been too busy trying to help the President. And I am not criticizing. I think it may develop to the point where it will have time left over to help the Congress some, but I am not going to look to the OST basically for help to the Congress. The President is looking to them for help to him. . . .

I believe completely in the OST. It had to come, because the President can't make these decisions out of the air. He has to have a good scientific body to advise him.

OFFICIAL: ... [H]ow many times did Wiesner appear in that first year after ... [OST was] created? About twenty-two times, with a [professional] staff of less than twenty people ... in the office. You can imagine the amount of effort that is entailed in writing testimony and getting ready for these hearings. It is a little disconcerting to hear that perhaps this hasn't been too useful to the various committees.

CONGRESSMAN: In the first place, he wasn't before me twenty times; and in the second place, I didn't know he was up on the Hill twenty times.

Plainly, the director of OST has given the Congress "a lot of testimony on things they were interested in," a Hill participant acknowledged. Anybody "at the apex of government in the President's office" can be useful to the Congress; but the Congress is never going to rely on an agency in the Executive Office of the President for information on "close-in policy ... developments"—because "it won't get it."

One of the problems of OST is really finding out how to do its own job. It is always complaining it doesn't have enough staff, and it will complain as long as it is there. . . .

. . . [W]hat happens is that somebody sitting in PSAC, or somebody in OST, has a position, and if it coincides with an action problem in the Congress, you have an ally, and if it doesn't, you have an enemy, and you just fight them to the death. We know, for example, that PSAC takes certain positions on civil defense. . . . If those views are contrary [to ours], we wouldn't go to PSAC for advice; we would figure out how to circumvent them.

In other words, you evaluate the issue as it comes, and not the institution as a whole. What is the issue and the position of the people? A lot of people who use the stationery of the President don't necessarily speak for him.

Formerly, an official reflected, a few prominent, respected men, like Vannevar Bush, served as a focal point to whom congressmen, administrators, and scientists could turn in the resolution of scientific-technical-political issues; they helped to

pull . . . things together, whether it was their job . . . or not. Aren't we seeking [in OST or the National Academy of Sciences] for an institutional substitute for what was done by a small group of people with great ability and wide knowledge of people? . . . I could talk to Van Bush, and he would talk to half a dozen different senators and he could give me the total picture of what can and can't be done. I don't find people [private scientists] around town [now] who can do that. . . .

CONGRESSMAN: The field is now too wide.

OFFICIAL B: I think Doc Seitz [Frederick Seitz, president of the National Academy of Sciences] is, to a certain extent, getting . . . to that kind of a role.

OFFICIAL C: Van Bush's invitations to breakfast fell off when he said the ballistic missile wasn't practical.[1]

Should the Congress Initiate Policy?

Many people felt that the Congress should originate policy independent of the executive; alternatively, others felt that the Congress should serve mainly to review and evaluate rather than to initiate policy.

In the view of one participant, the Congress could not develop policy independently. Congressmen simply did not have the time, the information, the staff, or the money to compete with executive agencies in working out new programs and policies. This conception of the Congress as essentially a reacting and reviewing body was challenged by a congressman, at least insofar as the Joint Committee on Atomic Energy was concerned. He offered the following reflections:

> The proper job of the executive branch is to initiate and develop programs and recommend them to the Congress. The job of Congress is to implement. Where the agency . . . doesn't do its job, you find confusion, or if you have a strong committee, you will find that committee will take over and, to some extent, do the job of initiation.
>
> I think the Joint Committee is a good example of that. [It] . . . has been criticized because [it has] . . . initiated some things which were opposed by the executive branch. However, I think a close study of the situation would show that . . . [it] filled a vacuum that existed. . . .
>
> [As an example, the Joint Committee on Atomic Energy] . . . was convinced that we should have nuclear submarines, but the executive branch was not. The Navy refused to even listen to the plans of Admiral

[1] In his book *Modern Arms and Free Men* (Simon & Shuster, 1949), Bush expressed doubt about the military usefulness of intercontinental missiles, mainly because of their great cost. ". . . [A]s long as atomic bombs are scarce, and highly expensive in terms of destruction accomplished per dollar disbursed, one does not trust them to a highly complex and possibly erratic carrier of inherently low precision, for lack of precision decidedly increases such costs. . . . For the near future, the really important and significant field of guided missiles lies in much shorter ranges . . ." (pp. 86–87). Also on grounds of cost, Bush discounted the development of nuclear power. ". . . [T]he application of atomic energy to peaceful industrial purposes is far off. The ultimate importance is still great, but the conception of a maze of power plants covering the earth, deriving their power from atomic fission . . . has largely disappeared for a considerable distance into the future" (p. 107).

Rickover. [The committee] . . . listened to them and . . . thought they were worth implementing. . . .

The hydrogen bomb was not suggested by the Defense Department . . . or the AEC. It was brought to the [Joint] Committee by some of the scientists who had this idea. . . . First four out of five, and then three out of five [commissioners] on the Atomic Energy Commission voted against it. But [the committee] . . . went ahead on it. . . .

Of course, when [it] . . . got right to the point of testing the H-bomb, then the military came in and sheepishly said, "Well, if it works, we can use it." After . . . the Nautilus and the Sea Wolf engines had been demonstrated in the hulls of submarines, then the Navy came in and said, "We can't get enough of them."

Congress is as much or more concerned about the political and economic aspects of an R&D program as the technical ones, a participant reminded the group. "How can we best the Russians; can we beat them to the moon? . . . In the supersonic transport, . . . the decision will be shaped as much by the actions of the European manufacturers as . . . by the technical problems of the sonic boom, or anything else. . . . [Congress] tends to react more . . . on a basis of these national and international factors than it does on a rational allocation of effort."

In the past, as most R&D expenditures went into military programs, many of the key issues were dealt with in private by the few congressmen who had access to the necessary classified information; and their colleagues had to accept their decisions "pretty much on faith." Now, a new range of issues was arising: How can science and technology serve civilian society? How can you bring scientists, engineers, politicians, entrepreneurs, ideas, and capital together to serve the nation's new social and technical needs? That was the kind of question the Congress now wanted to answer.

It was apparent from the discussion that to speak of "the Congress" as a whole was misleading, for there was a gradient of influence and knowledge among three groups of congressmen, each of whom had a different degree of influence on, a different kind of interest in, and a somewhat different kind of knowledge about R&D issues: the chairmen of key committees, the members of these committees, and ordinary rank and file congressmen. Chairmen of long-standing committees, like the Joint Committee on Atomic Energy, did not have to be told elementary facts about nuclear science and technology policy: they knew as much as or more than agency heads about it. Committee members, in turn, had an opportunity to acquire more knowledge and insight into major policy issues than other congressmen. "We who are on the [R&D] committees, who even get a tiny insight, as I begin to get a tiny insight . . . into some of these things—I am appalled at the three hundred and some members of the House who don't have any chance at all to get any insight and yet have to vote on these decisions." The average congressman tends to turn to a colleague whose judgment he respects for advice on matters that he cannot readily decide for himself.

Invited to comment after an evening's silence, a government official thought that the seminar had not paid enough attention to the problems which interagency R&D programs encountered in the Congress. There seemed to be "a geometric rise" in the number of interagency programs, he felt, and it was one important function of OST to coordinate them and present an integrated plan for their development. However, once that plan was presented to the Congress, "then, bango!—the first thing you find out is that the old line agencies have gone before congressmen that either have no interest . . . or have . . . downright hostility [to strengthening their research work], and so . . . the weak get weaker in science." The response he received was not very comforting. "The Congress is not going to accommodate . . . the shifting organizational and program elements [of the executive], so [that] if poverty cuts across six agencies we will set up a poverty committee. . . . [P]retty soon you would have a great number of committees, and you just can't operate that way. . . . [F]or better or worse, the Congress will consider these things piecemeal."

WILLIAM D. CAREY

Equipping Congress
To Deal with Science

I F I W E R E more confident that we have succeeded
in organizing the executive branch to deal with science and technology,
I might be more encouraged to advise on the organization of the Congress. As it is, I come bearing no heroic solutions. Frankly, I am by
no means sure that the problem itself has heroic proportions. If I were
obliged to make a list of the most urgent problems facing Congress in
the field of its organization and functions, I doubt very much that science would rank at the head of the list. So much for perspective.

We have been perhaps more critical of the behavior of Congress in
dealing with science than the facts justify. Where the major commitments of the government are concerned—atomic energy, space, defense,
and medical research—by my standards, the Congress has acquitted itself
well. It is chiefly, I believe, in the less articulate sectors of the research
program that some stresses and dissatisfactions have cropped up. Beyond
this, we have observed in some quarters a growing passion to focus "science policy"—vaguely defined—in the higher reaches of legislative structure.

It must be said, sadly enough, that the scientific community itself has

This paper, presented to the Brookings seminar on April 27, 1965, appeared in
slightly modified form in the *Saturday Review,* Nov. 6, 1965, pp. 57–58, under the title
"A Proposal for a Yearly Presidential Report on Science."

not always shown enthusiasm for improving congressional understanding of the research business. This was brought home to me a couple of years ago when I spoke before a large assemblage of research scientists and administrators.[1] I appeared coincidentally with the first stirrings of the crisis of congressional confidence in the growth and coordination of research. And I remember clearly that one individual after another rose to voice dismay at the prospect of the Congress injecting itself into inquiries into these matters. How can we prevent this from happening? What can be done to head it off? How can we keep research out of politics?

To me, this signified a state of mind that regarded research and development as untouchable, to be screened at all costs from legislative caprice. Research was doing nicely under the wing of the executive, and only trouble could result by tempting Congress to upset the equilibrium. It did not seem to occur to them that congressional oversight could manifest itself in a constructive form.

Much of this mentality has now subsided in the wake of the work of the special committees of inquiry, which took high ground. There have been no scandals, no public executions, and few indictments. There will always be the risk that a member of Congress will show exasperation with the moon program or research into the mating habits of frogs and that someone may twist an arm or two to influence the location of a plush research facility. But these risks are within the parameters of normalcy.

Still, I take the view that such tensions as have existed between the research brotherhood and the Congress cannot all be blamed on the latter. Some of the cohorts of science appear to have wanted all the prerogatives of a state religion without any of the embarrassments. This, too, I trust, has waned as the understanding of the need and nature of legislative oversight has improved.

In seeking to equip the Congress to deal effectively with science, it is not, I believe, necessary to foist a spate of new committees or institutional innovations on an already overloaded and overstructured legislative body. The place to start is at the other end of town.

If the Congress is failing to see the light, if it feels starved for facts, if it is baffled at finding science behind every bureaucratic rock, if it is

[1] See William Carey, "R&D and the Federal Budget," in *Proceedings of the Seventeenth National Conference on the Administration of Research,* held in Estes Park, Colorado, Sept. 11–13, 1963 (University of Denver, 1964), pp. 42–45.

lost to see the intrinsic merit in the more arcane nooks of basic science, if it hunts vainly for signs of a broad strategy for science, and if it cannot identify priorities for scientific choice, the Executive Office of the President must share the blame. We are simply not providing the answers. And if we are not providing them because we do not have them, then we need to ask whether we are doing enough to get them. In my judgment, Congress is not anxious to take over the policy initiative for scientific research. It merely takes the quaint view that *somebody* should seize the initiative and do it well and thoroughly.

A Yearly Report on Science and Technology

I have long preached, unsuccessfully, for the issuance once each year of a report from the Executive Office on the substance, organization, costs, goals, problems, and progress of science and technology. I have thought of this as a strategy document similar to the Council of Economic Advisers' annual *Economic Report.* A report such as this should tell us in highlight form where the nation's science has been, where it is now, and where it should go—and why—and with what rate of investment. It should deal with the roles of both the private and the government sectors of support and performance, and it should be qualitative as well as informational. I would be the first to grant that a report like this would not solve the entire problem, but it could supply in great part the element that is so conspicuously missing—a *framework* for considering the state of science and technology in the larger economy of public policy.

What is more, I should like to see such a report treated by Congress in much the same manner as the *Economic Report,* with public hearings and testimony from invited outside parties. This gets us directly to the question of congressional machinery. My preference would be for joint hearings by the House and Senate, possibly by a joint committee whose functions would be limited to examining the report and conducting the hearings and which would draw staff from the Science Policy Research Division of the Legislative Reference Service. I believe that the very requirement for such a comprehensive annual statement would itself be an action-forcing device on both the executive and the various committees in both houses of Congress and would serve to point up the right issues and determine who was accountable to do something about them.

But I am not persuaded that the Elliott committee version of a joint committee on research policy would be desirable.[2] Inevitably, such a committee would have little leverage on real-life situations; it would be too marginal to the legislative process to be of much account and would be reduced to staging dog-and-pony shows as a substitute for meaningful leadership—which can only flourish where there is power. A joint committee with no teeth and merely a general hunting license is unlikely to produce much except paperwork.

Briefing the Appropriations Committee Chairmen

A second innovation that strikes me as having a certain merit also begins with the executive branch. It relates to budgeting for research and development. I think it would be entirely practicable if the Budget Bureau were to approach the chairmen of the appropriations committees to suggest that each year there be a comprehensive presentation by the bureau and the Office of Science and Technology on the research and development components of the new budget. Such a confrontation should come immediately after the budget director and the secretary of the treasury have completed their normal annual presentation and defense of the President's budget. Such a briefing and question-and-answer session might go some distance to making the science budget less baffling than it is by tying together in understandable terms the fragments of R&D that are scattered all through the budget with resulting irritation to the budget subcommittees. At least, I offer the idea as a partial answer to the problem presented by the prevailing preferences of the Congress in considering budget estimates. It is a modest proposal, but one which poaches on no committee preserves, introduces no supercommittees, and could be accommodated with no great strain on anybody concerned.

The question which repeatedly arose in Congress in discussions leading up to the creation of the Elliott committee was: "Who, if anybody, is in charge of coordinating R&D?" That was the meat of it. What Congress wants more than anything else is evidence that the executive is running a tight ship and knows what it is doing. Congress, in its present incarnation, is perfectly capable of making up its mind about the moon

[2] The Elliott committee recommended creation of a nonlegislative joint committee on research policy; see *Study Number X: National Goals and Policies,* Report of the House Select Committee on Government Research, 88 Cong. 2 sess. (Dec. 29, 1964), pp. 55-56.

program, medical research, and the Mohole. But it is less prepared to certify that twelve or fifteen agencies have their meteorology programs in balance or that feedback from supported research is being put to good use. Congress cannot make sense out of the decision-making procedure of the agencies in defining—if they do—research priorities and in matching resources to them. And in this the Congress has company. If the Budget Bureau were pressed, we would have to answer in too many cases that we don't know *how* we do it, but we do it all the same.

The present stabilization of the research and development budget gives us a breathing spell which ought not to be wasted. I suspect that before long the expenditure curve will resume its upward movement. Then questions will again be asked. Meantime, the executive branch ought to decide what it wants to do about grants versus contracts, university cost participation in research, indirect expense allowances, inconsistencies in administrative controls, in-house versus contract research, the future of the national laboratories, and overconcentration of university research. We should also face up to the untouched issues of criteria in scientific choice and the irrational lack of balance in support or nonsupport of technological innovation. The time to hit these problems is during a period of constraint and competition at the margins of funding. It will take more than fine-sounding executive orders (many of them written by me), superagencies without muscle, or a wondrous array of interagency committees. To the extent that the executive runs its business well, the need and pressure for new congressional structure will be minimal.

In the end, more responsive executive branch performance is preferable to further complicating a legislative branch which is already more complicated and structured than it need be. If the Congress, nevertheless, decides on new machinery, it may even help, but I doubt that it will help enough to justify the additional wear and tear. Little is solved by moving problems up one or two more levels.

If legislative oversight has one indispensable value, however, it is that it focuses controversy. The "hairshirt" function is critical to representative government, and one doesn't find it in the executive arm. What we need, and do not have sufficiently, is some way for issues of science policy and priority to be sharpened and argued. In other words, we need a market place where the competition can make itself conspicuous. There is plenty of potential dissent within the scientific community, and it deserves an outlet. This is one more reason why I suggest so strongly that

Congress should require of the executive a periodic accounting and an airing of its performance and expectations in the full light of constructive criticism.

If we have made mistakes in handling science, they were the price paid for rapid expansion. Congress and the executive are probably equally responsible. But the costs have been well inside the range of acceptability. And we have learned something. We have unleashed a force in society that is here to stay and which contains an extraordinary creative potential. This is not exclusively the concern of either Congress or the executive but both. That potential will not express itself as a unity but instead in diversity—as a function of business investment, communications technology, transportation technology, molecular biology. It is no answer to hang on the door a sign reading "Science." Since science is diversity, it is not illogical for our machinery to reflect a parallel diversity, both in Congress and downtown. Diversity, mellowed by perspective, in this instance spells good organization.

DISCUSSION

Is an Annual
R&D Report Desirable?

TO THE EXTENT the executive does its business well, Carey said in his opening remarks,

. . . the need and the pressure for new congressional structure will be minimal; and, at the end, I come out on the side of a more responsive executive performance as an alternative to further complicating a legislative branch which is already more complicated . . . than it need be. . . . If legislative oversight does have one indispensable value, I think, it is that it focuses controversey. . . . [T]he "hairshirt" function is critical to representative government, and one doesn't find enough of it in the executive branch. . . .

There is plenty of potential dissent within the scientific community, and it ought to have an outlet. So this is one more reason why . . . Congress ought to require of the executive a periodic accounting and airing of its performance and its expectations in the full light of constructive criticism.

Were there not designated committees of the Congress to which such an R&D accounting should be made? a congressman asked. The answer he received may not entirely have pleased him: ". . . [W]e have, frankly, some trouble downtown rationalizing where responsibility begins and where it ends. . . . The same business appears . . . , at least potentially, to be germane in a number of . . . House committees, and . . . probably it comes down to a matter of initiative . . . as to who is going to attack which problem first, and in what depth. I have no quarrel with it. I call it diversity. . . ."

An Annual Report on R&D

With regard to the proposed annual report on R&D, the congressman observed, the responsibilities of the Congress would hardly be fulfilled by merely receiving from the executive a periodic accounting and airing of its performance. ". . . [W]e have constitutional responsibilities to establish policy. . . ."

An annual report on the status of science had been anticipated when the Office of Science and Technology was established, it was recalled. "What . . . dissipated that expectation?" A report had not been required by statute, an official indicated, but OST had "gone so far as to attempt to draw up such a thing. . . ." The attempt had foundered because of the difficulty of defining academic research, applied research, and development on a generic, government-wide basis. It had simply not been possible to envisage "a science and technology budget" distinct from the budget of discrete agency missions, although a step had recently been taken toward the delineation of a separate budget for academic science. Even there, it was hard to analyze the research programs of an agency without analyzing the missions they are designed to advance, nor was it easy to divorce the government component from other research conducted at universities.

However, on the latter point, it was suggested that the report should, indeed, deal with the nongovernment as well as the government sector; and on the former, that the agency environment need only be briefly sketched, for a report was not an encyclopedia and should give close attention only to selective developments. A report like the annual report of the Council of Economic Advisers, containing descriptive information on research expenditures and manpower, would present no special problem. But it was too much, one official thought, to expect OST, among its many other functions, to evaluate the technical promise of various areas of science and technology as well.

Nevertheless, another official insisted, "I think it can be done." DOD's Project Hindsight has demonstrated the feasibility of the technical analysis of a major R&D effort.[1] It was important that each agency conduct that kind of analysis, systematically and with care, in order to determine the effectiveness of its R&D programs.

Still, a participant from the Hill doubted the desirability of looking at science "across the board in government and society. . . ." Congress already received from two thousand to five thousand annual reports:

> If a report were written on science generally and came up to whatever committee—in fact, it probably should be presented as a congressional document, so it would be more accessible to the whole Congress—it would only be read for those items of interest and relevance at any given time to any given committee or any given member. It doesn't really further the requirements of Congress to have a generalized report, except as the Congress, as well as citizens generally, are interested in getting some kind of convenient reference on what is done in the scientific field.

That was not the proposal, said a defender of the report. The idea was to highlight "significant developments, significant or possible points of concentration or gaps or advances or problems . . ." in scientific and technological knowledge, resources, and policies.

Viewed over a period of time, a political scientist said, such a report should prove most useful. "Forty years ago we sent up the budget in chunks, in estimates. We didn't have a budget. . . ." But the bigger and more complicated the government got, the more it became necessary to examine systematically the scope of its activities. This was now gradually happening in R&D programs. Twenty years ago, very little was going on; today, a great deal—enough, it appeared, to warrant "systematic efforts to look at the whole thing," at how one program impinged on another, and at how to make better and more rational use of the nation's R&D resources.

"Why should a congressman want to think about agricultural research and Department of Defense research lumped into one figure?" asked a

[1] "Project Hindsight" is an ambitious Defense Department study of the source of major ideas leading to improved weapons systems (see D. S. Greenberg, " 'Hindsight': DOD Study Examines Return on Investment in Research," *Science,* Nov. 18, 1966, pp. 872–73).

critic. "I would challenge the fact that the economic report[2] has done very much good in terms of congressional decision-making. I don't know of any committee chairman . . . who pays very much attention to the overall parameters of the economic report. Maybe a few scholars or students do." He granted that the report contributed to the public's "economic literacy"; but it had little effect on congressional budgetary decisions.

But "literacy about science is also important," a participant rejoined:

> . . . [T]o most people what goes on in the government support of science and technology is a great technical mystery. . . . [T]he jargon is difficult . . . ; many witnesses appearing before committees of the Congress at times have felt tongue-tied to express themselves beyond the particular idiom or dialect of their specialty. . . . [T]hat country that supposedly derives its power from the people and from their money, that kind of a country, is entitled to a literate explanation of science, . . . accounting for and explaining what it is that we are doing with our current investment and where we propose to go.
>
> . . . [B]ack in 1947 or 1948, when the Steelman committee came into existence, a small band of men with a whole lot of courage . . . made some projections. They made some judgments about the value of basic science . . . to human, social, and economic growth. . . . And they projected what they felt would be a sensible goal ten years into the future. This kind of thing hasn't been tried since.
>
> [An effective report should treat science and technology] not in tiresome . . . particulars that would put anyone to sleep . . . but in terms of the excitement . . . , the values, that [science and technology] . . . represents . . . , the costs that it involves . . . , the purposes . . . , the needs . . . , the opportunities . . . , and the expectations. . . . If the President, . . . in his State of the Union message, can attempt briefly to set forth the country's expectations across the board, I fail to see why it cannot be done with respect to science and technology, and I think it is overdue.

Why the Resistance?

"I am very puzzled at the resistance to more information and an attempt to understand what is going on . . . ," said one social scientist, whereupon a second volunteered an explanation. Most of the group regarded science and technology as a means to an end. But the annual report that

[2] That is, the *Economic Report of the President,* transmitted to the Congress each January.

had been envisaged appeared to conceive of them as an end in themselves, as "an independent force in our society, with a re-creative, regen-
erative, ongoing capacity which is in itself something to be fostered,
cultivated, nourished, and maybe controlled; and . . . if it is . . . this
kind of a force, then . . . our existing ways of looking at it are not sufficient."

". . . [Y]ou used a naughty word—'controlled,' " countered the first
social scientist. "Maybe that is the reason for the resistance." [This view
received some confirmation at the next session, when an agency official
said, "May I give you a simple explanation of the last meeting with
Carey? Carey is representing the Bureau of the Budget. His proposal
would have meant much control over departments and agencies, and people therefore are against it. That is a simple explanation."]

The reason for *his* resistance, an agency official declared, was simple.
The report was supposed to help the Congress, but he did not think it
would. Assuredly, it would give the President another forum for ad-
vancing his programs, but he already had so many available he hardly
needed another.

The "crisis of confidence" in the executive's management of R&D
programs that led the Congress to launch the Elliott, Daddario, Reuss,
and other committee hearings hardly indicated congressional elation over
the executive's R&D management, another official rejoined. A better organized flow of information was needed to satisfy the Congress that the
executive knew what it was up to and to provide fruitful points of departure for further congressional inquiries.

The report was a good idea, a Defense Department official said, but to
avoid superficiality [and, perhaps, to reconcile both viewpoints within
the seminar!], it might be best to prepare it every other year. OST and
the Federal Council for Science and Technology haven't been able to
prepare any regular annual report, superficial or not, remarked a participant.[3] "Without apologizing for the OST," an official countered, ". . .
the preparation of the *Economic Report* is a major activity of the Council of Economic Advisers' staff for a significant period of time each
year." OST had a small staff and wanted to keep it small and to remain

[3] The Federal Council for Science and Technology had issued a report for 1962 but,
by the time of this seminar (April 27, 1965), no other. Later in the year, *The Role of
the Federal Council for Science and Technology: Report for 1963 and 1964* (that is,
for a two-year period) was published, and in 1967, *Activities of the Federal Council
for Science and Technology: Report for 1965 and 1966*. (All three reports, incidentally,
were published not by the council but by the Office of Science and Technology.)

selective about its activities. If a major report were to be prepared regularly, OST would have to enlarge its staff, which should not be done lightly.

What the Congress should learn from a report, it seemed to a congressman, was not only the goals executive agencies had embarked toward but "what dialogue took place and what controversy was involved" in establishing those goals—"who was beaten down, and how you finally got to that point, because perhaps . . . the people who took the opposite position may have been more right than the ones who finally prevailed." And, he added straightforwardly, "[t]his information is not readily available." It would be desirable if the Congress could review executive proposals (if necessary, off-the-record) before they became so firmly fixed that neither side can retreat and a head-on encounter develops.

CITIZEN: I am perplexed as to why Congress can't find out, when it wants to find out, about alternatives to the final policies decided upon. . . . [I thought] Congress can find out anything it wants to, if it sets its mind to it.

CONGRESSMAN: . . . I don't think we can find out. At any time the President wants to exert his executive privilege, we are not going to get information.

It was immediately pointed out, however, that, despite the doctrine of executive privilege, both the Armed Services Committee and the Joint Committee on Atomic Energy were informed about the budgets that the Defense Department and the AEC submitted to the Budget Bureau. Controversy had developed in the 1950's, when the Joint Committee had sought this information, but nowadays it was taken for granted. The AEC routinely "provides what is called the Holifield Report that just lays out . . . each project . . . from the laboratories on up." Controversy has rarely arisen, ". . . except on a particular project like SNAP-10A," when the committee authorized a project that the President had not requested in his budget.

For many years, the Joint Committee on Atomic Energy held annual hearings on the state of the atomic energy industry, when it could invite or, if necessary, subpoena witnesses from all quarters—from government, industry, labor, and the scientific community—"with much greater freedom and far less of the problems of conflicts of interest than the executive committees can. . . ." Why should not the Congress itself periodically conduct similar reviews of the status of science and technology? a private participant inquired. Only a partial answer was offered: the committee system did not lend itself to this. Why it did not was not fully explained, but the respondent seemed to infer that most committee members would not attend protracted regular hearings and that regularity of any sort was anathema to a body in which flexibility was as important as wind to a sailboat.

Some years ago, the British House of Commons had had an interesting arrangement, an official observed. A committee of younger M.P.'s kept tabs on the implementation of new laws and, five years later, reviewed their operation to see what revisions and improvements might be made. Something of this sort, he suggested, might be tried here in connection with important policies toward science and technology. For example, it would be useful to review the legislation on, and the performance of, the Communications Satellite Corporation at the end of five years.

Does Congress Need a Few Questions or Many Answers?

"I have been struck by the difference in effectiveness of those hearings that are conducted after some preliminary study is made by staff and those which are conducted without . . . [such] study," a close observer of congressional science affairs remarked. A staff study enables committee members to ask the first question, he explained, and "after being deflected by a witness who may try to outflank that question, they can ask the second question better . . . that is going to get to the root of the issue. . . ." ". . . [Q]uestions are helpful" but not sufficient, another participant felt, "because the people answering them . . . can anticipate and always have a way of weaseling around them. . . . [What] is really necessary and lacking is information—the answers which . . . don't come . . . when they are embarrassing." But a congressman disagreed:

> . . . [T]here is too much information in Congress. There is no doubt about it. . . . [T]herefore you never get a chance to learn all you should have known about the things that turned out to be very important to you aferwards.
>
> Too much information deflects the power of Congress, and Congress has enormous power, and, those of you [in the executive] . . . know very well [that] the way to get your way is to overload the Congress

slightly, not to underload it, and once you have overloaded it, you have succeeded completely.

. . . [M]ost congressional members do most of their committee work pretty much themselves, and the rest of the staff is directed toward other problems of being reelected, to be blunt. . . . The staffs of the committees are not looked upon with favor by most of the members. Very few congressional committee members that I can find . . . think very highly of the staff service that they get in terms of direct personal assistance. . . .

So the overload is there, and it is getting worse. The number of people is growing, per congressman. . . . The federal system is growing more and more important, so more and more decisions are being made at the federal level. . . . The technology is getting more complex. . . .

There is a famous thing called the State Department answer. . . . It is an answer which fits the President's policy and which nobody dares disagree with. . . . That means that the member of Congress is forever going around to the back door. He, in a sense, cannot deal with people's direct answers.

. . . I think frequently the President doesn't believes this half as much as the people who work for him. I am sure the President is willing to accept more criticism than the people who work for him are willing to find out he will accept.

The congressman believed that means should be developed to involve the scientific public in the budget review process. In other areas the interested public followed the budgetary and congressional process far more closely. "For example, if you make a change in the veterans' allocation, you know about it immediately; whereas in the scientific area, you don't know about it for years. We don't really have the scientific public reviewing the budget very much." However, it was remarked, the science budget is unusual in one respect, in that a group of private citizens —the President's Science Advisory Committee—looks over this budget, which is done by no other group representing a private community.

More should be done, an official thought, to encourage informal discussions between congressmen and members of the executive. The kind of quick give-and-take that could occur in an office or at lunch could be far more informative and valuable than the formal exchanges at hearings.

A Second Encounter

Over nine months later, in February 1966, the discussion returned briefly to the subject of a proposed annual report on the status of science and technology. Again, a congressman was unconvinced of the need for such a report.

CONGRESSMAN: The question is, Who is going to read it? The reports are meant for readers and not for the writers. Who is going to read this?

OFFICIAL A: Congressman Grabowski is going to read it. He put out a . . . press release and announced that he was going to introduce a bill . . . and he is going to read the report that you are not going to read. The editor of the *New York Times* thinks it is a great idea. Various other journals have shown some interest. . . .

CONGRESSMAN: . . . [H]ow many people plan to read the *Economic Report* in this room? . . . Do the economists around the country? Do the General Motors economists read it?

ECONOMIST: Yes.

CONGRESSMAN: Do these reports feed back to us?

OFFICIAL B: Yes.

CONGRESSMAN: Would a scientific report feed back?

CONGRESSIONAL STAFF MEMBER: The *Economic Report* is read religiously . . . by the Joint Economic Committee. In other words, there is a specialization of labor. This is their bread and butter. . . . This reporting proposition is a reflection of a desire by people like the *New York Times* . . . who don't want to dip into the material and need a convenient reference.

Many times, in recent years, congressional committees have inquired into the process of executive decision-making for science and technology, a participant remarked. Of late, Congress has produced far more reports than the executive on R&D issues. Surely, a report of the kind that was suggested would help to answer at least some of the questions the Congress raised. But a Capitol Hill participant remained skeptical. "It is the hardest thing in the world on Capitol Hill to find out how this decision-making goes on. It is done, but you never find it in the annual report."

"What is this [proposed] annual report other than an elaborate version of this 'Special Analysis'?"[4] asked a social scientist in some exasperation. "Can someone . . . explain the origin of this 'Special Analysis'?" Indeed, an official who had been critical of the proposed R&D report could.

[4] A reference to the "Special Analysis I: Federal Research, Development, and Related Programs" in each year's budget.

It was initiated by Harold Smith just before the end of the war on the basis [that] there were certain overall matters where public debate and public consideration would be much better informed if the Bureau of the Budget put an annex to the Budget document each year. . . .

In public works, [the] . . . desire was to focus attention on the totality and the problems between the Corps of Engineers, the Department of Agriculture, and the Department of the Interior. It has been a selective process presenting items of interest as seen from overall planners, in an effort to generate interest by people who wanted to debate the issues rather than to lobby for some special interest.

. . . [D]*o you feel this booklet* [that is, the "Special Analysis"] *is bad?*

No, I feel this is excellent.

Then why should more than this be bad?

The question was politely disregarded.

PART IV

A Broader View

JOHN F. MORSE

Old Saws and New Materials: A Consideration of Some Ethical Problems

WE HEAR MUCH these days of a flight from teaching in our colleges and universities. It is said to be caused, or at least accelerated, by the annual pumping of over $1 billion of federal research funds into those institutions. And it has been suggested by some, in what is possibly a *non sequitur,* that the times call for a new code of ethics to meet these new problems—that the old saws are inadequate for the new materials. The proposition is put bluntly as follows:

> The large majority who do not share this approach to life should consider the possibility of formulating ethical standards to curb the crassest opportunism in grantsmanship, job-hopping, and wheeling-dealing.[1]

There is a ring of old-fashioned stump oratory in the last few words. They have an imprecise meaning dear to the hearts of campaign orators —particularly those of the opposition party—and one almost expects to hear the shout: "Throw the rascals out!" coming from the back benches.

The words were pronounced, however, not from the dais of a political rally but from the Olympian heights of one of the country's great philanthropic foundations. The author, if not Jove himself, has over the years been accorded by educators an authority which the master of Olym-

[1] John W. Gardner, "The Flight from Teaching," in *Fifty-ninth Annual Report, 1963–64* (The Carnegie Foundation for the Advancement of Teaching, 1964), p. 20.

283

pus himself would not disdain. And he was describing the symptoms of illness, as he saw them, in our institutions of higher education.

I am not sure when changing jobs becomes job-hopping. I am not sure when seeking support for the exploration of an idea becomes grantsmanship. I am not even sure what wheeling-dealing is. But the words are clearly pejorative, and if as keen an observer and critic as John Gardner uses them to describe the climate as he sees it, the political-scientific-academic community should listen.

I believe it was Lincoln Steffens who noted that any falsehood repeated often enough would eventually gain acceptance as the truth. One of the favorite characters of my childhood was Chicken Little, who convinced most of her world that the sky was falling. I have an uncomfortable feeling as I read "The Flight from Teaching," or parts of Harold Orlans' *The Effects of Federal Programs on Higher Education*,[2] or the Reuss committee report, *Conflicts between the Federal Research Programs and the Nation's Goals for Higher Education*[3] that I am listening to a new generation of Chicken Littles. I believe Gardner's comments are applicable only to a small, although admittedly important, segment of American higher education. I am not at all sure that our problems are as acute as some observers insist or that the 1960's are as different from the 1930's as is alleged. Perhaps things are not what they used to be, but perhaps, too, they never were.

I do not believe, for example, that Yale policies under Angell and Seymour were very different from those under Griswold and Brewster. Certainly, as an undergraduate, I had my share of bored graduate teaching assistants who viewed their classes with thinly veiled malevolence. I can recall two assistant professors whom we all found exciting and eager and whose contracts were not renewed because of failure to publish. And I can recall more than one full professor who had published and unconsciously perished long before we were privileged to sit at his feet.

But most institutions in the 1930's were, and most institutions now are, almost totally lacking in research funds from any source. If research really were, even today, a prerequisite for academic advancement, three-quarters of our institutions would have no one on the faculty above the rank of assistant professor. In 1961, the National Science Foundation found that in 306 institutions that grant graduate degrees in science and

---

[2] Published by the Brookings Institution, 1962.

[3] Eighteenth Report by the Committee on Government Operations, H. Rept. 1158, 89 Cong. 1 sess. (Oct. 13, 1965).

engineering, 34 percent of scientists' time was devoted to research, while 57 percent was devoted to teaching.[4] Even these figures were misleading, however, for the percentage of time devoted to research dropped so sharply that in the bottom 200 institutions barely 10 percent of scientists' time was going into research. Taken in its broader context, then, if there is a flight from teaching, it is a flight which few are able to board, and at worst we are looking at a long line of stand-bys.

Constant self-appraisal is essential to the health of any organization. It is possible that the research-oriented institutions are so intent on extending knowledge that they are losing sight of their responsibility for transmitting it. I am not at all sure, for example, that any institution has thought through the question why it keeps expanding its staff of research associates and even research professors who do not teach. Or why it takes on research—if it does—in which no students are involved. But these are not ethical problems; they are policy problems. And it is the ethical problems that have been washed in by the flow of federal research funds that I was asked to consider.

Who Needs, and Polices, Moral Codes?

View-with-alarm reports, often well documented, from congressional committees, from executive branch task forces, from professional scientists, and from concerned laymen have so far roused in the academic community great attention, some concern, and little action. Is it possible that the majority of academic personnel see no need for formulating new ethical standards because they cannot identify themselves with the problems? Historically, most professional codes have been developed because of universally sensed feeling within the profession that a code was essential to its health. But a code developed by the "academic" profession for the guidance of a fraction of its members might smack more of policing than of self-regulation.

What are the problems and how serious are they? In an effort to determine the problems and find possible ways of attacking them, I corresponded with a number of persons who had given them serious thought. The responses were interesting and, with knowledge of the vantage

[4] See "Science and Engineering Professional Manpower Resources in Colleges and Universities, 1961," in National Science Foundation, *Reviews of Data on Research and Development,* No. 37 (January 1963), p. 9.

point from which each was written, predictable. All agreed there were problems, and to a degree they agreed on *what* those problems were. But they differed sharply as to their solution.

Two hard-hitting but scrupulously fair congressional staff members deplored faculty-raiding accomplished with federal funds and the new affluence of the research scientist who, through an incredible interlocking and overlapping of jobs which separately would add up to 120–40 percent of his time, doubles and triples his salary—largely at the expense of the federal government. One conceded that institutions as institutions might take the initiative and set their houses in order. But more important, he thought, was the role of the federal research-supporting agencies, which have been too fearful of being charged "with unwelcome interference in the universities." "After all," he wrote,

> the real leverage lies with the federal government. . . . I believe the process must start with the federal agencies. If they take a firm stand on the accountability for government money, insisting in particular that grants be used no less prudently than the university's own money, the chances are good that this would strengthen the hand of university administrators for elevating the values or at least restraining the faculty member who is driven by the desire for national recognition and/or material rewards to the detriment of his teaching.

This same attitude seems apparent in the Reuss committee report. The committee view is that it is through federal policies that order can be brought to higher education and that in the debate on proper remedies "the Government should not be just another participant in the debate. . . ."[5] Whatever else that phrase may mean, it would seem to suggest that the government, through revised policies, should determine and impose solutions.

Commenting on these same questions, a university president wrote,

> What good are ethical standards as a method of dealing with such a minority? If people who have graduated into a profession are not aware, from their own experience, of the unethical nature of opportunism, grantsmanship, job-hopping, and wheeling-dealing, a new statement of ethics will not be very helpful in affecting them. On this point, it might be relevant to consider how the scientific community can police itself against such a minority. The American Association of University Professors, for example, has never come to grips with this question of how to police its members for violation of its own standards of conduct. Can or should

[5] Eighteenth Report by the Committee on Government Operations, H. Rept. 1158, p. 6.

then the science community take steps beyond the statement of ethical standards to police the minority in its own membership which violates presently accepted precepts?

The mood of this letter is bearish. Yet the writer of it is providing skilled leadership in one of the country's great universities—one which would fit Douglas Brown's prescription for organization and executive leadership in a liberal university: "It is the faculty as a whole, supporting the wisdom and tact of a sensitive but courageous administration, that resolves . . . countervailing tensions into wholesome progress. Without ideas, strongly expressed, a university decays. Without order, a university becomes a loose collection of job shops."[6]

Perhaps the above statements define the parameters. Faculty as a whole, supporting sensitive but courageous administration, may be capable of setting the university house in order without the use of outside leverage. Government, if it sufficiently dislikes what it sees lying in the road ahead, *does* have the leverage and can be expected to apply it as needed. But individual faculties in individual institutions have not, to date at least, been able to serve as bellwethers for their whole profession; and a government lever can too easily become an oppressive force. There is, perhaps, a middle ground on which a new approach to the solution of new or at least increasingly complex problems can be built. A case history might serve to illustrate.

Fubini's Call for Voluntary Rules

In 1963, Eugene G. Fubini, then assistant secretary of defense, addressed the Seventeenth National Conference on the Administration of Research.[7] His topic, conflict of interest, was one which had been a subject of discussion for many years within the government but had only recently been regarded as a potential problem in the relationships between the academic world and government. It was probably inevitable that as the government and industry of necessity turned to the universities for advice and even for decision-making the potential for abuses of

[6] J. Douglas Brown, "On Organization and Executive Leadership in a Liberal University," *AGB Reports* (Association of Governing Boards of Universities and Colleges, March 1966), p. 15.

[7] See "Some Ethical Problems in the Administration of R&D," in *Proceedings of the Seventeenth National Conference on the Administration of Research,* held in Estes Park, Colorado, Sept. 11–13, 1963 (University of Denver, 1964), pp. 82–85.

privileged information would multiply almost geometrically. The world will never again be sufficiently simple, nor is it likely as specialization grows that it will ever have a sufficient number of experts in any given field, to avoid conflicts of interest. The problem, therefore, seems to be one of avoiding the dangers inherent in these conflicts.

Mr. Fubini constructed a hypothetical situation that might develop in the year 1972. Those who heard him were not sure that the case was really hypothetical nor that the date was a decade away. It is unnecessary to detail the complexity of the relationships Fubini envisioned. It is sufficient to point out that a university scientist could then and can now be the senior investigator on a government-supported research project, be a panelist to advise the same agency on research proposals submitted by his colleagues in the same field, serve as a consultant to industry specializing in this field, and be a major stockholder or even sole owner of a company operating in the field. He could even legitimately require for his own research equipment of which he, when he has his industrial hat on, is the sole manufacturer.

Fubini commented on the envy expressed by foreigners of this country's ability to call on university consultants. When asked how we could do it, he replied: "The ethics of the people who are involved, the intrinsic integrity of the people who are working on the subject, is always preserved." But then he went on to urge that the research administrators he was addressing give serious consideration voluntarily to developing a method of handling the conflicts problem. He recognized that "we have a lot of power in our hands when we are in the government. We don't always have the wisdom that we need to exercise these powers properly." He went on:

> ... [O]ne thing I don't want us to do is to be compelled to issue any regulation or law or anything like that. What I really need is advice and help. I would like to have all universities do what some universities have done: write down a set of rules, request every member of the faculty to sign a statement that he is abiding by the set of rules, and do it every six months; that's all. I don't care if the rules are different. If the rules are written, they are likely to be ethical.

The AEC Conflict of Interest Regulation

At approximately the time Fubini was speaking, the Atomic Energy Commission (AEC) chose the other route and, with little prior consultation, issued a new regulation to apply to all cost-type contracts. The regulation was as follows:

> The contractor shall require all employees who are employed full-time (an individual who performs work under the cost-type contract on a full-time annual basis) or part-time (50 percent or more of regular annual compensation received under terms of a contract with the Commission) on the contract work to disclose to the contractor all consultant or other comparable employment services which the employees propose to undertake for others. The contractor shall transmit to the Contracting Officer all information obtained from such disclosures. The contractor will require any employee who will be employed full-time on the contract work to agree, as a condition of his participation in such work, that he will not perform consultant or other comparable employment services for another Commission cost-type contractor under its contract with the Commission except with the prior approval of the contractor.[8]

The reaction of the academic world was predictable. A number of institutions accepted it with little protest. They were for the most part newcomers in the field of big science, were desperately trying to break into the inner circles of major research, were fearful of offending their "benefactors," and were ready to accept almost any strictures if they could be assured a continued flow of research dollars. On the other hand, universities longer and more firmly established in research protested with a vehemence that seemed to startle the AEC. They at least implied that they would terminate their AEC research if the commission insisted on imposing the regulation. As a result, although the regulation still stands on the books, it has never been applied.[9] It might be noted that, even if it were, there could be no assurance that it would accomplish what it set out to do. It seems the greatest naïveté to suppose that there is a danger in a conflict situation only if a scientist receives a part of his salary from his government-supported research. The danger is just as real if the university pays his entire salary.

A Code Acceptable to Both Government and Universities

The Fubini speech and the AEC regulations probably led to almost simultaneous activities in the Office of Science and Technology (OST) and

---

[8] *Atomic Energy Commission Procurement Regulations,* AECPR Circular 25, March 12, 1963.

[9] On July 30, 1966, the regulation was rescinded (*Federal Register,* vol. 31, p. 10324) and instead institutions are required to be in compliance with the ACE-AAUP statement, reproduced on pp. 337–40.

in the American Council on Education (ACE). At a meeting early in 1964, staff members at OST and at ACE conferred on the possibility of developing a statement on preventing conflicts of interest. They agreed that OST staff would develop a statement that would seek to outline the government's minimum needs and that the ACE staff would work on this statement in any way necessary to make it acceptable to the university world. The statement went through six or more drafts until it was mutually satisfactory. One further step remained.

The ACE is a voluntary organization of 1,194 colleges and universities and 230 educational organizations. There is no provision for the membership of individual persons. Its board of directors and its various commissions and committees are made up almost exclusively of university presidents and other administrative officers. It seemed clear to the staffs at OST and ACE that, if possible, the statement should be issued by the academic community rather than by the government. However, if the ACE alone were to issue the statement, it might be regarded as an administrative ukase rather than an attempt on the part of the total academic community to set its house in order. The staff of the ACE, therefore, turned to the American Association of University Professors (AAUP) to explore the possibility of joint sponsorship in the issuance of the statement. Again the statement went through several drafts until one satisfactory to the three parties concerned was approved and formally ratified by the board of directors of ACE and the council of AAUP. The statement was issued in December 1964 (see Appendix B, p. 337). Since that date, more than one hundred thousand copies have been distributed to universities at their request. Several times this number have been distributed by universities to their faculty members in mimeographed form, in faculty manuals, and in other media of communication.

During the months after the statement was issued, the ACE and the OST staffs continued to confer. The executive agencies—particularly the Department of Defense and the Atomic Energy Commission—expressed satisfaction with the initial step but indicated that they had no way of telling whether the statement would be effective in shaping the policies and procedures of the institutions with which they were dealing. Recognizing the legitimacy of the concern, the ACE agreed to take a further step. In May 1965, ACE President Logan Wilson addressed a letter to the presidents of the one hundred institutions most heavily involved in government-supported research. In it he asked for a statement of the universities' policies and procedures on conflict of interest. He further asked what, in the absence of such policies and procedures, each university was planning to do to implement the AAUP-ACE statement. The letter was accompanied by a questionnaire, which was deliberately loosely constructed in order to elicit a broad spectrum of responses. In fact, no one was quite certain what kinds of information would prove to be valuable.

The Universities' Response

Much has been written about the diversity of American higher education. There could be no better illustration of this diversity than the responses to the ACE letter. One university president answered in a "Who me?" vein and implied that he wished his faculty were sufficiently engaged to be placed in a conflict of interest position. Others had quite clearly anticipated the problem. One institution responded, "It has been the policy and practice of this University to require Board of Trustee approval of any request on behalf of a faculty member to serve as an extramural consultant in any capacity." At the other extreme, the president of a university which, in extent of involvement, general reputation, and political orientation, would seem almost identical to the one just cited wrote: "We do not have formal regulations. We have relied on the integrity of our faculty members to govern their conduct and to my knowledge, we have had no instance in which this confidence has been abused." The problem, of course, with the phrase "to my knowledge" is that it can mean "I know" or "as far as I know" and often the writer is uncertain of which meaning he wishes to convey.

As the responses came in, it was possible, whether we received a ten-page or a two-paragraph response, to sort and classify institutions easily. They fell into four categories, and the appropriate one could be determined on the basis of three criteria. The categories were (A) clearly satisfactory policies and procedures, (B) work in progress which would eventually lead to satisfactory policies and procedures, (C) vagueness as to policy and procedures that made determination difficult, and (D) clearly unsatisfactory policies and/or procedures.

The criteria determining the category into which an institution fell were threefold: (1) the formal adoption of the AAUP-ACE statement, or a comparable statement, as a matter of institutional policy, (2) a formal method by which a researcher would disclose to a superior the extent and nature of his outside consulting, and (3) a mechanism through which a researcher, faced with a potential conflict problem, might secure advice.

The first and third criteria seemed to present few problems. The second revealed a cat-on-a-hot-tin-roof syndrome, which may be expected to persist in future efforts to develop codes. Some institutions have no qualms about the use of such words and phrases as *require permission in advance,* or *must,* or *shall.* But others resort to exhortations or *express hope* or *suggest* that faculty members disclose their outside consulting.

Staff members of the American Council and later of the Federal Council for Science and Technology reviewed every response. There was such concurrence of view between these two separate evaluations as to almost suggest collusion. Of the 83 institutions which have so far responded, 49 have received an *A* rating, 9 have received *B,* 9 have received *C,* and 16 have received *D.* Seventeen have not responded.[10] Those institutions not rated *A* fall into three categories: those whose administrative wheels move so slowly that apparently two or more academic years must pass before action takes place, those which quite sincerely believe they have no problem, and those which flatly assert that they will not involve themselves in the outside affairs of their faculty.

When the ACE staff undertook this inquiry, it had little idea of what it would find or what it would do with its findings. But through close collaboration with the Federal Council for Science and Technology, an approach has been developed that may help in the solution of other problems. The culminating document in the evolution described above is a formal policy recently issued by the Federal Council for Science and Technology.[11] It states:

> *a.* The AAUP-ACE statement contains principles that are sound and colleges and universities are urged to adopt them.
>
> *b.* Each college receiving federal research funds should have written policies and procedures indicating the conditions under which outside

[10] As of January 1, 1968, the figures were: *A*—97; *B*—3; *C*—0; *D*—0. Recently, the Council has undertaken to review the policies of an additional 120 institutions (all those with a volume of $100,000 or more in sponsored research). The first returns show the following breakdown: *A*—69; *B*—10; *C*—9; *D*—2. Five have indicated that they are working on a policy statement and 25 have not yet responded.

[11] "Policy of the Federal Council for Science and Technology Relating to Conflicts of Interest by Staff Members of Colleges and Universities," issued by the Federal Council for Science and Technology, March 29, 1966.

activities are proper and providing for disclosure of such activities to an appropriate university official.

c. All federal agencies will accept as satisfactory evidence of the adoption of the above a finding to that effect by the Office of Science and Technology.

d. OST will coordinate the approach of agencies to those institutions not in conformity.

e. The progress of voluntary acceptance of these guides will be monitored by OST, which will, if necessary, consider further steps after a reasonable interval.

Clearly, the American Council on Education has no authority, or even wish, to impose policies or procedures on its member institutions, but it has, in this instance, been able to provide leadership in the attack on one problem. It is equally clear that OST has no authority to speak for all federal agencies, or to "clear" university policies in behalf of those agencies, unless delegated to do so. Nevertheless, in the absence of the action described above, every federal agency would undoubtedly have developed its own regulations, much as the Atomic Energy Commission did in 1963, and proceeded individually to see that they were carried out. If there is indeed a growing partnership between higher education and the government, a process directed toward bilateral solution of problems would seem far preferable.

Ten Problems of Moral and Educational Purpose

Other problems implied in John Gardner's essay that might be approached as the conflict of interest problem has been can be discussed only briefly here. Some might be tackled by organizations like the ACE. Others should surely be the responsibility of professional associations. There are undoubtedly other groups that might take the lead. Apparently, however, in the solution of complex problems, groups and associations are more likely to be effective than are individual institutions.

No one person can identify all of the problems that have been engendered by the growing and increasingly complex relationships between government and the university world. Each individual overlooks mountainous problems and sees others that do not exist. But let me set down, almost at random, a series of statements or propositions that have been made to me over the past several years by thoughtful, responsible, and concerned members of university administration and faculty and by public servants in the legislative and executive branches of government. All of the propositions would be rejected by some. None would be accepted by all. But to the extent that they are real, they represent problems of legitimate concern to those who care about the health of our nation.

1. Our universities in their search for prestige have lost sight of the difference between recruiting and pirating. Too often they lure to their campus the scientists they want with large salary increases and more and more magnificent equipment—all of which is eventually paid for by the federal government through charges to research contracts and grants.

2. On the other hand, scientists are increasingly losing any concept of loyalty to an institution. While demanding total academic freedom and enjoying tenure, they have no compunction about moving from one institution to another, almost without notice. They feel no gratitude to the institution that has made their professional growth possible and no responsibility for nurturing the institution's continued growth.

3. Too few institutions have defined their objectives and capacities. Too many have been willing to have their directions determined by the availability of federal funds and to assume obligations without assessing their ability to carry them out.

4. On the other hand, too many members of university faculties and too many government administrators, inadvertently or even knowingly, have subverted the purposes of universities by a process of direct negotiation which bypasses university administration. And they have overcommitted themselves beyond their capacity to perform what they have agreed to perform.

5. Too few universities have set up orderly procedures for the administration of research. Decisions they should be making and controls they should be exercising are transferred through default to federal agencies or are left to the discretion of the individual scientist.

6. On the other hand, too many university faculty reject the concept of university decision-making and control, preferring to deal directly with federal agencies in the belief that lack of intimate knowledge on the part of a federal-grants manager is more likely to lead to an affirmative than to a negative answer.

7. The universities are decreasingly concerned with their function of instructing undergraduates. This is not solely or even chiefly because of an increasingly heavy research load and, therefore, increasingly light

teaching load which the faculty are allowed to assume. It is also because research swallows the ablest graduate assistants, leaving only the weakest to serve as teaching assistants. Furthermore, the increasing use of research associates in some institutions removes from the market scientists who might elsewhere serve as teachers and researchers.

8. University faculty are abusing the principles of academic freedom and tenure by using their new-found prominence and their university platform to make pronouncements and influence governmental policy in areas where they have no special or professional competence.

9. In an age when ideas and knowledge are marketable to a degree unknown before, there is a growing danger that they will be concealed and suppressed until a market can be found for them. No amount of revised legislation in the fields of copyright and patent can replace a code of ethics in these areas.

10. The reason-for-being of a scientist on a university faculty is being forgotten. The phrase nonteaching professor is a contradiction in terms. Those who care only about the acquisition and not the transmission of knowledge pervert the whole purpose of a university. Yet they seem to be riding the wave of the future.

The handful of items listed above represents an attempt to illustrate what might be meant by the terms crass opportunism, grantsmanship, job-hopping, and wheeling-dealing. The list has been jotted down by one who is not a scientist and who is no longer a university administrator. An adequate list can be compiled only by those who day after day and year after year encounter the problems and who care sufficiently about the integrity of their profession and of the academic world to lay them out on the table and work toward their solution. We are now working with many new materials, and the old saws cannot be expected to cut through them.

DISCUSSION

The Value and Limitations
of a Code of Ethics

CLEARLY, SAID Morse, serious ethical problems arose in the relations of university faculty to the government. It was less clear that a "flight from teaching" had developed. However, the two problems were largely unrelated and had to be confronted with an open mind unconfounded by bromides such as that teaching and research were inseparable—which was manifestly untrue, for if it were true, no teaching at all was going on at the vast majority of higher [and, he might have added, lower] educational institutions at which no research was conducted.

Not one but at least three separate codes of conduct were required: for universities, for faculty, and for government personnel. The code for universities should cover everything from the pirating of faculty to the voluntary limitation of activities to those that lie within their institutional capabilities. The code for faculty should deal with their obligations to their profession, their students, their government, and (a matter remarkably neglected) their institution. Too many faculty would rather fight for their own freedom than for the welfare of the institution which enabled them to enjoy that freedom. Finally, the code for government personnel should require them to serve the interests of the government, of academic scientists, *and* of academic institutions. While it was proper for a civil servant to fight for the best interests of the government as he saw them, it was improper for him to subvert such government policies as the payment of costs and overhead or to work out deals with individual scientists which weaken their institutions and frustrate the spirit, if not the letter, of congressional intent.

As one seminarian saw it, the experience of the American Council on Education and the Council of the American Association of University Professors in attempting to get institutions to adopt *some* procedure for dealing with conflicts of interest indicated that few institutions had any formal way to cope with problems arising from their relations with the government. Perhaps, he continued, that was unfair:

> There are certain universities which have beautifully codified, well-developed procedures to handle almost any conceivable problem that might arise and a machinery set up to deal with new problems that are as yet unforeseen. Others have an absolutely laissez faire attitude springing . . . from two different points of view. "We don't have any problems. We just don't have any. We rely on the ethical sense of the individual." Or "It is not our business as a university. This is up to the individual faculty member."

Two eminent universities, X and Y exemplified these types. X "has a neat, tidy and completely acceptable set of procedures to handle almost any conceivable issue," whereas Y "has almost nothing in writing or even . . . in common law. . . ." But are conditions at Y any worse than at X? The questioner volunteered his own answer—No—and a paradoxical explanation:

> . . . [I]n an ideal world, conflict of interest regulations would work fine, but of course, in that world they would be unnecessary. . . . [I]n the real world in which we live, they are terribly necessary, but there isn't any workable [enforcement] procedure that doesn't impose costs which are considerably greater than any benefit that may be obtained.

Neither the answer nor the philosophy satisfied the first participant, who felt that university Y should formulate a conflict of interest code because without one ". . . no one has the slightest idea . . . on the Y campus as to whether they have a conflict of interest problem or not, because they have no way of coping with it. . . . At X, I should be astonished if any . . . scandal could possibly develop." Whereupon, it was promptly noted that precisely such a scandal had occurred at X (or, if not a "scandal," which might be too strong a word, then a decidedly awkward and widely publicized episode involving a faculty member who both advised a government research agency and appeared to benefit from the advice rendered). "How did the X regulations prevent this?"

One answer was that the regulations, in their present form, had not been adopted until after the episode. Another answer was that, while a code was of value in defining a model standard of conduct, it could not prevent breaches of that standard. ". . . [Y]ou can't prevent anything with a code. You can protect the general public with a code, but you can't be assured that there will be no charlatan. Lawyers are disbarred every year; doctors are . . . thrown out of practice every year, despite fairly well worked-out codes."

The Functions of a Code of Conduct

What, then, was the purpose of a conflict of interest code? "What do you gain by having a code?" This question was discussed at length.

One function was simply to provide all faculty members with a certain amount of common information, so that "a person who may feel he has some possibility of conflict . . . may in fact identify the possibility through reading such a document. . . ."

A second function was to help an institution protect its integrity. Private industry faced no conflict of interest problem comparable to that of the universities, it was remarked, because it long ago had to confront the problems that universities are only now facing. Industry "can't live without [conflict of interest codes]. . . . So they self-regulate. The universities are going to be forced to do this, because they have this same economic pressure and are getting involved [with the government] in the same way [as industry]."

A third function was the very practical one of disclosure, under which a potential conflict of interest is made known to others who can assess its significance and indicate whether a proposed activity should, or should not, be undertaken. Disclosure was important not only to prevent some conflicts of interest from arising but to *permit* others vital to the nation. The assumption was that, when men of integrity openly avowed their conflicts, if their conduct was not thereby raised to a higher level (since, as men of integrity, it was already high), it would, at any rate, be less subject to public recrimination and attack. ". . . [I]f everything is above the table and aboveboard, you are not likely to have very serious abuses." C. P. Snow observes in one of his novels that this is the way the problem is handled in the board room: a member declares his interest in the matter at hand and then proceeds to state his position.

But, it was asked, is this actually the present practice of university scientists serving the government in advisory capacities?

I read an awful lot of [congressional] hearings but I have never seen anybody, before proceeding to testify, state, "As you know, I hold a certain number of shares in such and such and we [our university] have several million dollars from certain agencies, and now let me tell you what I think should be done about this program." . . . [I]t wouldn't be a bad idea.

Do scientists and university representatives declare their interests today before they proceed to advise the government?

"Yes, they do," a government official responded. "They file with the government a statement of their outside financial interests." However, it was countered, this statement is held in confidence. It is not really a public disclosure. "We are told that . . . [a witness] was a lobbyist for Germany, but we are not told he is a lobbyist for Harvard." Why was public disclosure not the rule in testimony before the Congress?

Because, a participant from the Hill replied, "it may not be relevant to the particular information that he is giving. . . . [T]here isn't any standing rule about this. When you ask a witness to come before a committee, frequently he may be asked to qualify himself and, if a member sees fit, he may ask him if he has any interest in the subject matter in a financial way." The paramount purpose of a code of conduct in federally sponsored research, he continued, is to ensure that federal funds are "not being somehow abused by conflicting interest." A code serves that purpose by sharpening the perception of beneficiaries about the kinds of problems that may arise and by enabling them to make a public demonstration that they are acting responsibly.

A cynic might infer from some of the argument that the appearance of avoiding conflicts was more significant that the reality,[1] since it was repeatedly affirmed, on the one hand, that it was desirable (in the public interest) for the government to utilize experts who were thereby placed in a conflict of interest and that a formal declaration did not eliminate that fact but enabled a private interest and a larger public interest to be reconciled, and, on the other hand, that even if a man's conscience was clear it was best not to put him into what appeared to be a conflict of interest situation. The latter course was illustrated by two cases. A university representative related one:

> I am a member of the ———— Board. . . . Recently a case came up, and I looked at the rules of conflicts of interest, and according to the rules, there was no question that I could participate in the case; so I wrote a letter to the chairman of the board and said, "This is what the rules say, and I can participate, but what do you think?" . . . The rules permitted me, and I wanted to, [but] . . . I thought I had better check with him.
> Well . . . he called me in and said, "I don't care what the rules say,

[1] While a pragmatist might counter that, in affairs of this sort, appearance and reality may be equally important and indistinguishable.

if you get anywhere near this case I will murder you personally." So I stayed away from it.

A government official recounted the second:

> One time [a government agency] . . . decided to have a director of research. He came from . . . [a private company. The company] would continue to pay his salary at $40,000 a year, and he would direct the government's program.
>
> Well, there is a law which allowed a half-dozen or ten people to do something like that. But, you know, it really didn't make too much sense. And to help this fellow out we persuaded him that he ought to resign [from the company] . . . before he took the job. He was perfectly legal in doing it, but it was the kind of thing that really nobody would stomach, when it came to thinking. . . . It didn't make sense.

The Innocent and the Experienced

The foregoing company officer was honest and well intentioned but naïve, the official continued, and a good, well-administered code should reduce the danger of drawing naïve persons into real or apparent compromising situations. This danger might be particularly great at the hundreds of institutions which have only recently begun to participate substantially in programs of federally sponsored research and education, a private participant suggested:

> . . . [T]hey just have no experience . . . and with the best intention can fall flat on their faces. I have attended one . . . of the American Council [on Education] conferences with this vast and enlarging number of universities and colleges who are in the course of time getting involved in government programs, and I have been utterly astounded at the innocence, the . . . utter ignorance and innocence, of those people who just don't know really anything very much about the government. . . .

A political scientist suggested that this innocence of many academicians, and the general lack of information about what was actually going on—the frequency with which various ethical problems arose—made it difficult to establish realistic codes:

> I don't see how you can develop these codes in a vacuum. We are dealing with rather new situations . . . for the scientist in universities . . . , and . . . they don't know, and no one else knows, whether what they are doing is right or wrong until the facts are out on the table and you begin to develop a certain consensus. . . . Therefore, the first thing would seem to be to get more information, because there are many situations where

the scientists . . . believe they have been doing a valuable service by acting as points of interchange, by encouraging companies to produce equipment which they know is needed by themselves and others, and being involved in a number of different capacities. They actually make a virtue of this, in many cases with some justice. But when the facts are put out on the table other people look at them and a certain uneasiness may develop, and then you can begin to see where to draw the line between black and white. . . .

That innocence was responsible for most ethical problems or that more information was needed before adequate codes could be drafted was, however, disputed by several officials. "The code is not something you have to develop on the basis of a massive empirical experience," said one. "The code is merely the common sense of a situation." Another declared that most of the problems his agency had encountered arose at major institutions long familiar with federal programs, some of whose faculty nonetheless persisted in such unjustifiable practices as charging the government for more than 100 percent of their time.

The events that led to the preparation of the American Council on Education–AAUP conflict of interest statement also suggested that most of the problems arising in government-sponsored research occurred at large institutions, if only because they had more opportunities to develop problems. These events had involved efforts by the Atomic Energy Commission and the Department of Defense to ensure that faculty were neither receiving excessive payments from government projects nor compromising the integrity of government contracts to industry by revealing to one company (as consultant, director, or in any other capacity) information (which competing companies lacked) acquired in the course of service to the government.

Accounting for Time

The question of the time for which a professor could be reimbursed from government research funds, it was recognized, raised practical and ethical problems independent of any conflicts of interest that might, occasionally, also be entailed. To the complaint that some professors had received more than 100 percent of their salary from different government projects (though less than 100 percent from any one), an erstwhile professor (and, incidentally, a stern moralist) retorted that this was perfectly proper.

Let's assume the professor was engaged in full-time teaching and got a salary for that. This left him, under the normal procedure, anywhere from a third to a half of "his time" for his own reading, his own writing, his own research, his own consulting or anything he wanted to do with it. . . .

The university . . . encouraged him to do anything he wanted with that time . . . that would not conflict with his [teaching]. So the normal situation was that a professor could do full-time teaching and still have, we will say, twenty-five hours a week that he could spend on something else.

Now . . . when instead of doing full-time teaching he does, we will say, half-time [teaching and] half-time research . . . , he is still only, in his view, selling the one-half of his time which the university formerly bought. . . . He could still do that and have . . . 100 percent of additional time to spend if he is a hard worker.

That situation, another participant noted, could not be encountered in medical schools, where "for a long time, the concept has been 'whole time.' If you are 'full time,' that is all of the hours in the year."

"Conflict of time" was only marginally related to "conflict of interest," a government official conceded, and there had been some debate as to whether it should be included in the ACE-AAUP statement. Eventually, it was, as intrinsically an ethical issue:

If . . . [a principal investigator] tells the government he is going to spend a certain fraction of his time on it [a research project], then he ought to put that time in. . . . It doesn't really make any difference whether the institution is reimbursed or not for his effort. The fact is that the government hasn't gotten his leadership, and it was his leadership that caused the grant to be made in the first place.

Conflict of time was, of course, an ethical issue not only for the investigator but also for the university, which had to transmit the investigator's budget to the government and countersign and account for it. And the moral and practical problems of determining if the time and effort an investigator actually devoted to a project approximated what he had earlier estimated he *would* devote to it had become acute, since the time a faculty member spent represented either a new source of income for the university[2] or a contribution to the total costs of a particular project (the government had recently decreed the university must contribute at least 5 per-

---

[2] Not a source of net, but of gross, income, when granting agencies such as the National Science Foundation, which had originally refused to do so, began to reimburse universities for the proportion of time professors devoted to government-sponsored research during the academic year.

cent). ". . . [T]he University of ———— . . . and ———— . . . I would judge to be close to rebellion over the necessity to report an approximate estimate by the . . . project director on what percentage of effort he is putting into his research," a university spokesman averred.

The problem, another participant charged, was of the universities' own making, because they had been so "greedy" ["needy" might have been as accurate and more charitable] to get money from the government that they had subjected their faculty to such time accounting. The alternative course would have been to relinquish (as inherently unacademic) full reimbursement for faculty research time via project budgets for an earlier and more forceful campaign to obtain larger institutionaal grants.

Universities were also concerned about another conflict of interest: that between a professor's academic responsibilities and his private enterprises. "We had been supporting research in a certain area at a university," a government official recalled, "when the principal investigator . . . became one of the founding members of a little research company whose purpose was to do research of the same type. . . ." The situation was not uncommon, said another participant. "Half the professors [at ————] have their own companies, and they can throw money one place or the other." That was why an institutional standard of faculty conduct should be formulated which each professor will be aware of and for which each will feel responsible and—ideal prospect!—which "the public and the Congress and the trustees can approve. . . ."

The Background and Effects of the ACE-AAUP Code

The government officials most instrumental in pushing the adoption of a code had not believed that the conflict of interest problem was acute—if they *had,* they might have acted more directly, one official declared. "The government could lay down standards . . . by law or by regulation," as the AEC did. ". . . [I]t is a privilege for a university that gets a lot of federal dough to be able to frame its own code of conduct." Instead, the government acted with deliberate restraint. ". . . [I]t was decided very consciously not to issue this [the code] as a government statement," another official explained, "because it was . . . not the proper role of government to tell the universities how they should organize their activities. . . ." However, there had been in Washington an awareness of emergent conflict situations which, senior officials felt, it was their responsibility to bring to the attention of the academic community. Also in their minds was a fear that, should a few scandals occur, the Congress would act and "greatly tighten up a situation . . . to the detriment of the flexibility and freedom that we feel is necessary for research."

The ACE-AAUP code had, of course, led to widespread discussion of ethical problems among university faculty and administrators. "I doubt that there are many faculties who have really debated these issues among themselves in any freewheeling way and asked themselves and their colleagues about it," said a profesor, who evidently had in mind discussions involving the entire faculty of an institution. However, the ACE-AAUP code had been discussed at most of the one hundred universities initially addressed:

> With the exception of possibly fifteen institutions which had already developed codes governing prevention of conflict of interest . . . , these statements [adopted after the ACE-AAUP stimulus] have been developed either by an especially appointed faculty committee working with administration or . . . , in some cases, worked out administratively and then placed before faculties for discussion and ultimate ratification by the faculty in every instance. . . . That is why . . . [adoption] is so slow. To get the ratification by faculty senate and so forth is not a speedy process.

Patently, "the issuance of this statement . . . has caused a good many institutions to face up to their own problems," a government official stated. By his standards, 49 out of 106 institutions had (as of May 1966) adopted satisfactory policies, and others "are rapidly moving in this direction. . . . And the more institutions that adopt such policies, the more that will, because they are not in a very defensible position [to refuse on the grounds of 'academic freedom'] . . . if the bulk of them already have acceptable policies." To be sure, another participant noted, a few universities have not responded—in the main, probably, because of the forgetfulness or obliviousness of key personnel; and five or six institutions stated outright, "We do not propose to do anything about this."

Despite the statistics of institutional compliance, many participants doubted that codes actually changed conduct. Codes ". . . have a tremendous meaning in terms of calling attention to a problem . . . and . . . they may be very important in the relations of certain agencies with the

Congress . . . ," said one participant; but "I, at least, am a skeptic as to how valuable these codes are in actually . . . influencing the behavior of individual faculty members." Another was concerned that codes not make it *more* difficult for the best qualified men to serve the government. "How many honest men . . . are we keeping away from public service . . . for the sake of . . . preventing one or two wrongdoers?" Thus, the following week, "the Atomic Industrial Forum will be writing to the AEC suggesting . . . that if the AEC does not adopt its proposed [more liberal] regulations on organizational conflicts of interest . . . the organization that will be affected [most adversely] . . . will be the Atomic Energy Commission and not any of its contractors."

In an earlier seminar, a university scientist pointed out how vital it was to the success of a major scientific venture that able scientists commit themselves fully to do it. "Beware of the large new programs supported by committees of scientists who will return to their own interests as soon as their reports are written," he warned. "There are too many instances in which the United States has been trapped into supporting large programs recommended by committees whose members had really no personal stake, from the standpoint of their own scientific reputation, in the success of the program." However, he recognized that this posed a genuine ethical problem, "because what I am really saying . . . is that the only people you can believe are people who have a conflict of interest in making their recommendation," since "those who don't have a conflict of interest won't be responsible."

Should the Government Be Concerned about an Institution's Welfare?

A government official felt that a fundamental difficulty—moral, administrative, and financial—underlay government-university relations: the interests of federal agencies in universities were specialized.

> There isn't any agency of the government that is really looking at what is going on in the universities. Perhaps ideally the Office of Education should be doing this, but they haven't the capability to do it; so we are in effect tugging and hauling, pulling the universities this way and that way, and we are not giving . . . enough institutional-type . . . support of a general character that will permit the institution really to determine its own destiny.

A private participant concurred. ". . . [T]here is no agency of government so far as I know that gives a hoot . . . about the health of the institution as a whole, even in an abstract way. *People* in agencies do." But another government official disagreed:

> . . . I don't really believe it is the function of the government . . . to worry about any single institution as a whole or institutions as schools collectively. There are boards of trustees and chief executive officers in universities who are supposed to be looking after the welfare and the health of the institution. We have several institutions that are the wards of the federal government and not a one is . . . outstanding . . . in any respect. . . .
>
> On the other hand, I think the government does have a major responsibility not to call on the universities for things that it ought to do itself. If . . . we had had more concern about maintaining . . . top-flight government laboratories that we used to have . . . you wouldn't have a lot of the problems you now have in university-government relations. I think that it was a conscious effort [by private university advisers to the government] not to maintain government laboratories . . . that led to many of the things we now have.
>
> . . . [W]hat we need to do is to go back to fundamentals and differentiate between functions of the universities and functions of the government laboratories, and some of these problems will disappear.

There is a difference, a professor responded, between universities being wards of the government "and the government being willing to listen to arguments about the needs of a university as a whole." Trustees could not effectively look after the overall welfare of the institution "because there is no one that they can go to to make their case about the university as a whole." By recognizing overhead costs, the government was of course recognizing the existence of overall institutional needs, but attention to these needs was not the specific function of any government agency. ". . . [A]n argument that the university needs certain kinds of support in order to become more of an integrated unit, an intellectually coordinated unit, doesn't get a sympathetic response anywhere." "This," responded the official, "goes on in fifty state legislatures every year." (If the reader has deduced that the professor taught at a private university, he is right.)

"The problem of institutional support is the next great problem the Congress has to face, and it is a thorny one," a university spokesman declared, because of the difficulty of finding a politically realistic and technically practicable formula for extending such support. ". . . [H]ow do you select the universities . . . [and] what do you expect them to do? . . . [H]ow do you measure . . . [their] performance . . . to determine whether you . . . continue support?"

OFFICIAL A : . . . [T]he government may not know what it will call upon a university to do five years from now. It has to invest a certain amount of capital in the institution as an institution. . . . [T]here is a certain . . . overrun . . . on every project that ought to be seed money put into developing intellectual resources of the institution. . . .

OFFICIAL B : It sounds like a fee.

OFFICIAL A : It is an idea.

A third official believed that spokesmen for higher education had not made "any real effort" to develop the necessary ideas for an institutional-grant program that would deal with the problems that had been discussed; and this was at least in part due to the fact that many institutions were basically satisfied with present arrangements. ". . . [T]here are a lot of people who are in advisory positions who don't want the status quo changed. . . ."

On Advising and Consenting

This observation led, before long, to the final point raised that evening, which was introduced by a social scientist. He thought that the discussion had been confined too much to financial interests, whereas there were important conflicts that arose in the formulation of government science policies that involved no hint or taint of personal financial gain. For example, was it in the public interest for the same scientist to advise the government in a private capacity and then to receive that advice and act upon it as a legally responsible government official? Such men as Detlev Bronk or Harvey Brooks, he noted, had served in both capacities, first rendering the government private advice as members of the National Academy of Sciences and then acting on that advice as members of the National Science Board. (It might be added that Jerome Wiesner and Donald Hornig were placed in a similar position, giving the government private advice as chairman of the President's Science Advisory Committee and implementing that advice as director of the Office of Science and Technology.) No one would question the personal integrity or scientific distinction of these men; nonetheless, was it desirable, in prin-

ciple, for the same man both to advise and to consent—both to counsel
and to judge?

From a legal standpoint, a government official stated, the question had
been answered: "[T]here is no legal conflict of interest. . . ."

> Whether it is desirable from the point of view of public policy to have
> centered in one individual so many different responsibilities, I would ques-
> tion. . . . Personally, . . . if I was in a position to do so, I would rule they
> could not be members of the two bodies at the same time.

Two comparable conflicts of interest were noted by government participants. The National Academy of Sciences "is in conflict of interest because it is advisory to both the Congress and the executive branch." Also
in conflict is a member of the National Science Board who is also, as a
member of the academy or of PSAC, "called upon to evaluate in a broad
way the programs and actions of the National Science Foundation. . . .
[T]he question is, Is he evaluating his own work?" This matter of joint
membership on the National Science Board and either the academy or
PSAC had been looked into during Congressman Daddario's investigation of the National Science Foundation, a participant from the Hill
pointed out. He concluded from the testimony that men who were members of both the board and one of the other bodies favored no legal restriction on such joint membership and might well act in such a way as
to keep the board relatively weak; whereas those who belonged only to
the board were more inclined to prohibit joint service and to strengthen
the board's policy functions.

Defending joint participation in such groups, a government official
pointed to the resultant "cross fertilization . . . of ideas." If a scientist
finds that a particular policy issue cannot be dealt with by one body, he
can raise it in another.

> OFFICIAL A : On the balance . . . I would say that . . . [the government
> has] gotten better reports out of the National Academy because they have
> had a more realistic appreciation of the problems that face the govern-
> ment, and I daresay that the new directions in which the [National]
> Science Board has been going . . . has benefited greatly from this cross-
> flow of ideas.

> PRIVATE PARTICIPANT A : . . . [W]hat is so peculiar about the na-
> ture of science policy that sets it aside from our other public institutions,
> such as regulatory agencies or courts of justice, that, in this area alone,
> witnesses and judges should be the same?

> PRIVATE PARTICIPANT B : We have been in a promotional situa-

tion and not a regulatory situation. You do things when you are trying to stimulate and develop activity that you don't do later, after you have it in being. . . . [T]he situation is changing, and a set of arrangements that might have been satisfactory and in the public interest ten years ago may cease to be.

P R I V A T E   P A R T I C I P A N T   C : . . . [C]onflict of interest situations are absolutely inevitable, if you are going to get the best talent you have in the country to advise on certain issues policies. . . . Let's suppose that you have as chairman of the National Science Board the president of one of your most heavily supported institutions in the country. It is probable that he is going to feel that our system of distribution of federal funds as it stands right now is just about perfect. It also is probably going to have to be assessed by the board under him, as to the desirability of shifting our current patterns to achieve greater geographical spread of funds, [of] getting more money into the have-not institutions conceivably at the expense of some of the . . . have institutions. He is immediately in a conflict of interest situation and can't help it. You can't deny yourself the services of that man.

P R I V A T E   P A R T I C I P A N T   A : We have denied ourselves the services of one secretary of defense who, at least so far as the public thought, could not distinguish between the interests of the nation and [those] . . . of his corporation.

O F F I C I A L   B : This whole problem is part of growing to age of the scientific community. . . . As far as the [private] policy advisory committee and National Science Board are concerned, that, in my mind, is also transient. We don't have advisory judges; we don't have advisory legal people running our government affairs. The professions, except for the scientists, have taken up their public responsibility seriously, and they move in and carry the load in a responsible way. . . . [T]hey don't start loading [private advisers] . . . with government-responsible decisions. . . .

[Private scientists] . . . shouldn't be stooging around giving advice to the government. If they are so . . . important, and they are, they ought to be part of the government for a reasonable time and take the line authority. Until we encourage people to do it, and set up an environment which will attract and keep such people, we are in trouble. And we are in trouble.

O F F I C I A L   C : There is one interesting and very factual point . . . that I think you all should know about. . . . [T]he National Science Board . . . did once have a chairman who was president of a very well-supported university, who during the tenure of his chairmanship did not allow proposals [from his institution] to come to the National Science Foundation. All of this [was] before codes. . . . He had ethical standards of his own, and he applied them with a vengeance. . . . If you have individuals who have some ethical standards of their own . . . , you don't need codes.

And with that, the meeting adjourned. The man in question was clearly James Conant, who from 1950 to 1951 was both president of Harvard and the first chairman of the National Science Board.[3]

[3] It is no disrespect to Conant, but only fair to his successors, to point out that, during his incumbency as chairman of the National Science Board, the National Science Foundation's total research grants did not much exceed $1 million.

HARRY MELVILLE

The Support of Academic Scientific Research in the United Kingdom

GOVERNMENTAL SUPPORT of academic research in Britain is, for several reasons, now at an extremely interesting and even critical stage.

The Great Expansion in University Research

In the first place, the number of universities has almost doubled (a) by the founding of completely new institutions similar to those already existing and (b) the transformation of the former colleges of advanced technology into technological universities. The former are rapidly expanding their enrollments, and all made a quick start on research, as their staffs brought with them their own research students and assistants. Prior to assuming their new status, the colleges of advanced technology changed many courses and employed more and more senior staff; and of course, when they received their charters, they were enabled to grant their own degrees. Thus, a considerable new research potential is being built up, often different in character from that of older institutions, and the demand for research funds has markedly increased. This university expansion was planned by the government in response to the pressing demands from all kinds of employers—not only industry—for an increasing number of personnel trained to the bachelor, as well as graduate and professional school, levels. So far as manufacturing industry is concerned, particularly as it becomes more capital intensive, using bigger and more complicated production units, the need for more highly skilled manpower will automatically increase.

These developments have led to demands for research moneys that could only be met by an exponential rise in funds. During the immediate postwar years and, in fact, for almost two decades, much leeway had to be made up to equip universities with up-to-date research equipment together with the increased technical staff needed to exploit this equipment fully. For example, the volume of research grants awarded by the former Department of Scientific and Industrial Research increased at the rate of 25 percent compounded per annum. This constant pressure, even for funds which are relatively modest in magnitude, has caused concern to the government, particularly during the continuing financial crises of recent years. There is now, therefore, a distinct possibility that this highly favorable period has come to an end and that, though the support of university research has not reached a reasonable equilibrium, funds will increase at a lower rate for the next few years.

An additional important, but not necessarily dominating, factor in the government research budget is the position of European science. The United Kingdom has played an important part in European agencies for nuclear physics (CERN [the European Organization for Nuclear Research]) and for space science (ESRO [the European Space Research Organization]), contributing about 25 percent of their budgets (an amount equal to 20 percent of the government's Science Research Council budget). In all likelihood, British financial participation in European science will increase, maybe even faster than the domestic science budget. This can put a strain on domestic activities, if the participation involves long-range commitments required by the nature of the installations.

Less immediately important factors with greater implications for manpower derive from the future rise in industrial activity. The national plan of 1965 confidently foresaw a 4 percent growth in national product. This now seems unlikely, and a setback in the rate of industrial expansion might well have a disproportionate effect on the demand for men with high academic qualifications. Similarly in defense research, a curtailment of funds will comparatively quickly affect the demand for trained manpower.

The interaction of all these factors produces a situation of the utmost complexity which makes forward planning exceptionally difficult. The restraints that may have to be imposed reduce the probability of big investments in new lines of research and in new ways of supporting university research. While this paper will concentrate on the present scene, it may also be useful to comment on the pattern that has evolved to meet needs envisaged earlier, under more favorable financial circumstances.

Until about ten years ago, university research was mainly carried out by academic staff assisted by research students. The staff were paid by grants to the university from the University Grants Committee (UGC) —a body wholly funded by the United Kingdom Treasury. Similarly, necessary buildings were provided by the UGC. The funds for research students came from a great variety of sources. Few technical assistants were available at university departments. Funds for apparatus were extremely modest, and the head of any large department had to go out and virtually beg for assistance from any suitable quarter. In short, the academic scientist's full research potential was not exploited, and graduate student training did not make use of expensive equipment.

This situation has changed almost out of recognition. Because of the demand for essential construction and basic capital equipment in the country as a whole, it was simply not feasible in the immediate postwar period to devote adequate resources to rebuilding and reequipping the universities. However, during the last decade nearly all the science departments have been rehoused in new or modernized buildings. In addition, extensive equipment grants by the University Grants Committee have provided not only the usual undergraduate teaching equipment but also a great deal of apparatus suitable for research. These institutional grants are given not for specified research projects or programs but for the general prosecution of science. They support a great deal of research which is decided entirely by the staffs on the spot, without reference to any national or other plan. In effect, this establishes an immense operational base, for there are 7,700 science staff supported almost wholly by central government funds. Out of £23 million in recurrent UGC grants, some £11.5 million may be allotted to research, if one accepts the questionable assumption that staff devote half their time to such pursuits.

All universities in the United Kingdom have a common basic science pattern—mathematics, physics, chemistry, the biologies, and the earth sciences. Applied sciences are represented in most institutions, but the departmental structure varies a great deal. The growth of these subjects and the proliferation of subdepartments depends on how the university grows and on the willingness of the University Grants Committee to finance the kind of growth it would like. The resultant pattern is, therefore, in no sense a national one. Universities are keen to develop, and in an expanding era, each tends to do so in its own way. Whether this will continue in the more restrictive future is a matter yet to be decided, but, clearly, every university cannot hope to develop all academic disciplines even in pure and applied science.

Institutional vs. Special-Purpose Support

The foregoing description of the present state of affairs might seem so satisfactory that there would be little need for special government agencies to foster research. Not only does the need exist, for institutional funds are *not* sufficient for research, but the idea is firmly preserved that agency operations are essential for the proper development of scientific research in specific directions. It is not, therefore, a matter of adding a small sum here and there to that already available from the UGC. It is a question of providing roughly an equivalent amount in a highly selective manner so that promising ideas are fostered in a flexible system that can change, and be changed, rapidly. This fifty-fifty balance between general and specialized forms of research support has not resulted from a grand national plan. It has evolved by trial and error over a period of many years to suit the needs of the changing situation.

Some may argue that the institutional grant makes life too easy for the academic, enabling him to go on almost indefinitely doing research without control by any authority. It could lead to a waste of resources. Such criticism was once valid. Not long ago, many science departments were headed by one professor, who could make or mar the department for years. Nowadays, this situation has been completely changed, with the creation of many more chairs within a department, and it is unlikely that, at any one time, all professors will be scientifically inactive. The system of institutional financing provides a sense of stability and eliminates the continual need to seek external support for a certain level of research activity. Since no one really controls or even comments critically on a department's activities, it must be admitted that there could occasionally be some waste of resources. However, this is one of the cherished academic "freedoms." It can only be preserved if university staffs realize that what they are spending is almost entirely public money and that they have a social responsibility to make the best possible use of it.

The main agencies supporting scientific research are the Science Research Council, the Natural Environment Research Council, and to a lesser extent, the Medical Research Council and the Agricultural Research Council, the latter two being mission-oriented agencies with staffs and laboratories of their own. Funds for research come also from the defense agencies, the Atomic Energy Authority, and to a very much smaller extent, other departments. In contrast to their United States counterparts, which are more likely to contract for research and development, United Kingdom defense agencies (except for the Ministry of Aviation) are more likely to do their R&D intramurally. Industry and universities are employed for rather specific jobs closely knit with defense programs, not for basic research. Of course, a university is unlikely to accept such a research contract unless the department concerned has a real interest in prosecuting the work. Though most of this work is unclassified, as a general policy universities try to limit it to a minor fraction of extramural research funds.

The Roles of Graduate and Postdoctoral Students

An integral part of university research is the activity of graduate students. The combination of doing research and of being trained to do so is an established pattern strongly linked with the Ph.D. degree. The system works satisfactorily in chemistry—it is almost traditional, in fact, and the chemical industry depends on this training for a considerable portion of its intake of highly trained graduates. More than 50 percent of chemistry Ph.D.'s are employed in the chemical industry. In other pure science subjects—particularly physics—the situation is much less satisfactory; and in biology the same demand from industry does not exist. In the applied sciences, matters are complicated by the professional requirements—more applied scientists want to go into industry after having acquired a first [bachelor's] degree—often to the detriment of applied research at the universities. Here, however, the great majority are ultimately employed in industry.

The nature of training for the Ph.D. has been much questioned. Great improvements could be made in formal instruction by reducing the amount of original research undertaken. Then, there is the problem of the Ph.D. student incorrectly utilized as a research assistant to the academic staff. But despite such criticism and the desirability of keeping Ph.D. programs under continuing critical scrutiny, graduate training is necessary for a high percentage of science students—in fact, it is now undertaken by some 37 percent of those receiving a first degree in science. The number of Ph.D. candidates is so great and they are, moreover, such an integral and necessary part of the university system that the central government is really forced to take a considerable part in determining the kind of training they will receive. One scheme to encourage further advanced training is to provide scholarships to enable a student to obtain training in a contiguous field, prior to undertaking a Ph.D. in a different subject than his undergraduate major. With the development of interdisciplinary research, such "conversion" courses are absolutely essential if the student is to tackle his Ph.D. studies effectively.

Research students might be more successful in their studies and in subsequent employment if they had had some experience in industry. Two mechanisms exist for providing this experience. The technological universities utilize a "sandwich" course system in which, during his undergraduate career, a student alternates six months at the university and then six in industry. He thereby obtains a real appreciation of how industry operates and of the limiting conditions within which his scientific and technological work must be constrained. This type of graduate is immediately acceptable and effective, without further training, in industry. If these students engage in full-time research in industry, in pure or applied science, they should, again, prove extremely effective at it.

The nontechnological universities do not pursue this sandwich course system but often encourage students to do vacation work in industry. Though this is valuable, unless the firm takes immense trouble (and spends considerable sums of money), a student cannot thereby get a real grasp of industry. Recognizing the problem, the Science Research Council has developed schemes to enable students, after a period in industry, to return to universities for research. The hope is that they will thus acquire that combination of industrial and academic experience that will render them increasingly effective and useful in later life. However, as a man cannot normally be expected to make a financial sacrifice at this stage in his career, he has to receive an income at the university similar to that in industry. While industry is encouraged to bear part of the cost, such a student is bound to cost the SRC a good deal more than one who accepts a research award immediately after graduating.

Next come the policy problems of the postdoctoral research student. There is no question that a number of such people should be supported at both United Kingdom and overseas universities. Postdoctoral fellows give a department a flexibility it would lack if only permanent staff were available to conduct research. They can tackle problems too difficult for the graduate student and are not bothered by having to solve them in time to write a thesis. They can acquire skills in newly developing fields and should be able to do some teaching to disseminate the knowledge they are acquiring. Nonetheless, the number of postdoctoral students, and the tenure of their fellowships, must be limited. With industry, universities, and government in the market for scientists, it would be wrong to finance large numbers of postdoctoral fellows and to pay them larger salaries than they could get in normal employment. Accordingly, the number of postdoctoral fellowships offered by the Science Research Council has been kept to only 4 percent of the number of graduate students.

Scholarships and fellowships do not, however, adequately dispose of the problem of graduate research assistants. Under proper supervision, it is correct to use graduate research students as assistants to the permanent academic staff. But as some kinds of research require the construction and maintenance of highly complex and expensive equipment that may have to be operated on strict schedules round the clock, numerous qualified permanent staff are needed. Because of the high cost and high rate of obsolescence of machines like particle accelerators, computers, radiotelescopes, and space research apparatus for use in rockets and satellites, it has been essential for the government to support large staffs in order to use these instruments to the maximum possible extent. However, manufacturers are striving to produce instruments so foolproof that only routine maintenance is required, thereby reducing the need for highly skilled technicians. Even the labor required for the preliminary analysis of results may be reduced by various measures of automation such as the connection of on-line computers to automatic X-ray diffractometers or mass spectrometers and the automatic scanning of films from bubble chambers or photographic telescopes. Thus, specialized instrument services may enable the individual scientist or the small scientific unit to operate effectively and speedily without an increasingly large array of assistants.

Allocating Funds for Manpower and Equipment

At present, there are 7,700 academic staff in pure and applied science in universities in the United Kingdom, about 8,000 Ph.D. students, 400 postdoctoral fellows, and some 1,400 graduate research assistants and technicians. This is the manpower that has got to be provided with sufficient up-to-date equipment.

The nonearmarked basic bloc grant from the University Grants Committee is certainly not sufficient for a university to support effective research units in designated areas. One solution might be to calculate the total material costs that might be involved and then to award each university a bloc grant specifically for research, the amount being assessed by the quantity, quality, and character of the university's research. This grant would then be allocated by the university to each department. For many reasons, such a procedure is not really practicable in the United Kingdom. The assessment of a university's needs could only be made after the needs of departments and subdepartments had first been examined by expert external bodies. It would be difficult to allocate an institutional grant rationally without expert assessment of each department's claims. Once a system of institutional research grants was established, it would be extremely difficult to alter the pattern substantially.

A better solution is to create a central body or bodies that can examine the needs of the country as a whole for research in different subjects. Such a body can compare proposals within a discipline, determine their order of merit, and finally, distribute available money accordingly. Recipients are usually better satisfied with their allocation if they know that it has been determined by fellow scientists on the merit of the proposal. This kind of procedure is particularly necessary when funds do not match the demands for support.

But what constitutes a reasonable level of support? In a laboratory wholly supported from one source (for example, industry or government) a balance has to be struck between money for men and money for all other services. Management must monitor the situation continually and see that the right balance is struck. Theoretically, it should be possible to do the same in a university laboratory, since the manpower level is determined by the university. However, because universities receive support from many sources and because of their teaching activities, the situation is greatly complicated. The rough and ready way is to allow them to make their demands and distribute grants in response, making constant comparisons with nonuniversity laboratories to ensure that university manpower is utilized efficiently. Thus, it is not very difficult to assess whether a university laboratory is equipped with too few or too many instruments.

These remarks might be taken to imply that grants should be distributed according to the size of the department, each agency seeking to provide each laboratory with comparable equipment. This conclusion must be avoided at all costs, for it would ultimately lead to mediocre research. Excellence can be maintained by the critical examination of proposals, and money should be provided for excellent proposals. A shortage of money can produce effective competition. If competition is not overdone and a reasonable level of expenditure has already been attained, this is probably a desirable state of affairs.

However, when individual grants become large—that is, greater than £100,000—completely different criteria must be employed. To date, such large grants have been confined mainly to physics, astronomy, and space research. Many of these grants were originally small. As the cost of research in these fields has risen, it has become necessary to reconsider national policy with regard to them, particularly when large capital investments are in prospect. In radio-astronomy, for example, two complementary centers developed at Manchester and Cambridge. Other universities might have liked to establish facilities, but it was decided a few years ago that all future investment would be confined to these two. Accordingly, anyone wishing to do research in radio-astronomy must go to these two national centers, located wholly within university departments.

In nuclear physics, the problems are much more complicated. Only four out of over forty university physics departments have been or are being equipped with accelerators of modest size, and the number is not likely to be increased. These machines require operating staffs above the normal complement of physics departments, and operating expenses are also high compared with departmental budgets. Hence, the Science Research Council has to provide consolidated grants during the active life of the machine. Since this kind of nuclear physics is likely to continue indefinitely, arrangements have been made for these universities to assume an increasing share of the costs. In the case of high energy physics, discrete national laboratories are obviously also needed. As this type of installation's capital and running costs are larger than those of even large universities, they must be managed and staffed by the SRC.

These fundamental research installations are constructed solely for the use of university scientists. However, their operation and further development are dependent on their permanent staffs, whose professional standing would suffer if they were used merely as assistants to academic scientists. Staff physicists need programs of their own to keep scientifically alive and to improve the machine's performance and instrumentation. It is not easy to maintain the right balance, for if staff are overindulged, the academics may feel that their access to the machines is impeded by a lack of technical assistance and of machine time. As further capital investments will be made primarily at existing nuclear laboratories, in order to exploit their capacity more fully, the conduct of experiments (as distinct from the analysis of data) will be increasingly concentrated at these laboratories.

European Collaboration

Scientific collaboration in Europe is no new phenomenon. Apart from the movement of academics for hundreds of years without government assistance for travel, the most highly developed one-way traffic was probably in chemistry. Before the introduction of the Ph.D. in British universities, it was customary for graduate students to go to Germany for their doctorates. The tendency persisted until about 1933. Since the war, it has not resumed to nearly the same extent. The postgraduate awards of government agencies encourage well-qualified students to study on the Continent. Cost-of-living adjustments are also made for study in the more expensive countries. But though there is no financial barrier, less than half of one percent of Ph.D. students in science and technology study in European universities under government auspices, and a similarly small number of European students come to British universities. Flow in both directions should be much fostered. Interchange of people for short periods, the bewildering array of international conferences and summer schools in pleasant places, and the activities of international unions induce a universal movement of the academic population. High speed travel has helped. Most of that movement is not at personal expense. It would be no exaggeration to say that, in these respects, Europe is a scientific unity.

Collaboration in large-scale experimental work is another matter. Unlike the states of the United States, the states of Europe possess distinctive educational and scientific research systems of their own. In nuclear physics, and now in space, collaboration was really forced on Europe because of the magnitude of the operation. Smaller countries could gain access to a large accelerator only by the construction of a European facility, such as that of CERN. Larger countries, however, could have gone it alone. For example, the United Kingdom spends three times as much on its own national laboratories as on its contribution to CERN.

By creating favorable conditions, the best brains and skills of Europe could be attracted to one site, with unquestionable benefit to the quality of the laboratory. But an international laboratory can also have injurious effects on domestic nuclear physics. The essence of an international laboratory is the maintenance of a continuous flow of scientists through it. When a scientist has no equipment to work with in his home country, similar to that in the laboratory, he sees little point in returning. Thus, in the end, movement is stifled. The problem is more severe in the smaller countries, and the result could be that they will merely pay a subscription to a European facility which they cannot properly use. If this contribution constitutes a substantial part of their national science budget, a certain reluctance in maintaining their membership in the "nuclear club" may naturally develop. While all but one of the CERN member states have decided to meet the costs of the £26 million storage ring machine, the question for the immediate future is whether they will contribute to the construction of a 300 GeV accelerator while simultaneously continuing to contribute to the maintenance and development of CERN.

In space science, the problems are of quite a different character. Once again, collaboration is essential for the engineering, launching, and tracking of satellites. Using ESRO satellites, individual countries can mount their experiments at comparatively modest cost. They can get a fair share of what space is available on satellites, make an identifiable national contribution to science by analyzing their experimental data, and thus, in the long run, justify their subscription to ESRO.

Some would suggest the creation of many more European laboratories on the plea that only by combining resources can an effective effort be mounted to tackle some types of research. The further plea is that, again, some smaller countries cannot maintain outstanding centers in all the active subjects. If ever Europe becomes one state, politically, economically, and educationally, there might be a case for creating a relatively small number of outstanding laboratories at which all active scientists in the field would spend some part of their careers. Until this unity is achieved, the more immediate and practical solution is for countries to be selective in the range of topics they support at universities and research institutes. Unfortunately, the smaller countries must be more selective than the larger. But who should make the selection? Who should judge when an institution has passed its prime? Who should close it down?

In some countries, the science policy-making body reviews the scene, observes a scientific deficiency or gap, and seeks to fill it. The resultant tendency is to attempt to be good in all subjects. A measure of randomness in these affairs is more desirable.

But this brings us back to where we started—namely, that when large sums of money are involved, exchequer and parliament like to know why the money is spent, what is the plan for spending it, and ultimately, what results are achieved.

HOMER D. BABBIDGE, JR.

A View
from the Campus

A LOT HAS been said in recent years of the *partner-ship* of government and higher education, and it may be helpful to interrupt the wild Watusi of current developments long enough to inquire of the college president who is one of those partners how he's enjoying it all.

An "Education Administration" and a science-minded society have effected a revolution in government-education relationships in a short time. Estimates of total federal expenditures in the educational enterprise soar to heights unimagined a decade ago. New "thrusts" occur with the regularity of rock and roll rhythm, and new bureaus and agencies crop up faster than you can say "Rolling Stones."

And the typical college president is a little overwhelmed by it.[1] He invited government to the dance in the first place, thinking, I suppose, that his two-step was equal to any tempo. But he reckoned without the energy and enthusiasm of his new partner. It's not that he isn't gratified by the flattering response—she seems to be enjoying herself—but he's somewhat confused, and frankly, his feet are beginning to hurt. In the rare intermissions, the college president huddles with his colleagues in

[1] Since I am writing about the views of college presidents in general, these views should not be taken, necessarily, as my own.

323

an effort to analyze the situation, to see it in perspective, and if possible, to reassure himself that he's still "leading."

The college president doesn't like everything that's happening in Washington. He is, after all, a part of the educational establishment, and he sees that establishment being bypassed. He dislikes the "task force" approach to policy formulation and is especially unhappy about the secrecy—both with regard to membership and substance—of these deliberations. He witnesses a declining influence of national educational organizations and an apparent ascendancy of foundation influence in policy formulation. All this means that his—the college president's— voice is diminished in the policy arena.

All this wouldn't be so bad if the voices that *are* being heard were the voices of those who understood the problems of institutional management and leadership. College presidents have long chafed under the project-grant system of the scientific agencies of government, which tends to establish direct working relationships between the agency and the individual scientist. In James Shannon's phrase, this has made the campus a boarding house rather than a home for scientists. More profoundly, it has, the college president thinks, undermined institutional integrity and purpose; he likes to quote John Gardner:

> Sometimes institutions are simply the sum of the historical accidents that
> have happened to them. Like the sand dunes in the desert, they are shaped
> by influences but not by purposes. Or, to put the matter more accurately,
> like our sprawling and ugly metropolitan centers, they are the unintended
> consequences of millions of fragmented purposes.[2]

"Innovators" and "Users" of Higher Education

But the college president feels he can cope—one way or another—with the project-grant system. He is not unsympathetic, after all, with the view that faculty scientists should have a voice in the delineation of institutional purpose. But in recent years, two other sets of voices have addressed themselves to federal policy, at odds, in varying degrees, with the views of college presidents. They can be classified as the "innovators" and the "users."

The innovators are a straightforward enough group. They think the

[2] Remarks at the inauguration of James A. Perkins as president of Cornell University, October 4, 1965.

practices of American higher education are outmoded, sluggish, and unequal to the demands of the late twentieth century. Everything in the way of method and content is challenged. And a good many college presidents can, and do, agree with the charges. Though they're not at home in discussions of hardware and software, they *do* sense something of the magnitude of the forces for change that surround them. What annoys them about the innovators is their glibness—the casual way in which they talk about revolutions in an institutional framework that is notoriously resistant to change. The college president is near despair when the innovator proclaims that change in our institutions of higher education is a simple matter of "leadership." He wishes profoundly that the advocate of teaching by television could be sentenced to an hour with a chapter of the American Association of University Professors or, at least, to a half-hour before a squad of underclassmen.

But while the innovator is an annoyance to the harried administrator, the "user" is something more. In his most dire manifestation, he may constitute a real threat to the integrity of learning. The user is, in brief, one who sees in the educational enterprise a magnificent instrument for the achievement of social, economic, or political goals. And it must be conceded, I think, that much recent educational legislation smacks of just this. Colleges and universities have been urged to enlist in armies doing battle with everything from poverty to underdevelopment. Academic troops are being deployed against cancer, stroke, and heart disease. The suggestion that colleges may have been used to help the Central Intelligence Agency was only a logical extension and elicited some mischievous "I-told-you-so's."

There can be no doubt, I think, that the "uses of the university" to which President Kerr alluded,[3] have pronounced appeal for a socially minded, activist administration. And there can be no doubt, either, that college presidents are worried about the effects of such use upon their institutions. They know their colleges and universities are not universal joints, capable of turning in all directions. Nor are they bottomless pools of intellectual resource. They don't want to be unpatriotic or socially unresponsive, but college presidents increasingly wonder how many such projects they can take on and how much they can afford to contribute.

"Affording" is a big problem to college presidents. They bear the ultimate responsibility for parceling out limited resources and are more

[3] See Clark Kerr, *The Uses of the University* (Harvard University Press, 1964).

conscious than either faculty or government agencies of just how limited these are. "Cost sharing" is a reasonable enough concept when there is a perfect coincidence of interest between the two parties; but insofar as the coincidence is less than perfect, the concept begins to bind. And it doesn't help to have federal agencies paying a 10 percent profit to commercial firms for work in training and research, while bearing down on "cost sharing" and "matching" when dealing with educational institutions.

The demands being made on colleges and universities by the users do seem to be growing. Even when they purport to be fully funded, they are an added strain on—if no one else—the college president. Some feel they are being ravaged in the name of public service. All are conscious of being pulled and tugged at. In this mélange of programs, the college president worries that he may not only be following false leads or leading his institution off on tangents; he worries, too, that he may be missing a great chance to strengthen his institution at a critical point. And this fear of missing a chance may well make the institution more vulnerable to exploitation.

Academic Reforestation

The degree to which college presidents feel their institutions have been exploited can be measured by their growing concern for a broad-scale national program of replenishment. Many of them feel that the demands of the public for their services are not to be denied but that the users have a responsibility to replenish—not just pay for—the resources they have consumed. One proposal for "academic reforestation" is the so-called Miller bill, which would provide virtually unrestricted formula grants to institutions that are making demonstrable contributions to scientific advance.[4] Other proposals, with similar objectives, can be anticipated. A given supply of milk can produce just so much cream; beyond that, the basic supply must be expanded.

What the college president wants more than anything else from the federal government—or from anyone else, for that matter—is grant support on an institutional basis that can be deployed at the discretion of the institution. Some would spend it on science, some on art; some would use it to repair weak spots, others to build pinnacles of excel-

[4] See the discussion of this bill by Christian Arnold, pp. 97 ff.

lence. But each would like the authority to make that decision. And each believes it would contribute to institutional integrity and to the rich diversity we're always talking about.

A pipe dream? Perhaps. But the college president persists in the notion that the institution he represents is important to the national well-being and that a policy of strengthening such institutions per se would be a sound public policy. He appreciates that not all federal funds can take this form, but he hopes that the present pattern of tightly limited, mission-oriented, prepackaged support can be augmented by a margin of true aid that can be used *by* the institution *for* the institution.

Washington Representation

But beyond the voices and the policy influence of innovators and users, there are other developments on the national scene that excite strong feelings among college presidents. Prominent among these is the phenomenon of "Washington representation." Viewed in one light, it's only natural. There is money there in profusion and (inevitably) in confusion; and the last one there is a loser. Thus, institutions have posted full-time money-watchers, even fully staffed offices, on the scene. Commercial organizations and law firms offer to help. Myriad, assorted insects flock around the incandescent glow of new federal programs.

Yet other institutions hold out. Partly out of pride, or because they can't afford it, or because they feel it's undignified. Some feel it's ineffective, others that it's self-defeating. Still others are content to rely on the national organizations that were first on the scene to disseminate the information essential to effective grantsmanship. But it may not be long before "everybody's doing it" and the holdouts will be under great pressure to conform. We will then, some say, be treated to a spectacle not unlike Manhattan in a transit strike, the system clogged with agents scrambling over one another after money their employers are not sure they really want.

But the fact of the matter is that the college president is overwhelmed by the complexity of federal organization. He reads that there are forty-six different agencies in the business, and he shudders. He needs help to find his way around, and if he's opposed to Washington representation, he has to build some kind of expertise into his campus structure. He wonders aloud, though, if the government itself can't help by simplifying its structure. All this talk of "separate missions" aside, can't someone in Washington worry about the whole of a college or university? The U.S. Office of Education, laboring under the weight of enormous new program responsibility, is still the sentimental favorite of some for the role. Unfortunately—for this purpose—the multiplication of categorical programs has caused the office to move in the direction of concentrating all its staff and resources on handling the flood of regulations and paper work with no one left to plan a program of flood control. Others want the responsibility elevated to the Office of the President; though they're quick to concede that there's a point beyond which the Office of the President cannot be expected to run the operating affairs of the federal government. College presidents, accepting the inevitability of the catacombs of government, would like at least to see them better mapped or have guides provided.

And then there are the family squabbles that have been instigated by the proliferation of federal programs. The "have" institutions, doing pretty well under a set of existing ground rules, have no desire to change them. The "have-not" institutions demonstrate remarkable agility and imagination in contriving new possibilities for support. And so long as the level of support is limited by considerations of national defense, the conflict is turned inward, and the pressures felt within the family. The only escape from this internecine struggle lies in raising further the level of federal support, adding new programs rather than replacing the old with the new.

In sum, the proliferation of federal programs in education has plunged the academic world into a sea of excitement, confusion, and uncertainty. One college president sums up the feelings of many by retelling the message of an old magazine cartoon: Two Englishmen, waist deep in a quagmire, over the caption, "Quicksand or not, Gridley, I've half a mind to struggle."

Three Objectives

If he did struggle, what would the college president struggle for? Three objectives, at least, seem to emerge as having general support among the group.

First, the college president would advocate more involvement and representation for key administrative officers in the various deliberations of government that have to do with higher education. The president does not see himself as the sole spokesman for the well-being of higher education, but he feels his voice should be clearly heard by those who are responsible for institutional relationships.

Second, the president would urge a better balance between project support and institutional support. For those institutions that are now getting significant project-grant support, an increase in institutional support would add greater stability to what seems at times a kind of two-legged stool. And for those institutions that are not now beneficiaries of project support, increased institutional aid might make it possible to forgo the rat race of competition for project funds.

Third, the college president would struggle to achieve, somewhere within the government, some machinery for taking a look at the total impact of federal programs on higher education. He senses that the ramifications are greater than generally realized and feels strongly that the administering physician should concern himself with these side effects.

But even without these reforms, and for all the anxiety and exhaustion he has to show for it, would the college president give up the present pattern of federal programs? Would he turn back the clock? I think not.

Federal programs have, after all, done a great deal to strengthen institutions in the truest sense and promise to do even more. The academic facilities program, despite its high matching requirement and inadequate funding, is helping make possible the construction of a broad range of needed structures. The gesture of creating a national humanities foundation has been heartening. The institutional-grants programs of the National Science Foundation and the bloc grants of the National Institutes of Health represent a trend that can be applauded.

And even the programs with which he finds fault are tolerable to the college president. He finds on examination that a structure, however precarious and inelegant, has been built on these programs, and the removal of any one of them could cause it all to tumble. And so, wincing, he accepts what is there and hopes that it will be buttressed and shored up with additional programs and modified by legislative change into a more agreeable structure.

The college president draws for his optimism on the fact that current educational development is a moving vessel, subject to handling and maneuvering. He is grateful for the fact that there is wind in the sails of federal policy, for he recalls the years of languishing in irons. He dreams, of course, of the day when he can sail downwind; but he realizes that as long as the wind is there, progress is possible. Indeed, he is inclined to feel that all the tacking he has to do now is effecting *some* progress.

And in his soberest moments, the college or university head realizes that he and his institution must decide, ultimately, how much the federal government can help. Are not many of the opportunities open to him only Satan's lures? Must he not have the integrity and the will power to walk past parts of the Great Society Smorgasbord? And to absorb the criticism that he's "missing a great opportunity to put the institution on the map"?

Integrity is a quality the college president knows *he* has. But he's a little worried about the head of the Biology Department. And that brigand at the University of X—why he'd do anything to get a federal dollar!

Appendixes

Letter from Donald Hornig
to Senator Pastore

EXECUTIVE OFFICE OF THE PRESIDENT,
OFFICE OF SCIENCE AND TECHNOLOGY
Washington, March 27, 1964

Hon. John O. Pastore
Chairman, Joint Committee on Atomic Energy
Congress of the United States
Washington, D.C.

DEAR SENATOR PASTORE:

This is in response to questions on national policy for high energy physics raised during my appearance before the Joint Committee on Atomic Energy on March 3, 1964. First, I would like to set forth the general considerations which shape national policy in this area.

The reason for our great interest in high energy physics is that it is unique in concerning itself with the most fundamental laws governing the constitution of matter and the elementary particles of which matter is constructed. What is meant by fundamental laws is that in principle all other laws and properties can be derived from them. Although the consequences of the discovery and understanding of fundamental physical laws cannot be foreseen at the time they are made, it has been true historically that in the long run these understandings have had a very great impact on science and technology and on all mankind.

For example, the laws of electromagnetism, discovered in the late 19th century, now are the foundation of our entire radio, TV, electronic, and electric power industries. Similarly, the laws governing the forces of the nucleus have led to the discovery of nuclear energy. Our ability in the past to exploit these fundamental laws has contributed extensively to national security and economic growth.

High energy physics is indeed making rapid progress toward the goal of understanding the elementary particles and the underlying laws. In the past ten or fifteen years research in this field has enormously extended our knowledge. Very recently, the discovery of the omega minus particle has set the stage for still deeper understanding.

One test of the value and importance of a field of science is the quality of the scientists who are attracted to it; in this respect high energy physics draws many of our most talented people. Scientists and engineers attracted to the field, both accelerator designers and physicists, have made important contributions to technology (for example, high power radar tubes) and to all of the areas in which the AEC is working.

For these reasons, it is in the national interest to continue vigorous exploration of this fundamental branch of science, and maintain our leadership.

Long-range planning of support, and long-range policy in the broadest sense, are especially necessary for high energy physics because:

(a) High energy physics experimentation has grown very costly and in its next phase will be even more expensive despite careful attention to limiting costs. Although its costs are still greatly exceeded by the space program and many applied developments, it will doubtless remain for some time one of the most expensive fields in pure science. The nature of its problem makes this inevitable.

(b) The lead time for planning and building an accelerator that will substantially advance the high energy frontier is eight years or more.

Although the foregoing administrative problems necessitate long-range planning of support, it is not possible to blueprint a long-range program in detail because of unforeseeable developments in science and the necessity of assessing the program in the light of changing fiscal needs and resources.

Government expenditures in high energy physics encompass both support of existing accelerators and funds for new construction. The support of existing facilities, as now proposed in the President's budget, is essential to maintaining our leadership. In planning future steps we shall always face the question of a wise division of support between machine use and new accelerator construction, with its implication, in turn, of a new level of use.

These considerations were prominent in the study carried out last year by the Joint Panel of the General Advisory Committee to the Atomic Energy Commission and the President's Science Advisory Committee. Three important technical conclusions, also, stand out clearly in that study: (1) proton energy is the single most important parameter to be extended in order to make a major advance in high energy physics; (2) accelerators for much higher energy (a few hundred up to a thousand Bev) are technically feasible; (3) a two-step advance to the highest energy foreseeably attainable now appears to promise, in the long run, the most fruitful and efficient use of our resources. This two-step approach has been concluded, after extensive deliberation, to be the best policy of all groups who have recently considered this question.

Recent discoveries in high energy physics make the scientific case for a very high energy machine even stronger today. Confidence in the feasibility of such machines also remains firm.

Thus, the main elements of the long-range policy for high energy physics in the United States that guide planning within the Executive Branch are:

1. It is in the national interest to support vigorous advancement of high energy physics as a fundamental field of science.

2. The high energy physics program is a national program, not related solely to the mission of any one agency. However, the AEC is serving, and is uniquely fitted to serve, as its primary custodian. Although the implementation of policy in this field rests primarily with the AEC, support by the NSF and agencies of the Department of Defense will be of considerable benefit to the agencies and the universities.

3. The level and character of support for high energy physics must be determined and periodically reassessed in the context of (a) the overall national science program (rather than in relation to the applied research and development programs of the AEC), (b) advances in the field itself, and (c) the then existing fiscal situation.

At present, it appears that the high energy physics program will require continued growth, especially in the provision of advanced accelerators and equipment. This should be done on a selective basis so that a productive program is maintained without the need for diversion of manpower and funds from other vital fields of research which are contributing to basic knowledge, education, and training.

4. Planning should proceed for advancement by two significant steps, at appropriate intervals, to an energy of the order of 1,000 Bev; the second accelerator to be available for experimentation in 15–20 years, depending on the developments in the science and the design studies.

5. The operation of existing accelerators and the associated research must be supported, including steps to increase their scientific productivity, where necessary to maintain a sound national program and to make significant contributions to science. Accelerators which become unproductive should be closed down or reduced in level of operation. New accelerators should be constructed only to provide significant extension of parameters or a new order of scientific capability.

6. Since major new high energy facilities of the future will be very few and very large, their organization must be carefully planned so that they can serve effectively the entire national community of high energy physicists.

7. In view of the high cost of new very high energy accelerators, opportunities for international cooperation in accelerator construction and use should be actively explored.

I hope that this statement of long-range policy for high energy particle physics will be of assistance to your Committee.

Sincerely,
DONALD F. HORNIG

APPENDIX B

On Preventing Conflicts of Interest
in Government-Sponsored Research
at Universities*

THE INCREASINGLY necessary and complex relationships among universities, Government, and industry call for more intensive attention to standards of procedure and conduct in Government-sponsored research. The clarification and application of such standards must be designed to serve the purposes and needs of the projects and the public interest involved in them and to protect the integrity of the cooperating institutions as agencies of higher education.

The Government and institutions of higher education, as the contracting parties, have an obligation to see that adequate standards and procedures are developed and applied; to inform one another of their respective requirements; and to assure that all individuals participating in their respective behalfs are informed of and apply the standards and procedures that are so developed.

Consulting relationships between university staff members and industry serve the interests of research and education in the university. Likewise, the transfer of technical knowledge and skill from the university to industry contributes to technological advance. Such relationships are desirable, but certain potential hazards should be recognized.

A. Conflict Situations

1. Favoring of outside interests. When a university staff member (administrator, faculty member, professional staff member, or employee) undertaking or engaging in Government-sponsored work has a significant financial interest in, or a consulting arrangement with, a private business concern, it is important to avoid actual or apparent conflicts of interest between his

* A joint statement of The Council of the American Association of University Professors and The American Council on Education, December 1964.

337

Government-sponsored university research obligations and his outside interests and other obligations. Situations in or from which conflicts of interest may arise are the:

a. Undertaking or orientation of the staff member's university research to serve the research or other needs of the private firm without disclosure of such undertaking or orientation to the university and to the sponsoring agency;

b. Purchase of major equipment, instruments, materials, or other items for university research from the private firm in which the staff member has the interest without disclosure of such interest;

c. Transmission to the private firm or other use for personal gain of Government-sponsored work products, results, materials, records, or information that are not made generally available. (This would not necessarily preclude appropriate licensing arrangements for inventions, or consulting on the basis of Government-sponsored research results where there is significant additional work by the staff member independent of his Government-sponsored research);

d. Use for personal gain or other unauthorized use of privileged information acquired in connection with the staff member's Government-sponsored activities. (The term "privileged information" includes, but is not limited to, medical, personnel, or security records of individuals; anticipated material requirements or price actions; possible new sites for Government operations; and knowledge of forthcoming programs or of selection of contractors or subcontractors in advance of official announcements);

e. Negotiation or influence upon the negotiation of contracts relating to the staff member's Government-sponsored research between the university and private organizations with which he has consulting or other significant relationships;

f. Acceptance of gratuities or special favors from private organizations with which the university does or may conduct business in connection with a Government-sponsored research project, or extension of gratuities or special favors to employees of the sponsoring Government agency, under circumstances which might reasonably be interpreted as an attempt to influence the recipients in the conduct of their duties.

2. Distribution of effort. There are competing demands on the energies of a faculty member (for example, research, teaching, committee work, outside consulting). The way in which he divides his effort among these various functions does not raise ethical questions unless the Government agency supporting his research is misled in its understanding of the amount of intellectual effort he is actually devoting to the research in question. A system of precise time accounting is incompatible with the inherent character of the work of a faculty member, since the various functions he performs are closely interrelated and do not conform to any meaningful division of a standard work week. On the other hand, if the research agreement contemplates that a staff member will devote a certain fraction of his effort to the Government-sponsored research, or he agrees to assume responsibility in relation to such research, a demonstrable relationship between the indicated effort or responsibility and the actual extent of his involvement is to be expected. Each university, therefore, should—through joint consultation of administration and faculty—develop procedures to assure that proposals are responsibly made and complied with.

3. Consulting for Government agencies or their contractors. When the staff member engaged in Government-sponsored research also serves as a consultant to a Federal agency, his conduct is subject to the provisions of the Conflict of Interest Statutes (18 U.S.C. 202–209 as amended) and the President's memorandum of May 2, 1963, *Preventing Conflicts of Interest on the Part of Special Government Employees.* When he consults for one or more Government contractors, or prospective contractors, in the same technical field as his research project, care must be taken to avoid giving advice that may be of questionable objectivity because of its possible bearing on his other interests. In undertaking and performing consulting services, he should make full disclosure of such interests to the university and to the contractor insofar as they may appear to relate to the work at the university or for the contractor. Conflict of interest problems could arise, for example, in the participation of a staff member of the university in an evaluation for the Government agency or its contractor of some technical aspect of the work of another organization with which he has a consulting or employment relationship or a significant financial interest, or in an evaluation of a competitor to such other organization.

B. University Responsibility

Each university participating in Government-sponsored research should make known to the sponsoring Government agencies:

1. The steps it is taking to assure an understanding on the part of the university administration and staff members of the possible conflicts of interest or other problems that may develop in the foregoing types of situations, and

2. The organizational and administrative actions it has taken or is taking to avoid such problems, including:

a. Accounting procedures to be used to assure that Government funds are expended for the purposes for which they have been provided, and that all services which are required in return for these funds are supplied;

b. Procedures that enable it to be aware of the outside professional work of staff members participating in Government-sponsored research, if such outside work relates in any way to the Government-sponsored research;

c. The formulation of standards to guide the individual university staff members in governing their conduct in relation to outside interests that might raise questions of conflicts of interest; and

d. The provision within the university of an informed source of advice and guidance to its staff members for advance consultation on questions they wish to raise concerning the problems that may or do develop as a result of their outside financial or consulting interests, as they relate to their participation in Government-sponsored university research. The university may wish to discuss such problems with the contracting officer or other appropriate Government official in those cases that appear to raise questions regarding conflicts of interest.

The above process of disclosure and consultation is the obligation assumed by the university when it accepts Government funds for research. The process must, of course, be carried out in a manner that does not infringe on the legitimate freedoms and flexibility of action of the university and its staff members that have traditionally characterized a university. It is desirable that standards and procedures of the kind discussed be formulated and administered by members of the university community themselves, through their joint initiative and responsibility, for it is they who are the best judges of the conditions which can most effectively stimulate the search for knowledge and preserve the requirements of academic freedom. Experience indicates that such standards and procedures should be developed and specified by joint administrative-faculty action.

Seminar Members, Speakers, and Guests, 1964-66

Members

Philip H. Abelson, *Science*
Harvey Brooks, Harvard University
John C. Calhoun, Jr., Department of the Interior and Texas A&M University
William M. Capron, Brookings Institution
William G. Colman, Advisory Commission on Intergovernmental Relations
Emilio Q. Daddario, U.S. House of Representatives
Clarence H. Danhof, Brookings Institution
Bowen C. Dees, National Science Foundation
Hugh L. Dryden, National Aeronautics and Space Administration
Kenneth M. Endicott, M.D., National Cancer Institute
Kermit Gordon, Brookings Institution
George A. Graham, Brookings Institution
Philip Handler, Duke University
Caryl P. Haskins, Carnegie Institution of Washington
Charles J. Hitch, Department of Defense
J. Herbert Hollomon, Department of Commerce
Francis Keppel, Department of Health, Education, and Welfare
Charles V. Kidd, National Institutes of Health and Office of Science and
    Technology
John W. McCollum, Greenleigh Associates
George F. Metcalf, Martin Company
Robert S. Morison, M.D., Rockefeller Foundation and Cornell University
Robert W. Morse, Department of the Navy
Charles A. Mosher, U.S. House of Representatives
Lucien N. Nedzi, U.S. House of Representatives
Harold Orlans, Brookings Institution
L. Harvey Poe, Aerojet-General Corporation
James T. Ramey, Atomic Energy Commission

Herbert Roback, Military Operations Subcommittee, Committee on Govern-
ment Operations, U.S. House of Representatives
Henry S. Rowen, Bureau of the Budget
Jack P. Ruina, Institute for Defense Analyses
Wallace S. Sayre, Columbia University
Herbert Scoville, Arms Control and Disarmament Agency
Frederick Seitz, National Academy of Sciences
Chalmers W. Sherwin, Department of Defense
Robert L. Sproull, Department of Defense and Cornell University
Elmer B. Staats, Bureau of the Budget
Gerald F. Tape, Atomic Energy Commission
Weston E. Vivian, U.S. House of Representatives
Eric A. Walker, Pennsylvania State University
James E. Webb, National Aeronautics and Space Administration
Edward Wenk, Jr., Legislative Reference Service
John T. Wilson, National Science Foundation
Logan Wilson, American Council on Education
Dael Wolfle, American Association for the Advancement of Science

Speakers

Hendrik W. Bode, Bell Telephone Laboratories
Harvey Brooks, Harvard University
William D. Carey, Bureau of the Budget
Kenneth M. Endicott, M.D., National Cancer Institute
J. Herbert Hollomon, Department of Commerce
John Morse, American Council on Education
Harold Orlans, Brookings Institution
Howard E. Page, National Science Foundation
Wolfgang K. H. Panofsky, Stanford Linear Accelerator Center
Fred A. Payne, Jr., Department of Defense
Don K. Price, Harvard University
Herbert Roback, Military Operations Subcommittee, Committee on Govern-
ment Operations, U.S. House of Representatives
David Z. Robinson, Office of Science and Technology
Chalmers W. Sherwin, Department of Defense
Elmer B. Staats, Bureau of the Budget
Alvin M. Weinberg, Oak Ridge National Laboratory
Edward Wenk, Jr., Legislative Reference Service

Guests

Robert B. Abel, Office of Naval Research
Arthur S. Adams, The Salzburg Seminar

Mac C. Adams, National Aeronautics and Space Administration
John B. Anderson, U.S. House of Representatives
Captain Burton H. Andrews, Department of Defense
James W. Armsey, Ford Foundation
Captain Henry A. Arnold, United Aircraft Corporation
Stanhope Bayne-Jones, M.D., Washington, D.C.
David Z. Beckler, Office of Science and Technology
Marver H. Bernstein, Princeton University
Robert C. Berson, M.D., Association of American Medical Colleges
Raymond L. Bisplinghoff, National Aeronautics and Space Administration
Charles R. Bowen, International Business Machines Corporation
Douglas Brooks, Travelers Research Center
Robert D. Calkins, Brookings Institution
William D. Carey, Bureau of the Budget
Lawrence R. Caruso, Princeton University
Robert R. Casey, U.S. House of Representatives
Richard L. Chapman, Brookings Institution
Leon W. Cohen, University of Maryland
John T. Conway, Joint Committee on Atomic Energy, U.S. Congress
Edgar M. Cortright, National Aeronautics and Space Administration
John M. Drewry, Committee on Merchant Marine and Fisheries, U.S. House
    of Representatives
Howard Eckles, Department of the Interior
William N. Ellis, Research and Technical Programs Subcommittee, Committee
    on Government Operations, U.S. House of Representatives
Mrs. Edna Gass, Research and Technical Programs Subcommittee, Committee
    on Government Operations, U.S. House of Representatives
Brigadier General Edward B. Giller, Department of the Air Force
Robert Gilpin, Princeton University
Dale Grimes, University of Michigan
William Harris, Battelle Memorial Institute
Chet Holifield, U.S. House of Representatives
William L. Hooper, Office of Science and Technology
Rear Admiral H. Arnold Karo, Coast and Geodetic Survey
Thomas E. J. Keena, Office of Congressman Emilio Daddario
Geoffrey Keller, National Science Foundation
Franklin P. Kilpatrick, Brookings Institution
Herbert L. Kinney, Atomic Energy Commission
Robert E. Learmouth, National Cancer Institute
Hugh F. Loweth, Bureau of the Budget
Paul W. McDaniel, Atomic Energy Commission
Daniel Markel, Committee on Commerce, U.S. Senate

Donald G. Marquis, Massachusetts Institute of Technology

Louis H. Mayo, George Washington University

Michael Michaelis, Arthur D. Little, Inc.

Frederick A. Mosher, Carnegie Corporation

Richard E. Neustadt, Harvard University

Homer E. Newell, National Aeronautics and Space Administration

Herman Orentlicher, American Association of University Professors

Fred A. Payne, Jr., Department of Defense

William Pounds, Massachusetts Institute of Technology

Norman F. Ramsey, Harvard University

George W. Rathjens, Jr., Institute for Defense Analyses

David Z. Robinson, Office of Science and Technology

Robert S. Sargent, Department of Defense

Willis H. Shapley, National Aeronautics and Space Administration

David T. Stanley, Brookings Institution

Stephen V. Stephens, Brookings Institution

Stephen Strickland, American Council on Education

Russell I. Thackrey, National Association of State Universities and Land-Grant Colleges

T. Phillip Waalkes, M.D., National Cancer Institute

William A. Wallenmeyer, Atomic Energy Commission

Thomas G. Ward, M.D., Microbiological Associates

Christopher Wright, Columbia University

Adam Yarmolinsky, Department of Defense

Philip B. Yeager, Committee on Science and Astronautics, U.S. House of Representatives

Index

Index

Abelson, Philip H., 94, 129
Academic science in Great Britain: high energy physics, 179, 319; policy, 8, 19, 276; practical objectives, 131; research support, 311 ff.
Academic Science and Engineering, Committee on, 17*n*
Accelerators, 9, 12; built by AEC, 166; proposal by Midwestern Universities Research Association, 80*n*, 171
Advanced Research Project Agency (Department of Defense), 47
Advisory panels for science, 33, 150, 167, 257; *see also* Office of Science and Technology; President's Science Advisory Committee
Aeronautics; *see* National Advisory Committee for Aeronautics; National Aeronautics and Space Administration
Agricultural research, federal funding of, 85, 99–100, 217, 226
American Association of University Professors, and code of ethics, 286, 290, 337
American Council on Education, and code of ethics, 290, 337
American Mathematical Society, 158
American Medical Association, 4
Ames National Laboratory (Iowa), 63
Appropriations, House and Senate Committees on, 239, 268
Argonne National Laboratory (Ill.), 63, 173, 175
Argonne Universities Association, 175
Arizona, University of, 106
Arnold, Christian K., 7, 89–100
Ashby, Eric, 39
Associated Universities, Inc., 166
Association of American Universities, 5

Astronomy, 154
Atmospheric Research, National Center for, 60
Atomic Energy, Joint Committee on: hearings, 9*n*, 124, 185; reports, 167*n*, 168*n*; and Stanford accelerator, 171
Atomic Energy Commission: accelerators, 9, 166, 184; conflict of interest regulations, 288; R&D budget, 215
Auerbach, Lewis E., 28*n*
Avery, O. T., 163

Babbidge, Homer D., Jr., 4, 12, 323–30
Basic research (National Science Foundation classification), 55; evaluating, 80; funding, 26, 77*n*, 83, 156, 221; *see also* Mission-oriented research; Research and development
Berkner, Lloyd, 12
Bev (unit of energy), 166*n*
Big and little science, 58, 128, 189 ff., 197; *see also* High energy physics; Pure science
Biological sciences: allocation of funds, 108, 149, 159; rating of molecular biology, 130
Bode, Hendrik W., 18, 123–36
Bowman, Isaiah, 157*n*
British academic science; *see* Academic science in Great Britain
Brookhaven National Laboratory (Long Island, N.Y.), 60, 166, 172, 175
Brooklyn, Polytechnic Institute of, 106
Brooks, Harvey, 7, 11, 17, 53–76, 81, 128, 145–51
Brown, J. Douglas, 287
Budget, Bureau of the: master agreement for university grants, 41*n*; publications, 93*n*, 237*n*; *see also* "Special Analysis I"

347

INDEX